# Manual of Pneumatic Systems Optimization

# Manual of Pneumatic Systems Optimization

Henry Fleischer, P.E., CMfgE
*Vice President, Research and Development*
*Numatics, Inc.*

## McGraw-Hill, Inc.

New York   San Francisco   Washington, D.C.   Auckland   Bogotá
Caracas   Lisbon   London   Madrid   Mexico City   Milan
Montreal   New Delhi   San Juan   Singapore
Sydney   Tokyo   Toronto

**Library of Congress Cataloging-in-Publication Data**

Fleischer, Henry.
    Manual of pneumatic systems optimization / Henry Fleischer.
        p.    cm.
    ISBN 0-07-021240-6
    1. Pneumatic control—Mathematical models—Handbooks, manuals,
etc.  I. Title.
    TJ219.F55   1995
    629.8'045—dc20                                          95-14225
                                                                CIP

    2 3 4 5 6 7 8 9 0  DOC/DOC  9 0 0 9 8 7 6


ISBN 0-07-021240-6



*The sponsoring editor for this book was Robert Hauserman, the editing
supervisor was Bernard Onken, and the production supervisor was
Donald Schmidt. It was set in Century Schoolbook by Priscilla Beer of
McGraw-Hill's Professional Book Group composition unit.*


*Printed and bound by R. R. Donnelley & Sons Company.*

McGraw-Hill books are available at special quantity discounts to use
as premiums and sales promotions, or for use in corporate training pro-
grams. For more information, please write to the Director of Special
Sales, McGraw-Hill, Inc., 11 West 19th Street, New York, NY 10011. Or
contact your local bookstore.

*Dedicated to the eight pivotal girls (wife, mother, sister, two daughters in law, and three granddaughters) and three significant boys (father and two sons) in my life, representing the past, present, and future.*

# Contents

# Preface

This treatise on the optimization of pneumatic systems can be employed equally by the student of fluid dynamics and the intelligent layperson on the factory floor. Some parts are concise, in keeping with the increased comprehension of the well-grounded engineer-designer, while unfamiliar sections are more detailed for purposes of background and understanding. We have focused on some illustrative examples, which become more complex as we progress into each chapter in order to cover all aspects of pneumatic systems. In this fashion each of you, the readers, can proceed at your own respective pace and depth of involvement and can disregard certain sections according to your particular level of interest and experience.

We are offering some new information and theories based on tests that were not conducted under the strictest laboratory-controlled conditions (e.g., temperature). This is quite understandable since we are neither an institute of higher learning with extensive funding (relatively speaking) in human and monetary resources nor a large corporation with a sizable R&D (research and development) budget. However, being blessed with a working environment which encourages challenges and fosters questioning, and having more than the average share of spirited curiosity, we conducted investigations within our limited means. On the basis of these findings, we are presenting some novel strategies which represent a departure from the current method of sizing pneumatic components and selecting pressures. In time you may find that our theories may require modification due to more elaborate probing. Some premises may require revision, while others may be discarded. Adding new postulates is a given which in due course will also be improved on or replaced. We are not totally correct, nor can we ever be. However, we are closer to the truth than is capable with the prevailing techniques. The objective is to continually refine the process. We hope to shed new light into a corner long ignored. We desire to *open*—rather than close—a new area of thinking. Our acceptance should not be measured by how correct our answers are but rather by our ability to further open the doors of truth. For the ultimate truth in the scientific realm is an ideal which can be only approached but never reached. Like all authors, we have done our best to live up to our commitments. But you, the readers, are the ultimate judges.

*Henry Fleischer*

# Acknowledgments

It is unusual for a person outside academe to have the opportunity to write a text while still being thoroughly immersed in the primary activity of holding down a full-time position in industry. This observation reflects the regard the management of Numatics, Inc. holds for the written word.

Unbeknownst to me, many individuals at Numatics, Inc. must have taken the initiative to solve problems without my assistance to spare me those precious few moments when I was absorbed in the organization of this text. Since I am unaware of who they are, I thank them collectively for their valuable assistance to me in completing this book.

Most married authors are indebted to their spouses and children for immeasurable assistance and patience in preparation of a book manuscript. In my case, completing this manuscript would have been inconceivable without my wife Rhoda. She has the uncanny ability to elicit from me exactly what I am trying to say. Angrily (because I didn't think of it before), I write it as she suggests, for she is correct. If there is any aspect you find difficult to understand, it must be a concept that I felt was adequately explained and thus failed to consult her on. My son Bruce's technical expertise was instrumental in clearing several very difficult barriers. My son Niles was helpful in resolving some troublesome obstacles. Isn't that what sons are for!

Bill Carls, the previous president of Numatics, had the foresight to recognize the value of a program that could predict the performance times of cylinders. He encouraged, stimulated, and influenced us to continue the work to a successful conclusion. John Welker, the present president of Numatics, continued in the same footsteps. John was the first Numasizing missionary and unequivocally supported the project of writing the text. Bill Carls planted the seed, and John Welker made certain it blossomed.

John Bond's ability to convert raw data into formulas helped me arrive at several vital conclusions. Mike Liberty's organizational prowess and his penchant for detail helped steer me on a straight course. Dave Ureche and Donna Harris also provided professional assistance. Frank Shepard, with his unlimited patience in the lab, carried the day. Last but not least, thanks to Chuck Fletcher for spawning this subject a long time ago.

Chapter

# 1

# The Evolution of Pneumatic-System Technology

*"Do not go where the path may lead. Go instead where there is no path and leave a trail."* RALPH WALDO EMERSON

The patterns of energy consumption in the United States, which are reflected in the general lifestyles of average U.S. citizens, have placed a tremendous burden on the U.S. economy. The U.S. balance-of-trade deficit, uninterrupted since 1975, is due overwhelmingly to excessive importation of oil. Crude-oil imports accounted for almost half of the U.S. trade deficit in 1990 and for over half in 1991 (Fig. 1.1), and the preliminary figures for 1993 remain essentially unchanged. The United States thus imports about 45 percent of its oil. The U.S. Department of Energy predicts that unless we (i.e., U.S. citizens) alter our patterns of consumption and production, the figure will leap to 65 percent by the year 2010.[1] Per capita, the United States consumes much more energy than does the United Kingdom, Japan, or Germany (Fig. 1.2). These figures reveal a condition which effectively prevents us from being competitive. The cost of these excesses is reflected in the price of every product we manufacture.

Certain events further exacerbate our energy problem. The dependence on oil from the volatile Middle East puts us continually at the mercy of the oil cartel's price manipulations. This was clearly evident during the Persian Gulf War in 1991 and especially at the time of the 1973 Middle East (Yom Kippur) War.

---

[1]P. Hong, "The Keys to Energy Security: More Drilling, Less Swilling," *Business Week,* p. 42, April 20, 1992.

| Item (example) | 1990 | 1991 |
|---|---|---|
| | ( in billions) | |
| Crude oil | $ 43.8 | $ 37.2 |
| Electrical machinery (fuses, circuit breakers) | $ 33.6 | $ 35.1 |
| Data-processing and office equipment | $ 26.9 | $ 30.1 |
| Clothing | $ 25.6 | $ 26.2 |
| Telecommunications equipment | $ 22.2 | $ 23.5 |
| Agricultural products | $ 22.3 | $ 22.2 |
| New cars from Japan | $ 19.2 | $ 20.4 |
| General industrial machinery (escalator parts) | $ 14.5 | $ 14.4 |
| Power-generating machinery (turbine engines) | $ 14.5 | $ 14.2 |
| Car and truck parts | $ 15.2 | $ 14.1 |

(a)

**Figure 1.1**   (a) Top U.S. imports. (*Source: U.S. Commerce Department.*)

Other situations, such as the Exxon *Valdez* oil spill in 1989, with the continued reliance on aging, rusting, and unregulated tankers 6 years later still spilling and fouling the waters from the South Pacific to the North Atlantic; the perpetual global climate changes; and the depletion of the ozone layer further aggravate the energy dilemma. These unfavorable phenomena are all attributable to either the distribution or the extensive burning of fossil fuels, both of which are, unfortunately, essential for the lifestyle we lead and have come to expect. Taken together, these issues and facts with their dire effects signify an acute need for a national energy strategy as the United States represents the single largest market for imported oils.[2] The profound and widespread geopolitical, economic, social, and ecological consequences these issues created, and continue to generate, necessitate appropriate governmental measures because they are beyond the individual's control. It is essential, though, that they be properly supported with concurrent industrial and civic activities.

---

[2]J. Enders, "Delicate Task of Oil Transport Rests on Old Ships," *The Flint Journal,* pp. A1, A6, March 28, 1993.

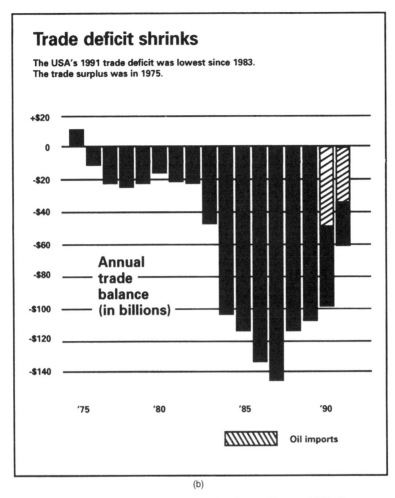

(b)

Figure 1.1   *(Continued)* *(b)* Trade-deficit shrinkage. *(Source: U.S. Commerce Department.)*

We are now paying for these consequences with fewer jobs, due partially to the decades of our throwaway and wasteful actions. The expense of these and other practices, included in all our fabricated goods, continually increased until we were priced out of the market. The cost of energy constitutes a portion of this price tag, for we have treated it with the same disregard that we have treated other commodities. These ingrained attitudes prevailing in all sectors of our society, which was once the envy of the world, are luxuries we can no longer afford. The evidence is formidable, and the essential actions to be taken are patently obvious.

## ELECTRICITY

| | USA | Japan | Canada | United Kingdom | United Germany |
|---|---|---|---|---|---|
| Capacity (1987) – 1000s kW | 743,377 | 176,419 | 100,600 | 64,772 | 107,635 |
| Production (1987) – million kWh | 2,685,627 | 698,970 | 496,335 | 300,247 | 529,992 |
| Consumption (1987) – million kWh | 2,727,458* | 698,970 | 452,379 | 311,882 | 537,586 |
| Consumption per capita – kWh | 11,193 | 5,739 | 17,526 | 5,484 | 6,916 |
| Consumption per capita – % of USA | 100.0% | 51.3% | 156.6% | 49.0% | 61.8% |

## COAL

| | USA | Japan | Canada | United Kingdom | United Germany |
|---|---|---|---|---|---|
| Reserves (1987) – million metric tons | 290,840 | 1,120 | 7,550 | 5,070 | 88,120 |
| Production (1987) – 1000s metric tons | 831,754 | 13,049 | 61,207 | 104,435 | 494,208 |
| Consumption (1987) – 1000s metric tons | 751,840 | 102,512 | 50,670 | 117,187 | 506,149 |
| Consumption per capita – metric tons | 3.1 | 0.8 | 2.0 | 2.1 | 6.5 |
| Consumption per capita – % of USA | 100.0% | 25.8% | 64.5% | 67.7% | 209.7% |

## NATURAL GAS

| | USA | Japan | Canada | United Kingdom | United Germany |
|---|---|---|---|---|---|
| Reserves (1989) – billion cubic meters | 5,150 | 38 | 2,637 | 590 | 363 |
| Production (1988) – million cubic meters | 472,490 | 2,100 | 98,220 | 45,750 | 28,670 |
| Consumption (1987)–million cubic meters | 498,847 | 41,865 | 57,558 | 65,233 | 71,180 |
| Consumption per capita – cubic meters | 2,047 | 344 | 2,230 | 1,147 | 916 |
| Consumption per capita – % of USA | 100.0% | 16.8% | 108.9% | 56.0% | 44.7% |

## CRUDE PETROLEUM

| | USA | Japan | Canada | United Kingdom | United Germany |
|---|---|---|---|---|---|
| Reserves (1989) – million barrels | 26,500 | 55 | 6,786 | 5,175 | 412 |
| Production (1988) – million barrels | 2,981 | 5 | 586 | 867 | 28 |
| Consumption (1987) – million barrels | 4,680 | 1,147 | 467 | 502 | 644 |
| Consumption per capita – barrels | 19.2 | 9.4 | 18.1 | 8.8 | 8.3 |
| Consumption per capita – % of USA | 100.0% | 49.0% | 94.3% | 45.8% | 43.2% |

* 2.73 trillion kWh = 28.2 Quads (1987)
  3.02 trillion kWh = 31.2 Quads (1990)
  (10331 BTU required to generate 1 kWh)

**Figure 1.2**   World energy utilization. (*Source: PC Globe, Inc., Tempe, Ariz., 1991.*)

Collectively we must reverse this trend, for the alternative is not only unacceptable but totally unthinkable. We must extract the cost of waste from our products. This would be a small contribution toward placing us back into contention in the international arena. However, there are still many areas in the energy field alone that demand our attention, such as

1. The lack of a comprehensive energy plan.
2. The need to reduce our addiction to fossil fuels.

3. The need to employ whatever we do use more efficiently by methods as advocated by energy providers such as Pacific Gas and
Electric.[3]

4. The need to search for alternate energy sources and the need now,
during, and after we've either located new sources or drastically
improved the efficiency of our present ones to aggressively conserve rather than build for our immediate future energy requirements. In 1988 it cost seven times more to produce one kilowatthour (1 kWh) from a new energy source than it did to save
one. In 1994 that 1988 figure increased 12-fold for building a conventional coal-fired utility and 40-fold for a nuclear-powered facility to generate rather than conserve 1 kWh, including incentives.[4]

The author's company, Numatics, Inc., a fluid power establishment,
has confronted the industrial energy parcel of this perplexing problem
and specifically the compressed-air sector with a program for conserv-
ing energy without loss of productivity called "Numasizing."

In 1990 fossil fuels accounted for 88.6 percent of all the energy consumed in the United States; by 1992 that figure dropped to 88.3 percent (Fig. 1.3). It would therefore appear that reducing our reliance
on fossil fuels would be of major interest to us in the light of the foregoing information. Apparently not, for even though the 1973 oil-
embargo crisis heightened the public's energy awareness, the consumption of fossil fuels has diminished by only 6.3 percent[5] from the
1973 figure of 94.6 percent. An extensive conservation effort was then
launched, along with a frantic search for alternative energy sources,
which gradually dwindled. It was hoped that the Persian Gulf War
would rekindle this need for the federal government to be stimulated
into taking appropriate steps, for on the agenda of national priorities,
there still is no single issue, either locally or globally, which has had
or will have as great an overall impact on our lives as that of energy.
Efficient utilization of energy must be added to the other essential
considerations (production, cost, reliability) in the selection of machines and all their components, whether electrical, hydraulic,
mechanical, or pneumatic. (*Note:* Throughout the course of the text I

---

[3]A. H. Rosenfeld and D. Hafemeister, "Energy-Efficient Buildings," *Scientific
American,* pp. 78, 80, April 1988.

[4]Broadcast of Morning Edition (7:30 AM) in early May 1994 on station WFUM
[National Public Radio (NPR)] by R. Charles on nuclear reactors: "$125 to conserve
with incentives per kilowatthour; $1500 to construct a traditional coal-fired facility to
produce 1 kWh; $5000 to construct a nuclear-powered utility to produce 1 kWh."

[5]U.S. Energy Information Administration (1973 Fossil Fuels totaled 94.6 percent).

## 1990 SOURCE
### 38,390,000 BPDOE (Barrels Per Day Oil Equivalent )
### (81.26 Quadrillion BTU's or Quads)

OIL
41.3%
15,850,000 BPD

| 7,190,000 BPD IMPORTED 45% | COAL 23.5% 9,020,000 BPDOE | NAT. GAS 23.8% 8,120,000 BPDOE | HYDRO 3.6% 1,390,000 BPDOE | NUCLEAR 7.6% 2,910,000 PBDOE |

OTHER
0.2%
100,000 PBDOE

INDUSTRIAL
14,200,000 BPDOE
(30.1 Quads)
37%

COMMERCIAL
6,150,000 BPDOE
16%

COMMERCIAL
TRANSPORTATION
5,370,000 BPDOE
14%

RESIDENTIAL
7,670,000 BPDOE
20%

PERSONAL
TRANSPORTATION
5,000,000 BPDOE
13%

## CONSUMPTION

Electrical Segment of Industry
4,860,000 BPDOE (10.26 Quads)
34%

Compressed Air Segment of Electricity
1,070,000 BPDOE (2.26 Quads)
22%

10% Savings  107,000 BPDOE  (.22 Quads)
20% Savings  214,000 BPDOE  (.45 Quads)
compared to
Prudhoe Bay Oil Fields  1,800,000 BPD

**Figure 1.3**  (a) U.S. energy system.

These two charts are based on Energy Information Administration (EIA) surveys. There were some slight differences between the 1990 review and the updated figures for 1990 as published in the October 1991 report. Some variations also showed up when comparing the figures of *Nations Business, Electrical World, Pipeline and Gas Journal,* etc. with those of the EIA. Since the deviations were minor (mostly due to independent rounding), I have reconciled all of them so as to render uniform results. From a conceptual viewpoint and from the ultimate potential savings and increased productivity

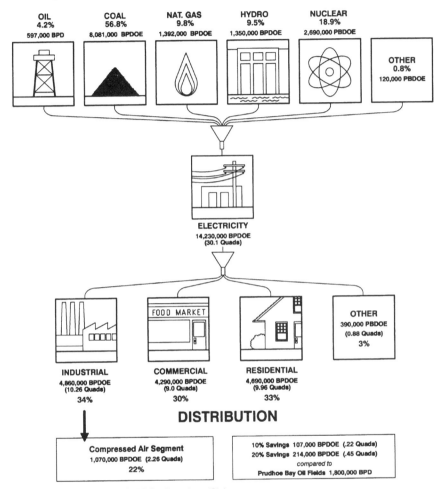

Figure 1.3  (*Continued*) (*b*) U.S. electric utilities.

aspect, they have no bearing as the differences are minuscule. Also, I have incorporated into these figures the fact that 1,033,100 Btu (EIA from utilities) is required to generate 100 kWh of electricity (due to losses in conversion and transmission), while 300 kWh is needed to produce 1,024,000 Btu of heat (1 kWh = 3413 Btu). [*Source: U.S. Energy Information Administration, 1990 and 1991; also part of 1992, the most recent year for which statistics are available. DOE/EIA 0384 (90), DOE/EIA 0384 (92), DOE/EIA 0384 (93).*] Note: 1994 preliminary statistics will not be available until June 1995.

am attempting to use the most recent year for which complete statistics are available.)

There are some in the ecological community who insist that the lack of potable (drinkable) water is the major issue facing this planet today. They predict that this problem will progressively increase unless we find a reasonable solution.

Two thirds of the world's surface is composed of water, more than enough to go around. Potable water would not be a problem if an ample supply of energy were available (since water desalination and distribution in themselves present no difficulty). For example, the Kuwaitis desalinate every drop of their water with no hardship, as they are blessed with a plentiful supply of energy in the form of oil. We therefore disagree with the environmentalists and return to energy as the most critical cause for concern.

The sun, wind, and tides—to identify just a few of the natural phenomena—are the most powerful and everlasting sources of energy available to us. They all have the potential to diminish our foreign oil dependence, thus averting the environmental problems identified with fossil fuels. The elements are all there, including most of the technologies needed to harness and implement them. We must have a call to arms, a singlemindedness of purpose, to sufficiently challenge us if we are to fulfill this dream.

To date, we still have not developed a complete and coherent national energy policy or an all-inclusive approach to deal with the bulk of the energy issues. President Franklin D. Roosevelt was the first to make such an attempt. At the brink of World War II, he directed his staff to make certain that the United States would have ample energy supplies. The most recent strategy in this area was that of President Bush, which represented the tenth bid by a U.S. president to establish a viable policy. The most visible shortcoming with the Bush energy strategy was that it didn't champion conservation and efficiency more strongly.[6] It is too early to know the details of the type of program and considerations that will emerge from the Clinton administration, for it is not high on Clinton's agenda. However, it is interesting to note that Hazel O'Leary, who now heads the U.S. Department of Energy (DOE), intends to place more emphasis on research in renewable energy, clean-coal technology, and energy efficiency. She also intends to seek more private-sector partnerships. She has called for less dependence on foreign oil and no increases in energy taxes on coal, oil, and gasoline. This is contrary to the few comments President

---

[6]"National Energy Strategy: Powerful Ideas for America," U.S. Government Printing Office, Washington, D.C., 1991. As viewed in *Physics Today*, July 1991, pp. 22–30.

Clinton made on his position on these matters.[7] We must wait until the opposing points of view have been resolved. Until then, with the current state of the world political atmosphere, the judicious management of energy has once again been placed on the government's back burner, leaving it up to the industrial and commercial sectors to spearhead the conservation drive.

The claimed reduction in Middle East tensions has caused our guard to drop somewhat, and we are once again being lulled into a false sense of complacency. R&D, in endeavoring to locate new energy sources, must be an ongoing commitment over decades by government, industry, and the general populace. Our past palliative, short-term fixes were totally ineffective. Still, everyone realizes it is critical that we seek energy self-sufficiency because of our increased dependency on foreign oil imports. In addition, and more importantly, the age of fossil fuels in general will cease to exist as we know it today in a century or less because of the inherent pollution that these fuels create and the global environmental conditions that are grossly damaged by their combustion products. In fact, the prevailing feeling among environmentalists is that the life expectancy of fossil fuels may be no more than 50 years. We remain vulnerable, and yet we continue to burn fossil fuels unabated and without any sense of urgency.

We all acknowledge the fact that we must attain this independence from fossil fuels. We also recognize that in order to accomplish this, we must shift to appropriate alternate sources of energy, which is, more than ever, urgently required and will take time. The need to gain a greater regard for the state of affairs (borne out by the preceding data and conditions) is hampered in this country by lethargy. This attitude is not reflective of all but far too typical of many and thus helps to explain our willingness to be seduced by low prices and adequate supplies of gasoline. However, once we are cognizant of this need, we can move away from fossil fuels and in particular, oil. To ease the transition (repeating again for emphasis), it would be prudent to conserve wherever possible. The major deterrent to conservation and energy management in this country, as we view it, is the difficulty in understanding not the phenomena and basic physical principles involved, but rather the tremendous apathy toward the subject. The purpose here is twofold: (1) to help reverse this general attitude of indifference toward conservation in the specific sector of pneumatics and (2) to unravel the mystery surrounding the subject of

---

[7]*Engineering Times* (published by the Naional Society of Professional Engineers), vol. 15, no. 3, pp. 1, 6, March 1993.

pneumatics. In this fashion it is hoped that some will be encouraged to champion the cause and implement the potential improvements in both conservation and productivity.

A distinction between pneumatics and hydraulics seems appropriate here:

1. *Pneumatics* is the branch of physics that deals with mechanical properties of gases such as compression ratios, pressure, and density and applies the principles of compressed or pressurized gases as a source of power to solve engineering problems. The most widely used compressed gas in the field is air, and thus its use has become synonymous with the term *pneumatics.*

2. *Hydraulics* is the branch of physics that deals with the mechanical properties of liquids, such as pressure, density, and viscosity, and applies the principles to solve engineering problems.

Gases and liquids are both fluids as opposed to solids. Pneumatics and hydraulics together constitute a branch of industry known as *fluid power.* Pneumatics is a segment of industrial energy which has been overlooked and/or neglected because it is not normally viewed as a means of power generation. But that's exactly what its purpose is, and therefore it must be conserved and used as wisely as the traditional media of oil, gas, coal, and water.

Numatics, Inc., has addressed the issue of energy conservation and productivity improvement by explicitly tackling the methods that the industry employs to apply pneumatics in today's marketplace.

It is the hope of the writer to educate you, the reader, in the use of this technique, which is relatively easy. By comparison, the more difficult task will be to make you aware of the severity of the situation. Introducing new technology is always problematic for a variety of reasons. This book will serve the industrial community well if it convinces those involved in the use of fluid power to examine this well-proven technique, which can develop a sizable energy-conservation source painlessly and effortlessly. Interestingly, if for no other reason, since industry consumes so much energy, it would make economic sense for it to adopt this conservation method. Using this method can help free up valuable capital for other forms of business expenses to give the needed impetus to launch industry back on the competitive track.

The question that initially arose was whether this unchartered area of pneumatics could be sufficiently fruitful to warrant examination. The figures spoke for themselves. The United States used 81.26 quads (1 quad = 1 quadrillion Btu or $1 \times 10^{15}$ Btu) of energy in 1990 and 82.36 in 1992 (Fig. 1.3). The 1992 figure is equivalent to 38,900,000 barrels per day of oil equivalent (bpdoe). I will use the acronym bpdoe as you can probably more readily relate to the familiar barrels of oil rather than British thermal units. You can then have a better perception of the enormous amount of energy involved on a daily basis. Each barrel contains 42 U.S. gallons (gal) of oil. An automobile tank holds an average of 16 gal. We are speaking of the equivalent of over 1,600,000,000 gal per day, which amounts to more than 100,000,000 tankfuls of gas per day. Since there are approximately 100,000,000 automobiles of all types in the United States, it is the equivalent of each car expending one tankful of gas each and every day of the year.

Industry's share of this pie is 14,200,000 bpdoe (36.9 percent), of which 4,860,000 bpdoe is devoted to electricity (34.2 percent of industry's share and 12.6 percent of the total pie) (see Fig. 1.3); 1,070,000 bpdoe of this oil is used for electricity to generate compressed air (22% [1,070,000/4,860,000] of industry's electrical share, 7.5 percent [1,070,000/14,200,000] of industry's share and 2.8 percent [1,070,000/38,900,000] of the total; see Fig. 1.3). As can be seen in Fig. 1.4, compressed air is a major factor in a plant as an energy source when compared to the other sources and thus demands attention. If the efficient use of pneumatics saved only 10 percent, it would be equivalent to an oil well producing 107,000 barrels of oil per day (boopd) forever. To put it in another perspective, the Prudhoe Bay Oil Fields (considered sizable by any account) yield 1,800,000 boopd,

## EMPLOYEE INVOLVEMENT GROUP
# HIGH COST    ENERGY

| | LAST MONTH COST | YEAR TO DATE |
|---|---|---|
| ELECTRIC | $ 405,584.66 | $ 3,494,180.86 |
| AIR | $ 79,272.00 | $ 785,974.14 |
| STEAM/COAL | $ 31,599.76 | $ 495,267.17 |
| WATER | $ 8,979.35 | $ 94,419.95 |
| Month Total | $ 528,189.17 | $ 94,418.95 |

## GET INVOLVED!    DATE _SEPT-84_
## SUGGEST SAVINGS

Figure 1.4   Automotive assembly plant statistics: sample bulletin-board chart.

although their life expectancy is only a short 30 years. If the savings were 20 percent, then that would bring this newly found oil field to one ninth that of Prudhoe Bay. It is not necessary to sink a single foot of shafting in order to recover any of this "oil," yet we proceed with the same indifference oblivious of the inevitable aftermath.

Let us digress for a moment to digest the profound implications of a potential savings of 214,000 bpdoe (20 percent savings). A household having a 20-cf (20-ft$^3$) refrigerator, clothes washer, room air conditioner, and dishwasher requires an average of 2.29 barrels of oil per year to operate them.[8] This 214,000-bpdoe oil well can operate 10,800,000 households having these appliances for one entire year, year in and year out.

We can reconcile the 7,190,000 barrels per day (bpd) imported in 1990 (Fig. 1.3) with the crude-oil costs of $43.8 (see footnote 1) billion for the same year using the following equation:

7,190,000 bpd × 365 days × $17.00/barrel (approx.) = $44 billion/year

To date the conventional method for reducing compressed-air usage is to obtain more efficient compressors, plug leaks, shut off nonoperating air devices, and so on. Considerable education and effort has been expended in this area with commensurate results. These are all commendable and beneficial projects worthy of continual monitoring to maintain the savings. But we believe that another approach has the potential for even greater savings. It not only encompasses the advantages of the aforementioned traditional categories, such as reducing leakage, but also incorporates a new element into the equation.

At the point of use, compressed air is used primarily to apply force. The principal mechanism for producing this force is a pneumatic cylinder. Our major emphasis is thus placed on the cylinder, for it affords the most fruitful means of saving energy. The general practice for selecting air valves and conductors has been to select a valve and pipe size equal to the port size of the cylinder chosen. In many instances this practice results in oversizing the valve and conductor, sometimes by as much as two or three sizes. In fact, for some applications, the use of conductors larger than required will hinder the performance of the system. In other instances the choice of too small a valve and conductor will also prevent the realization of optimum performance. Concluding with prime components by this archaic method of selection occurs strictly by happenstance.

---

[8]*USA Today Research,* March 1992.

Optimum selection of components should be added to optimum energy utilization, reliability, productivity, and cost as all are intertwined and relevant. The growing demand for a more exacting procedure to select pressures and size devices can be fulfilled only if all the considerations discussed above are equally weighted and judged.

Numasizing, the method that Numatics employs to satisfy all these prerequisites for using compressed air more judiciously to achieve an energy savings of 10 percent, 20 percent, or more, is built on two cornerstones: the utilization of dual pressures as opposed to the universal use of a single pressure and $C_v$, the capability of a pneumatic device. Both are covered in detail in Chaps. 2 and 3.

The proposed method of selection, as we proceed with our first example, will dramatically demonstrate that a $3\frac{1}{4}$-in-bore air cylinder ported $\frac{1}{2}$ NPT (national pipe thread) does not necessarily require a $\frac{1}{2}$-NPT valve (normally having a $C_v$ of approximately 4.0) nor a $\frac{3}{4}$-in hose (the traditional choice for a $\frac{1}{2}$-NPT port). None of the cases, appealing to different objectives, required a $\frac{3}{4}$-in hose as the ideal choice, and in only one of the three objectives was a $\frac{1}{2}$-NPT valve necessary to meet the target. As we will see shortly, there are many objectives to select from, depending on customers' needs.

The conventional method of using the same pressure at each end of an actuator (cylinder, rotary, etc.) in most cases is not only useless but wasteful. Rarely does a cylinder carry the same large load at each end (extend and retract ends; see Fig. 1.5). In fact, on careful scrutiny, a major load is present in only one direction in the vast majority of cases. The load in the reverse direction is small by comparison, as it merely returns the working tool or is simply frictional. Yet, the mindset is such that an identical pressure is used, with ensuing impact, to generate the force necessary to overcome the minor load end. To prevent this impact, a flow control valve or similar device is used to reduce the airflow and thus the speed, and therein lies the rub.

Productivity is often sacrificed because of ignorance of alternate solutions to reduce impact. To compound the felony, because symmetry is also an intrinsic human characteristic, a second flow-control valve is located for the major load end. This presents an additional impediment, even in the full-open mode of the flow control, further slowing the cylinder end, which is already taxed with a large load. If the speeds are not achieved with the flow-control valves, it may be necessary to use larger and more costly valves and components. These larger units are necessary in order to overcome the added resistance of the flow-control valves (typical installation) which prevented reaching the response-time constraints in the first place. This is covered in depth in Chaps. 6 and 8, with examples delineating when it is and is not appropriate to use these devices.

# Problem Specifications

Weight of Carriage retract ($L_r$) ............ 20 lbs.
Weight of Load & Carriage extend ($L_e$) ....... 450 lbs.
Angle of Incline ........................ 45°
Coefficient of Surface Friction ............. 0.3
Time to Extend ($T_e$) ..................... 0.3 sec. (initially 0.74 sec.)
Time to Retract ($T_r$) ..................... 0.2 sec. (initially 0.36 sec.)
Pressure Available (Supply) ............... 100 PSIG
Cylinder Stroke ........................ 3.75"

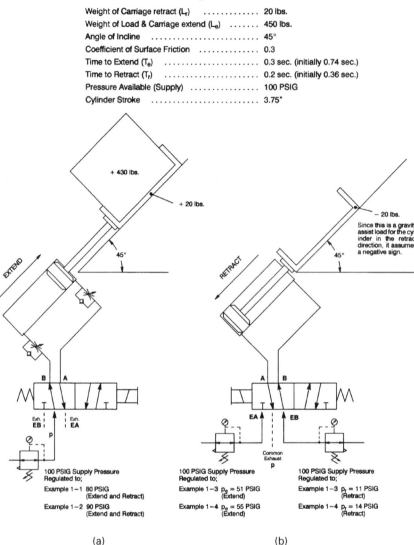

(a)                              (b)

**Figure 1.5**  Cylinder loads with (a) single pressure and (b) dual pressure.

It is noteworthy to point out that, in the example shown in Surveys 1-1 to 1-4, an air savings of over 36 percent was achieved by virtue of using dual pressures. This is more the norm (than the 10/20 percentage ratio stated earlier) for those whose objective, in the >10,000 surveys completed to date, was energy conservation. The industries serviced thus far cover the full spectrum of manufacturing in every geographic location of the world. Yet, this represents a minute fragment of the possible energy savings that could be generated in the United States alone. Views of the single- and dual-pressure circuits accompany the solutions of the examples in Surveys 1-1 to 1-4 at the end of the chapter.

Air cost to generate 12,000,000 cycles per year using a single pressure source of 80 psig (lb/in$^2$ gauge)                                              $1167.00

To obtain 24,000,000 cycles/year air would cost     $2334.00

Air cost to generate 24,000,000 cycles/year using dual pressures of 55 and 14 psig, respectively     $1490.00

$$\text{Percent savings} = \frac{(\$2334 - \$1490) \times 100}{\$2334} = 36.2\%$$

It was stated earlier that this method also includes means to save energy in the conventional areas such as leaks. If the pressure is reduced, there is a commensurate reduction in leakage. In the results shown above, the $2334 cost contains $174 due to leakage, whereas the dual-pressure solution has only $39 attributable to leakage. See Surveys 1-1 to 1-4 for detailed breakdowns.

As for the other cornerstone, $C_v$, that's thoroughly covered and explored in Chap. 2. Still, I will briefly review its function so as to establish its role in the overall scheme. Pragmatic field engineers consider it essentially a dimensionless number because of its many variables. It expresses the flow capability or conductance (reciprocal of resistance) of any fixed-orifice pneumatic device such as a valve, a cylinder port, or a fitting. It is analogous to the conductance of an electrical device.

Every pneumatic device, bar none, as in electricity, has a conductance value. These values, again as in electricity, can be combined to render a system $C_v$ ($C_{vs}$). The cylinder performance times are inversely related to the $C_{vs}$ and directly proportional to the system's exhaust volume ($V_{es}$ or $V_{rs}$ depending on which direction the single-rod double-acting air cylinder is proceeding in). As the $C_{vs}$ increases, the cyclic rate of the cylinder improves, measured in cycles per minute (cpm); and as the volume increases, the cyclic rate of the cylinder is reduced. It is consequently essential that each component be selected carefully for both $C_v$ and volume, as both energy and productivity are affected. They are the vehicles for determining the performance times of actuators.

[*Note:* Here and throughout the text we continually refer to volume rather than mass because these are the only parameters of concern in pneumatics for the following reason. The mass of air is dependent on pressure, volume, and temperature. Temperature is not taken into account because the typical range of use hovers within a small window which makes it insignificant. Anything outside of this 40°F window is handled as a special case. As far as the pressures are concerned, we performed all the tests (details are given later in chapter) at pressure levels associated with the normal field operating range, thereby removing them from the equation and leaving only the total system extend and retract volumes to contend with. The specific gravity of air is so negligible that we don't concern ourselves with it from a practical point of view.]

By methodically calculating the necessary information for each cylinder, one can determine the potential cyclic rate for a machine. Included in this determination is an assessment of whether the cylinders operate in synchronization or sequentially. If the designer is dissatisfied, components as well as pressure changes can be evaluated immediately to ascertain the effect on speed. It is therefore conceivable to virtually arrive at all the necessary components to achieve the required cpm value *before a single line is drawn*. This is one of the functions of Numasizing. In addition, Numasizing enables the circuit designer to select the optimum components (valves, conductors, fittings, flow controls, cylinders, surge tanks, compressors, etc.) and pressures. It not only takes into consideration all the physical specifications of a pneumatic circuit (conductor length and diameter, available pressure, cylinder loads, fittings, desired extend and retract times) but assesses objectives as well.

It is not my intent to imply that energy conservation, energy efficiency, and optimal utilization of energy are the sole or even the major objectives of this concept. Numasizing is not relegated to dealing only with energy. Quite the contrary, it achieves many other equally important objectives such as determining the minimum size components, increasing productivity, reducing concerns dealing with the environment, or a mixture of several or a blend of many concerns. We focus on energy here because of its vital importance for all the aforementioned reasons. We emphasize this notion because in a small measure it aids us not only in the current transition period to new and improved energy technology but beyond, for it teaches us to use what we have more wisely.

At the outset of our investigations in 1969 we (myself and others at Numatics, Inc.) were originally searching for an accurate method of sizing valves. The fluid power industry lacked an accurate and reliable means of predicting performance times of valve-conductor-cylinder assemblies functioning under any and all combinations of loads and pressures. A specific void was there, demanding to be filled. We undertook an inquiry, which turned out to be massive, into the response times of actuators in conjunction with associated components operating over the entire range of their load capabilities under incremental variations in supply pressures.

The inquiry focused mainly on double-acting air cylinders having dissimilar loads because the majority of applications, as discussed earlier, fall into this category. We confirmed early in our testing program that correlating pressures to loads allows reductions in valve and other component sizes (smaller $C_v$ values) without jeopardizing productivity in the majority of cases. We were concentrating primarily on minimum-size components, with particular emphasis on valves. However, it soon became apparent from our initial results and research of over 50,000 recorded observations that the concept was considerably broader, encompassing all the facets and purposes outlined thus far.

To date we continue to experiment and test, having amassed an additional 200,000 observations, to enlarge the database, improve on the methods, refine the results, and obtain further information. It is an ongoing process of clarification and purification. To illustrate the flexibility of this technique, let us study the same circuit from a variety of viewpoints ranging from the original equipment manufacturer (OEM) and end user to the facilities engineer and general manager. What results is a customized circuit designed to include all the specified needs.

Each application necessitates selecting entirely different components and pressures depending on where the emphasis is placed. Perhaps your plant, like so many of today's plants, is operating at or near peak compressor capability, yet you are desirous to install added pneumatic equipment without necessitating purchasing additional compressor capacity. Logically this appears to be contradictory. A survey, however, can uncover areas that would permit shedding enough energy without loss of productivity on existing installations. The economies would yield the necessary quantity to accommodate the intended new equipment. The recommendations may at times require valve and pressure changes on the existing machinery, but that would be far less expensive than the purchase of additional compressor capacity along with the associated equipment and required floor space.

Also, as illogical as it may appear sometimes, the use of dual pressures can increase productivity and simultaneously reduce operating and leakage costs. As we proceed throughout the text, there will be ample field examples elaborating on and confirming this premise.

Let us return now to review the various objectives in the light of these concepts and apply them to a typical application. We will limit our explorations to four specific viewpoints or paths at this time:

1. The first viewpoint will be the OEM or the purchasing agent, whose major concern is the use of minimum-size components (least capital expenditure), while meeting engineering specifications. Interestingly, some OEMs see the practice of the dual-pressure principle in turn as a sales tool for their customers. The OEM can justify the additional expense burden since it can be amortized over a few months (see summary results in Fig. 1.6).

2. The second viewpoint is traditionally the end-user's route (production), whose responsibility is to guarantee the means to increase future productivity and to accomplish it at minimal cost.

3. The third part is the one the facilities engineer would take at an end-user facility which is rapidly approaching its compressor capacity and yet must accommodate more pneumatic equipment. Thus the facilities engineer is responsible for purchasing components that would optimize the utilization of air, and may also be interested in reducing air usage of existing applications, without sacrificing productivity, so as to ensure the ability to supply the additional needed compressed air.

4. The fourth path (which may be preferred by the facilities engineer) is a variation of path 3 as it involves a minor pressure increase, thus necessitating a slightly greater horsepower (hp) requirement to fulfill one of the suggested minimum specifications.

Regarding path 4, allow me to delve into a little detail so early in the text, but this is an excellent introduction to deal with this hp aspect. We see from the summary sheet in Fig. 1.6 that in order to satisfy one of our requirements, so as to avoid any production problems, an increase in pressure is necessary, resulting in an increase in hp needs and thus in the utility bill. The issue that is often raised is how the increase in hp relates back to the utility bill and what the relation between the utility bill and the total air savings is. We will be solving several problems treating all these questions later on in the text, but this will give us the proper understanding now to avoid future explanations. The hp difference between Surveys 1-3 and 1-4 is 0.29 hp (4.20 − 3.91), and if we multiply that by 0.746 (746 W = 1 hp), we obtain 0.216 kW. From the specifications we also learned that this cylinder is operating 4000 h/year (50 weeks/year × 5 days/week × 16 h/day); therefore the added kilowatthours expended for the year is 866. The cost of air of $0.30/1000 scf was used to calculate the total cost, which includes the utility portion, and is based on $0.0675/kWh. This is fairly representative of compressor operation at 100 psig in the metropolitan Detroit area. There are wide deviations from this figure in some locations of the United States. It would behoove the designer who is computing the costs to carefully check this charge.

# Summary

Taken from computer printouts which follow. Abbreviations of all items are addressed in front of text.

| Survey Number & Viewpoint | Valve Size $C_v$ | Cycles Per Minute | Cylinder Bore Size (Inches) | Hose Conductor (Inches) | Pressure Used (PSIG) $P_e$/$P_r$ | Required HP[II] | Cost Of Air/Year (Dollars)[III] | Capital Expenses (Dollars) | Labor Cost/1000 Pcs. (Dollars)[V] | Technique Used To Obtain $T_e$/$T_r$ |
|---|---|---|---|---|---|---|---|---|---|---|
| 1–1: OEM or (End User Purchasing) | (L1) 1.0 | 50 | 3.25 | 3/8 | 80 / 80 | 3.29 | 1167 | 219.40 * | 6.76 | Flow Controls (4FC3B's) [I] |
| 1–2: End User (Manufacturing) | (L2) 1.7 | 100 | 4.00 | 5/8 | 90 / 90 | 8.80 | 3120 | 247.09 ** | 3.49 | Flow Controls (4FC3B's) [I] |
| 1–3: End User (Facilities) | (MK55) 5.5 | 100 | 4.00 | 5/8 | 51 / 11 | 3.91 | 1387 | 320.34 *** | 3.39 | Dual Pressure below recommended |
| 1–4: End User (Facilities) | (MK55) 5.5 | 100 | 4.00 | 5/8 | 55 / 14 | 4.20 | 1490 | 348.94 **** | 3.40 | Dual Pressure with one 4FC3B |

\* L1 Valve + 3.25" Cylinder + (2) 4FC3B Flow Controls

\** L2 Valve + 4.00" Cylinder + (2) 4FC3B Flow Controls

\*** MARK 55 Valve + 4.00" Cylinder + (1) Additional Pressure Regulator

\**** Same as *** with (1) 4FC3B Flow Control

In reviewing the above summary survey results, one can easily see the benefits for each of the various disciplines.

The comparison of the HP requirements.

The comparison of the labor cost / 1000 pieces using the different components.

The comparison of the attained cycles per minute.

The comparison of the pressures required.

The comparison of the operating costs.

What are the various stroke times at terminal velocity?

Can also determine the effect of additional elbows in the network.

Can establish the optimum cylinder bore based on pressure and load.

Can establish the optimum conductor diameter based on length.

Comparing the components for size and capability.

I) L1, L2, MK55 and 4FC3B are Numatics, Incorporated valves. However, any valve having the same $C_v$ will render similar cylinder performance times.

II) Compressor HP required on a continuous basis to operate cylinder.
Suggested HP for a dedicated compressor to be 3X to 4X continuous rating to render 2 to 3:1 off time to on time.

III) Based on $ 0.30/1000 SCF (In turn based on approximately $ 0.07/kWh)

IV) Labor cost to operate machine which houses cylinder and is based on $ 20/man hr.

**Figure 1.6** OEM and end-user survey results; taken from computer printouts in Surveys 1-1 to 1-4. Abbreviations of all items are addressed in the Glossary.

Thus, in our case the additional cost amounts to \$58/year, which is a small price to pay for peace of mind. The utility allotment should fall between 50 and 67 percent of the entire air expense (a window large enough to encompass the variations due to area and utility conditions). In our case the additional charge was \$103, the total difference between the two surveys (\$1490 − \$1387). The final percentage of 56, in our situation, is the relationship of the utility bill to the overall air cost (\$58/\$103 = 0.56). This is reasonably close to what the percentage is running in the Detroit region.

The information resulting from the Detroit metropolitan area field survey described in the preceding paragraph has been divided into two categories. The individual survey performance results can be found in Surveys 1-1 to 1-4 at the end of this chapter along with the summary information sheet (Fig. 1.6) and diagram of problem setup and specifications (Fig. 1.5). Everything is included there except the $C_v$ data sheet. The $C_v$ data for this survey is located at the end of Chap. 2, which expressly deals with this subject.

Essentially, this entire concept is intended to allow the designer of automated equipment to concentrate more on the creative aspects of the machinery, leaving the design details to a prepackaged program. These and other factors make cost comparisons and economic feasibility studies less arduous. By streamlining these provided processes, the designers become more efficient as the use of their talents become more effective.

```
NUMATICS NUMASIZING (R) SUMMARY SHEET                    Date:   04/10/95
NU301EED  Ver 3.01 (c) 1989 Numatics, Inc.              SURVEY # 1-1
==========================================================================
Prepared for:                   Prepared by:    Michael Liberty
Company:                        Company:        Numatics Inc.
Address:                        Address:        1450 N. Milford Rd.
City,State,Zip:                 City,State,Zip: Highland, Mi. 48357
Telephone #                     Telephone #     (810) 887-4111
Fax #                           Fax #           (810) 887-9190
--------------------------------------------------------------------------
                                Avg/Tot/Oth      Extend      Retract
INITIAL CUSTOMER PARAMETERS:
  Total weight of load (lbs)                    450.00      -20.00
  Angle of load from horizontal       45
  Coefficient of Friction           0.30
  Number of actuators                  1
  Total load per actuator (lbs)                 435.53        0.70
  Minimum line pressure (PSIG)       100
  Design pressure used (PSIG)                     80.0        80.0
  Shifts/day (1 shift=120,000 m/yr)  2.0
  Cycles per year                12000000

ACTUATOR:
  Description:   Single Rod High Flow Numatics Actuator with 1/2 NPT ports
  Bore/stroke/rod          3.25" bore x 3.75" stroke x 1.000" rod
  Fitting                    3/8" - 1/2 NPT STR

CONDUCTOR & ASSOCIATED COMPONENTS:
  Branch conductor /leg                 N/A
  Branch manifold fitting /leg          N/A
  Branch cond equiv ftg lg /leg (in)    N/A
  Quick disconnect model /leg           N/A
  In line flow control model /leg                4FC3B       4FC3B
  Main conductor           3/8" rubber hose 96" long with 5.0 elbow(s)
  Main manifold fitting                 N/A
  Main cond equiv ftg lg (in)           79

VALVE ASSEMBLY & ASSOCIATED COMPONENTS:
  Description     2 Pos L1 on 1/4 NPT base with ext reg
  Fitting                    3/8" - 1/4 NPT EL
  Silencer model             M4 (1/2 NPT)

SYSTEM PERFORMANCE TIMES:
  Att'n stroke time (sec)                         0.74        0.36
  Required stroke time (sec)                      0.74        0.36
  Stroke time @ term vel (sec)                    0.28        0.31
  Att'n cyclic rate (CPM)            50.00
  Required cyclic rate (CPM)         50.00
  Cyclic rate @ term vel (CPM)       87.19
  System delay time (sec)            0.023
  Dwell time after stroke (sec)                   0.00        0.10

SYSTEM INFORMATION:
  Required system Cv                              0.71        0.60
  Attained system Cv                              0.72        0.61
  Att'n system air flow (SCFM)                    12.6        24.0
  Att'n branch air vel (400 FPS max)    N/A               N/A
  Att'n main air vel (400 FPS max)                  44       106
  Att'n % delta p (46% max)                          4        24
  % Act. capacity used (75% max)                    66         0
  Min pres necessary for ld w/S.F. (PSIG)         70.0        0.1
  Air per cycle (SCF)                0.30
  Att'n act leakage cost/yr @ $ 0.30 /KSCF   87     40        47
  Att'n operating air cost/yr @ $ 0.30 /KSCF 1080  560       520
  Cost /1000 cyc @ att'n times @ $ 20.00 /hr  6.76
  Att'n power input total (HP)       3.29

COMMENTS:
  OEM DESIRES MIN SZ COMPONENTS - FC'S CRANKED DOWN TO OBTAIN REQUIRED TIMES
```

```
NUMATICS NUMASIZING (R) SUMMARY SHEET                    Date:   04/10/95
NU301EED  Ver 3.01 (c) 1989 Numatics, Inc.              SURVEY # 1-2
=========================================================================
Prepared for:                    Prepared by:    Michael Liberty
Company:                         Company:        Numatics Inc.
Address:                         Address:        1450 N. Milford Rd.
City,State,Zip:                  City,State,Zip: Highland, Mi. 48357
Telephone #                      Telephone #     (810) 887-4111
Fax #                            Fax #           (810) 887-9190
-------------------------------------------------------------------------
                                    Avg/Tot/Oth    Extend      Retract
INITIAL CUSTOMER PARAMETERS:
  Total weight of load (lbs)                       450.00      -20.00
  Angle of load from horizontal         45
  Coefficient of Friction             0.30
  Number of actuators                    1
  Total load per actuator (lbs)                    518.41        9.13
  Minimum line pressure (PSIG)         100
  Design pressure used (PSIG)                        90.0 ?      90.0
  Shifts/day (1 shift=120,000 m/yr)    2.0
  Cycles per year                 24000000

ACTUATOR:
  Description:   Single Rod High Flow Numatics Actuator with 1/2 NPT ports
  Bore/stroke/rod             4.00" bore x 3.75" stroke x 1.000" rod
  Fitting                     5/8" - 1/2 NPT STR

CONDUCTOR & ASSOCIATED COMPONENTS:
  Branch conductor /leg                  N/A
  Branch manifold fitting /leg           N/A
  Branch cond equiv ftg lg /leg (in)     N/A
  Quick disconnect model /leg            N/A
  In line flow control model /leg                  4FC3B       4FC3B
  Main conductor            5/8" rubber hose 18" long with 0.0 elbow(s)
  Main manifold fitting                  N/A
  Main cond equiv ftg lg (in)             0

VALVE ASSEMBLY & ASSOCIATED COMPONENTS:
  Description    2 Pos L2 on 3/8 NPT base with ext reg
  Fitting                     5/8" - 3/8 NPT STR
  Silencer model              M4 (1/2 NPT)

SYSTEM PERFORMANCE TIMES:
  Att'n stroke time (sec)                            0.30        0.20
  Required stroke time (sec)                         0.30        0.20
  Stroke time @ term vel (sec)                       0.18        0.17
  Att'n cyclic rate (CPM)               99.22
  Required cyclic rate (CPM)           100.00
  Cyclic rate @ term vel (CPM)         132.76
  System delay time (sec)               0.023
  Dwell time after stroke (sec)                      0.00        0.10

SYSTEM INFORMATION:
  Required system Cv                                 1.40        1.35
  Attained system Cv                                 1.42        1.38
  Att'n system air flow (SCFM)                      42.9        60.4
  Att'n branch air vel (400 FPS max)       N/A              N/A
  Att'n main air vel (400 FPS max)                   52          87
  Att'n % delta p (46% max)                          10          24
  % Act. capacity used (75% max)                     46           1
  Min pres necessary for ld w/S.F. (PSIG)           55.1         1.0
  Air per cycle (SCF)                   0.42
  Att'n act leakage cost/yr @ $ 0.30 /KSCF    122    44          77
  Att'n operating air cost/yr @ $ 0.30 /KSCF 2998  1543        1435
  Cost /1000 cyc @ att'n times @ $ 20.00 /hr 3.49
  Att'n power input total (HP)          8.80

COMMENTS:
  END USER DESIRES FUTURE INCREASE TO 100CPM AT MIN CAP EXP. FC'S USED.
  ALTERED COND D & L, VLV & CYL. REPL ELS W/10X MIN ID BENDS. ONLY 10PSI S.F.
```

```
NUMATICS NUMASIZING (R) SUMMARY SHEET                    Date:    04/10/95
NU301EED  Ver 3.01 (c) 1989 Numatics, Inc.              SURVEY # 1-3
=========================================================================
Prepared for:                       Prepared by:   Michael Liberty
Company:                            Company:       Numatics Inc.
Address:                            Address:       1450 N. Milford Rd.
City,State,Zip:                     City,State,Zip: Highland, Mi. 48357
Telephone #                         Telephone #    (810) 887-4111
Fax #                               Fax #          (810) 887-9190
-------------------------------------------------------------------------
                                       Avg/Tot/Oth   Extend    Retract
INITIAL CUSTOMER PARAMETERS:
Total weight of load (lbs)                           450.00    -20.00
Angle of load from horizontal             45
Coefficient of Friction                 0.30
Number of actuators                        1
Total load per actuator (lbs)                        519.99     9.02
Minimum line pressure (PSIG)             100
Design pressure used (PSIG)                           51.3     11.4
Shifts/day (1 shift=120,000 m/yr)        2.0
Cycles per year                     24000000

ACTUATOR:
Description:  Single Rod High Flow Numatics Actuator with 1/2 NPT ports
Bore/stroke/rod           4.00" bore x 3.75" stroke x 1.000" rod
Fitting                   5/8" - 1/2 NPT STR

CONDUCTOR & ASSOCIATED COMPONENTS:
Branch conductor /leg               N/A
Branch manifold fitting /leg        N/A
Branch cond equiv ftg lg /leg (in)  N/A
Quick disconnect model /leg         N/A
In line flow control model /leg                      NONE       NONE
Main conductor            5/8" rubber hose 18" long with 0.0 elbow(s)
Main manifold fitting               N/A
Main cond equiv ftg lg (in)           0

VALVE ASSEMBLY & ASSOCIATED COMPONENTS:
Description   2 Pos Mk 55 on 1/2 NPT base with ext req
Fitting                   5/8" - 1/2 NPT STR
Silencer model            M4 (1/2 NPT)

SYSTEM PERFORMANCE TIMES:
Att'n stroke time (sec)                              0.30       0.20
Required stroke time (sec)                           0.30       0.20
Stroke time @ term vel (sec)                         0.08       0.07
Att'n cyclic rate (CPM)                  99.94
Required cyclic rate (CPM)              100.00
Cyclic rate @ term vel (CPM)            237.00
System delay time (sec)                   0.023
Dwell time after stroke (sec)                        0.00       0.10

SYSTEM INFORMATION:
Required system Cv                                    3.14       3.15
Attained system Cv                                   3.23       3.23
Att'n system air flow (SCFM)                         27.5      15.2
Att'n branch air vel (400 FPS max)       N/A                  N/A
Att'n main air vel (400 FPS max)                      49        69
Att'n % delta p (46% max)                              2         4
% Act. capacity used (75% max)                        81  ?      7
Min pres necessary for ld w/S.F. (PSIG)              55.1       1.0
Air per cycle (SCF)                      0.19
Att'n act leakage cost/yr @ $ 0.30 /KSCF   35         25        10
Att'n operating air cost/yr @ $ 0.30 /KSCF 1352      984       368
Cost /1000 cyc @ att'n times @ $ 20.00 /hr  3.39
Att'n power input total (HP)             3.91

COMMENTS:
END USER STILL DESIRES 100CPM BUT AT MIN HP. FC'S REMOVED. INC VLV SZ.
USING DUAL PRESSURES. HOWEVER, OVER 75% OF CYL CPCTY (51PSIG TOO LOW).
```

```
NUMATICS NUMASIZING (R) SUMMARY SHEET                    Date:   04/10/95
NU301EED  Ver 3.01 (c) 1989 Numatics, Inc.              SURVEY # 1-4 & 3-7
========================================================================
Prepared for:                    Prepared by:     Michael Liberty
Company:                         Company:         Numatics Inc.
Address:                         Address:         1450 N. Milford Rd.
City,State,Zip:                  City,State,Zip:  Highland, Mi. 48357
Telephone #                      Telephone #      (810) 887-4111
Fax #                            Fax #            (810) 887-9190
------------------------------------------------------------------------
                                       Avg/Tot/Oth   Extend     Retract
INITIAL CUSTOMER PARAMETERS:
Total weight of load (lbs)                          450.00      -20.00
Angle of load from horizontal            45
Coefficient of Friction                0.30
Number of actuators                       1
Total load per actuator (lbs)                       519.98        9.01
Minimum line pressure (PSIG)            100
Design pressure used (PSIG)                          55.2        14.2
Shifts/day (1 shift=120,000 m/yr)       2.0
Cycles per year                     24000000

ACTUATOR:
Description:   Single Rod High Flow Numatics Actuator with 1/2 NPT ports
Bore/stroke/rod               4.00" bore x 3.75" stroke x 1.000" rod
Fitting                       5/8" - 1/2 NPT STR

CONDUCTOR & ASSOCIATED COMPONENTS:
Branch conductor /leg                    N/A
Branch manifold fitting /leg             N/A
Branch cond equiv ftg lg /leg (in)       N/A
Quick disconnect model /leg              N/A
In line flow control model /leg                       4FC3B      NONE
Main conductor                5/8" rubber hose 18" long with 0.0 elbow(s)
Main manifold fitting                    N/A
Main cond equiv ftg lg (in)               0

VALVE ASSEMBLY & ASSOCIATED COMPONENTS:
Description    2 Pos Mk 55 on 1/2 NPT base with ext reg
Fitting                                  5/8" - 1/2 NPT STR
Silencer model                           M4 (1/2 NPT)

SYSTEM PERFORMANCE TIMES:
Att'n stroke time (sec)                               0.30        0.20
Required stroke time (sec)                            0.30        0.20
Stroke time @ term vel (sec)                         0.10        0.08
Att'n cyclic rate (CPM)                  99.94
Required cyclic rate (CPM)              100.00
Cyclic rate @ term vel (CPM)            210.08
System delay time (sec)                 0.023
Dwell time after stroke (sec)                        0.00        0.10

SYSTEM INFORMATION:
Required system Cv                                    2.42        2.83
Attained system Cv                                   2.50        2.88
Att'n system air flow (SCFM)                         29.3        16.7
Att'n branch air vel (400 FPS max)       N/A                      N/A
Att'n main air vel (400 FPS max)                      50          70
Att'n % delta p (46% max)                              3           4
% Act. capacity used (75% max)                        75           5
Min pres necessary for ld w/S.F. (PSIG)              55.2         1.0
Air per cycle (SCF)                     0.20
Att'n act leakage cost/yr @ $ 0.30 /KSCF   39          27          12
Att'n operating air cost/yr @ $ 0.30 /KSCF 1451      1044         407
Cost /1000 cyc @ att'n times @ $ 20.00 /hr 3.40
Att'n power input total (HP)            4.20

COMMENTS:
IDENTICAL TO 1-3 EXCEPT USED RECOMMENDED MIN PR OF 55 PSIG W/ONE FC
```

# 2

# Conductance ($C_v$)

Compressed air is a multifaceted topic, similar to many disciplines. As such, it is difficult to select the one ideal entrance to start us through the subject matter in a logical sequence. Nevertheless, let us begin our journey by first defining and then analyzing $C_v$, one of the cornerstones of our sizing technique. This will help dispel the mystery that surrounds it as well as indicate why we use it. $C_v$ is nothing more than the conductance of a pneumatic device. Pneumatic conductance is reported as a number expressing the ability of a fluid to flow under a pressure differential $\Delta p$ or pressure drop and is often referred to as *flow capability* or more commonly as the *flow coefficient*. It is the reciprocal of resistance, which is a measure of the inability to flow under similar conditions. Thus the greater the $C_v$ value, the better the flow. $C_v$ is analogous to electrical conductance.

Every electrical device in a room, without exception, has a resistance value or its reciprocal conductance value. One can determine the conductance value of each device, as well as combine all these values for a room total. The individual and the entire currents drawn can then be calculated on the basis of this conductance and the impressed voltage in the circuit. This information will permit the sizing of the branch and trunk lines to feed all the appliances. One can then proceed to ascertain the size of the main switch and the specific switches for each appliance or outlet in the room. One can now do the same for the other rooms and thus come up with a total for the establishment and, depending on the safety factor involved, arrive at the overall size of the generating capacity required. This formula can now be duplicated for all homes and businesses in a town. All the towns can be totaled so that, if desired, one can even determine the generating needs for the entire planet. A world main can be calculated with all its subvalues, etc., derived from the conductance specifications for each individual item, along with all the required switching gear.

In pneumatics you should do the same thing for the very same reason, namely, knowing your loads and requirements and sizing everything accordingly. As in electricity, every pneumatic component has a $C_v$ conductance value. We therefore can combine the $C_v$ values of each to obtain the total for the entire machine. As mentioned above for electricity, this permits us now to obtain the flow requirements, based on this conductance and the available pressure, in order to select the main conductor as well as the individual lines. From this we can deduce the size of the main valve (a pneumatic valve is the equivalent of an electrical switch, which in this case will either allow or not allow air to pass in opposition to electrons) as well as that of all subordinate valves. Finally, we can calculate the needs for the other machines and arrive at the plant's requirement for a compressor (pneumatic equivalent of an electrical generator). By similar reasoning we can determine the world's total compressed-air needs. Here, too, everything evolved from the conductance of each discrete component.

Expressing all fixed-orifice pneumatic devices in terms of their flow coefficients is like having all monetary systems designated in so many ounces of gold so that dollars, francs, lire, pounds, and other currencies can be compared to one another for purposes of evaluation and exchange. Analogous to this, flow coefficients may therefore be used to compare the flow capability in terms of $C_v$ of one pneumatic device to another for purposes of selection and rating.

The conductance of a device plays the same general role in pneumatics as it does in electricity. Nowhere is it as clearly demonstrated as in the comparison of the following two basic equations (the first equation, for electricity, is Ohm's law; the second is the basic flow equation at critical flow for pneumatics):

Ohm's law: $E = IR$

Basic flow equation at critical flow: $Q = 0.489\,C_v p_{1a}$

where $R$ is in ohms ($\Omega$) and $Q$ is in standard cubic feet per minute. Before discussing the similarities between these two expressions, let me cite and elaborate on the formula for determining the compressed-air flow rate as adopted by the National Fluid Power Association (NFPA) and then derive the specific equation for flow at critical backpressure, commonly referred to as *flow at critical pressure* or simply *critical flow*. The origin of the formula can be traced to Bernoulli's theorem. At given conditions of pressure, temperature, and specific gravity, the flow rate of a device is directly proportional to the flow coefficient as follows:

$$Q = 22.48 C_v \left( \frac{\Delta p p_{2a}}{\Gamma_{1a} G} \right)^{0.5}$$

where $Q$ is flow at 14.7 psia atmospheric pressure, 68°F temperature, and 36% relative humidity expressed in standard cubic feet per minute (scfm).

A conventional commercial pressure gauge is set up to read 0 at standard atmospheric pressure and is expressed in pounds per square inch gauge (psig). However, at this reading we are actually surrounded by pressure; therefore, this 0 psig expressed in absolute terms is really 14.7 pounds per square inch absolute (psia). Using 0 to represent atmospheric pressure is simply a convenient reference point. To obtain absolute pressure from gauge pressure, one must always add 14.7 to the gauge reading. This is based on the weight of the entire column of air above an area of one square inch at sea level. It is force per unit area. The weight of this column of air is 14.7 lb. The majority of the weight is closest to sea level as the air molecules are more tightly packed (compressed) at the base, and therefore the air is more dense and thus heavier. At the top of Mt. Everest, 30,000 ft above sea level, the weight of the column of air bearing down on an area of one square inch weighs only 4.37 lb, and therefore the absolute pressure at the summit is only 4.37 psia.

A standard cubic foot (scf) of air is the volume occupied by one cubic foot of air at sea level where the barometric pressure is 14.7 psia [denoted as one atmosphere (1 atm)], 68°F, and 36% relative humidity. If the gauge pressure in a piece of equipment were 27.4 psig (42.1 psia), the number of atmospheres would be (42.1/14.7)3. For an application of this concept, see Example 2.5 later in this chapter. The following terms are used in equations in this chapter:

$C_v$: The flow coefficient of any fixed-orifice pneumatic device using the proposed NFPA flow rig (shown later in chapter; Fig. 2.8) and procedure[1] is expressed as $C_v$. $C_{vs}$ replaces $C_v$ when dealing with a system rather than a single device (combining $C_v$ values described later in chapter).

$\Gamma_{1a}$: The temperature is expressed in absolute terms in degrees Rankine (°R) (°R = °F + 460). $\Gamma_{1a}$ for the family of curves on the flowchart (later in the chapter, Fig. 2.9) is 528°R (68°F + 460 = 528°R). These curves are applicable for 68°F ± 20°F. Beyond this range the formula should be used. The same reason for expressing pressure in absolute terms applies to temperature or any other physical property.

---

[1]American National Standard ANSI/(NFPA) T3.21.3-1990; *Flow Rig and Procedure,* 1st ed., Jan. 25, 1990.

$p_{1a}$: The initial measure of the fill pressure or the maximum upstream pressure available to the actuator prior to the inception of the movement of its piston (static mode) at temperature $\Gamma_{1a}$ is expressed in psia. Placing a number subscript (integer) after any term indicates that it is expressing that value at a specific condition; e.g., "1" may be the initial situation and "2," the final. Placing a subscript "a" after any term indicates that it is expressing that value in absolute terms; e.g., $p_1$ = Initial pressure of 100 psig whereas $p_{1a}$ = initial pressure of 114.7 psia (100 + 14.7).

$p_{2a}$: The final measure of the fill pressure or the minimum downstream pressure, in the actuator, that $p_{1a}$ reaches at the conclusion of its movement (dynamic mode) at temperature $\Gamma_{1a}$ and is expressed in psia. Once movement has ceased, the pressure builds back up to $p_{1a}$.

$\Delta p$: The pressure drop expressed in psi = $p_{1a} - p_{2a}$. I must emphasize that $p_{1a}$, $p_{2a}$ and $\Delta p$ pertain to only that end which is being filled (pressurized). It is the changes that $p_{1a}$ is undergoing during the pressurizing of the stroke for that particular end of the cylinder. This filling-pressure principle is applicable in turn to either the extend stroke or the retract stroke. The filling end is always accompanied by the pressure exhausting function on the opposite end. (The variations or similarities between the filling pressures at each end of the cylinder which successively fill and exhaust will be dealt with in another chapter and should not be confused with this $\Delta p$.) We therefore experience in turn the extend filling pressure becoming the retract exhausting constituent when the opposite retract end is being filled and vice versa.

$G$: Specific gravity assumed to be 1 for air at 14.7 psia atmospheric pressure, 68°F temperature, and 36% relative humidity. $G$ varies from 1.00 to 0.97 across a temperature spectrum ranging from 0 to 100°F due to the effect of relative humidity (over its entire range of 0 to 100%; see Fig. 2.1). Using the two extremes in the equation reduces the maximum effect on flow to under 1.5 percent for almost all possible plant floor conditions. Let us further assume that the compressed-air temperature at the point of use can reach 130°F during extreme conditions; its influence is still less than 3 percent as we take the square root of the figure. We therefore ignore the effect of relative humidity and use 1.00 to cover all conditions encountered for ease of calculation. Some individuals who pursue this subject prefer to view $G$ as the ratio of the molecular weight (MW), simply identified as $M$, of the gas under test to that of air, which in reality is a method for determining the specific gravity of the unknown gas when using air as unity. The MW of air is 28.98: $G$ = MW of gas used/28.98.

| Temp. °F | Relative Humidity Per Cent | | | | | | | | | |
|---|---|---|---|---|---|---|---|---|---|---|
| | 10 | 20 | 30 | 40 | 50 | 60 | 70 | 80 | 90 | 100 |
| 0 | .9999 | .9999 | .9999 | .9998 | .9998 | .9997 | .9997 | .9996 | .9996 | .9995 |
| 10 | .9999 | .9998 | .9998 | .9997 | .9996 | .9995 | .9994 | .9994 | .9993 | .9992 |
| 20 | .9999 | .9997 | .9996 | .9995 | .9994 | .9992 | .9991 | .9990 | .9988 | .9987 |
| 30 | .9998 | .9996 | .9994 | .9992 | .9990 | .9987 | .9985 | .9983 | .9981 | .9979 |
| 40 | .9997 | .9994 | .9991 | .9987 | .9984 | .9981 | .9978 | .9975 | .9972 | .9969 |
| 50 | .9995 | .9991 | .9986 | .9982 | .9977 | .9972 | .9968 | .9963 | .9959 | .9954 |
| 60 | .9993 | .9987 | .9980 | .9974 | .9967 | .9960 | .9954 | .9947 | .9941 | .9934 |
| 70 | .9991 | .9981 | .9972 | .9963 | .9953 | .9944 | .9935 | .9925 | .9916 | .9907 |
| 80 | .9987 | .9974 | .9961 | .9948 | .9935 | .9922 | .9909 | .9896 | .9883 | .9870 |
| 90 | .9982 | .9964 | .9946 | .9928 | .9910 | .9892 | .9875 | .9857 | .9839 | .9821 |
| 100 | .9976 | .9951 | .9927 | .9903 | .9878 | .9854 | .9830 | .9805 | .9781 | .9756 |
| 110 | .9967 | .9935 | .9902 | .9869 | .9837 | .9804 | .9771 | .9738 | .9706 | .9673 |
| 120 | .9957 | .9913 | .9870 | .9827 | .9783 | .9740 | .9697 | .9653 | .9610 | .9567 |
| 130 | .9943 | .9886 | .9830 | .9773 | .9716 | .9659 | .9602 | .9545 | .9488 | .9432 |

**Figure 2.1**  Specific gravity of moist air at standard sea-level pressure. (*Reference data from J. P. Rollins, ed., Compressed Air and Gas Handbook, 4th ed. Compressed Air and Gas Institute (CAGI), 1973, Chap. 10, General Reference Data, pp. 10–51.*)

The flowchart in Fig. 2.9 is based on the aforementioned formula, $[Q = 22.48C_v[(\Delta p p_2)/(\Gamma_{1a}G)]$, for a $C_v$ of 1; $p_1$ and $p_2$ in Fig. 2.9 are given in psig for convenience. It is essentially the graphical representation of the equation. To obtain the flow at any other $C_v$ rating, simply multiply the flow at the $C_v$ of 1 by the $C_v$ of the component in question. As is evident from the formula, there is a direct linear relationship between $Q$ and $C_v$. [*Note:* The flow-rate formula applies only when $p_{2a}/p_{1a}$ is ≥0.533 (critical backpressure ratio for air, critical pressure ratio, or just critical ratio). At this ratio, of absolute downstream pressure to absolute upstream pressure, sonic velocity is approached (i.e., Mach number 1). When $p_{2a}/p_{1a}$ is less than the critical ratio of 0.533, the value of $p_{2a}$, used in the preceding formula, should be equal to the critical pressure (here, too, the term *back* is commonly discarded but implied). In this case, the critical pressure is obtained by multiplying $p_{1a}$ by the critical ratio for air (i.e., 0.533). Every gas has its individual critical ratio. See Fig. 2.12 for a list of the critical ratio for several gases along with the formula for determining their value. Also, the minimum that $p_2$ can be is 0 psig (14.7 psia). For all cases where $p_1$ is <12.9 psig (27.6 psia), flow can never reach critical since it cannot be <14.7 psia or atmospheric pressure. This is because the minimum that the fraction $p_{2a}/p_{1a}$ can be is 0.533 (14.7/27.6), and that is only at $p_{1a} = 27.6$ psia. If $p_{1a}$ is <27.6, the fraction can never dip down to 0.533 as $p_{2a}$ will remain at 14.7 psia. Anything less than 27.6 psia when multiplied by 0.533 will generate a number in the vacuum range (<14.7 psia), and obviously atmospheric pressure under standard conditions cannot be <14.7 psia. For example, the lowest the fraction can be at 10 psig (24.7 psia), if it is exhausting to the atmosphere, is 14.7/24.7 or 0.595. Since it is >0.533, it has not reached critical or maximum flow. The corollary is that $\Delta p$ can never be >12.9 psi when $p_{1a}$ is ≤27.6 psia. As $p_{1a}$ dips below 27.6 psia and is exhausting to the atmosphere, $\Delta p$ continues to decrease; e.g., a $p_{1a}$ of 24.7 psia will have a maximum $\Delta p$ of 10 psi as its $p_{2a}$ is a minimum of 14.7 psia.]

Figure 2.12, on physical and chemical properties of gases, includes both the molecular weight and the specific gravity, either of which affords us the opportunity to determine the flow for different gases, such as how much argon can flow through a valve having a $C_v$ of 1.5 at 68°F and 100 psig with a pressure drop of 5 psi and a specific gravity (sp. gr.) of 1.379:

$$Q = 22.48 C_v \left( \frac{\Delta p p_{2a}}{(\Gamma_{1a} G)} \right)^{0.5}$$

$$= 22.48 \times 1.5 \left( \frac{5 \times 109.7}{528 \times 1.379} \right)^{0.5} = 29.3 \text{ scfm}$$

Air under the same conditions will flow 34.4 scfm. If we know what the flow would be for air and are interested in knowing what the flow would be for another gas under identical conditions, we simply take the air flow and divide it by the square root of the specific gravity of the unknown gas. For example, if we know that air flows at a rate of 34.4 scfm through a certain device and the square root of the specific gravity of the desired gas, argon, is sp. gr. 1.174 $(1.379)^{0.5}$, then 34.4/1.174 is 29.3 scfm.

To simplify the flow equation for air, in which we are primarily interested, we will substitute 1 for the $G$ term, as it was previously established to be essentially 1, and substitute 528°R for $\Gamma_{1a}$, which results in the following equation:

$$Q = 0.978 C_v (\Delta p p_{2a})^{0.5}$$

We will further reduce the equation for the special case of critical flow:

$$p_{1a} = p_{2a} + \Delta p; \qquad 1 = \frac{p_{2a}}{p_{1a}} + \frac{\Delta p}{p_{1a}}$$

If $p_{2a}/p_{1a} = 0.533$, then $\Delta p/p_{1a} = 0.467$, $p_{2a} = 0.533 p_{1a}$, and $\Delta p = 0.467 p_{1a}$. Now $Q = 0.978 C_v (0.467 p_{1a} \times 0.533 p_{1a})^{0.5}$.

$$Q = 0.978C_v \, (0.2489[p_{1a}]^2)^{0.5}$$
$$= 0.489C_v p_{1a}$$

We can now return to the comparisons between Ohm's law and the pneumatics critical flow equation:

Ohm's law    $E$ = impressed voltage, expressed in volts

$E = IR$    $I$ = current flow, expressed in amperes

$R = 1/C_n$    $R$ = resistance (reciprocal of conductance, expressed in ohms)

$E = I/C_n$    $C_n$ = device conductance (reciprocal of resistance, expressed in mhos)

$I = C_n E$    $C_{ns}$ = system conductance when dealing with several devices, expressed in mhos

Summarizing this derivation, we have

Pneumatic equation for critical flow    $Q$ = airflow, expressed in scfm

$Q = 0.489C_v p_{1a}$    $C_v$ = device conductance, expressed in $C_v$

$C_{vs}$ = system conductance when dealing with several devices, expressed in $C_v$

$p_{1a}$ = pressure in absolute terms, expressed in psia

In reviewing these two basic equations, we find a striking similarity. The same relationship exists between transmitting electrical signals and pneumatic signals through their respective conductors. This is especially evident when we substitute the pneumatic terms for their electrical equivalents into Ohm's law. In the context of electricity, the term *impressed voltage* is used to imply pressure, and thus its counterpart in the flow equation is pressure. The conductance as described earlier carries the same meaning in each discipline, and thus $C_v$ is substituted for $C_n$. Finally, $I$ representing the flow of current, essentially the number of electrons expressed as amperes, has as its parallel $Q$, which denotes so many molecules of air, which is expressed in scfm. Thus $I = C_n E$ becomes $Q = C_v p_{1a}$, which is comparable to the original flow equation at critical flow without the constant 0.489 as seen above.

Although no universal attempt has been made in pneumatics to assign a term equivalent to resistance, its reciprocal conductance is expressed as a number simply known as $C_v$. (*Caution:* Do not confuse this pneumatic $C_v$ with the thermodynamic $c_v$, which refers to the specific heat of a fluid at constant volume.)

The Instrument Society of America (ISA) issued two standards, one in 1973, the other in 1974, using $C_v$ to specify the size—or, more precisely, the capability—of pneumatic valves. Several years ago, the National Fluid Power Association (NFPA) undertook the task of establishing a method to measure $C_v$ for any fixed-orifice pneumatic device. After many years of investigation and testing, they successfully issued the first edition on January 25, 1990, ANSI/NFPA Standard T3.21.3-1990. Many manufacturers of pneumatic components, including Numatics, Inc., have been using this standard method to rate their products.

The following is a brief review of the work of three physicists[2] and a comparison of the mathematics involved in determining the combined conductance and resistance as they relate to pneumatics and electricity, to further indicate the close affinity between these two subjects:

Formula for combining pneumatic conductances arranged in series:[3]

$$\frac{1}{(1/C_{v1}^2 \times 1/C_{v2}^2 + 1/C_{v3}^2 + \cdots 1/C_{vi}^2)^{0.5}} = C_{vs}$$

The original work done by Slawsky and Lutzky were in flow factors which we found by experimentation and analysis to have a direct linear relationship to the flow coefficients we are currently using.

Formula for combining pneumatic resistances arranged in series:

$$(R_{p1}^2 + R_{p2}^2 + R_{p3}^2 + \cdots + R_{pi}^2)^{0.5} = R_s$$

Formula for combining electrical conductances arranged in series:

$$\frac{1}{1/C_{n1} + 1/C_{n2} + 1/C_{n3} + \cdots + 1/C_{ni}} = C_{ns}$$

Formula for combining electrical resistances in series:

$$R_1 + R_2 + R_3 + \cdots + R_i = R_s$$

*Pneumatics:* Assume that three pneumatic components with conductance values of 1, 2, and 3 $C_v$ are arranged in series. Therefore, their individual resistances (reciprocals) are 1, ½, and ⅓, respectively. Their combined conductance and resistance is

---

[2]Milton M. Slawsky and Martin Lutzky of the National Bureau of Standards, in conjunction with Albert E. Schmidlin of Walter Kidde Company.

[3]Henry Fleischer, "Why You Should Know Your $C_v$," *Hydraulics and Pneumatics*, Aug. 1980.

$$\frac{1}{(1/1^2 + 1/2^2 + 1/3^2)^{0.5}} = 0.857C_{vs}$$

Reciprocal = 1.17 resistance

$$[(1)^2 + (1/2)^2 + (1/3)^2)]^{0.5} = 1.17 \text{ resistance}$$

Reciprocal = $0.857C_{vs}$

*Electricity:* Assume that three electrical components with conductance values of 1, 2, and 3 mhos are arranged in series. Therefore, their individual resistances (reciprocals) are 1, ½, and ⅓ Ω, respectively. Their combined conductance and resistance is

$$\frac{1}{1 + \frac{1}{2} + \frac{1}{3}} = 0.55 \text{ mho}; \quad \text{reciprocal} = 1.83 \text{ } \Omega$$

$$1 + \frac{1}{2} + \frac{1}{3} = 1.83 \text{ mho}; \quad \text{reciprocal} = 0.55 \text{ mho}$$

It is quite evident that the addition of any device to an existing series circuit, whether it is pneumatics or electricity, will reduce the overall flow coefficient, since the total resistance is increased. It further follows that the effect of removing a device from a series circuit can cause an increase in the system flow coefficient, since the total resistance is reduced. The order in which devices are located in a series circuit does not affect the final result. The flow coefficients are additive for devices connected in parallel.

The combining chart (Fig. 2.13) can be used to combine any number of known $C_v$ values graphically by taking them two at a time and using the result to combine with the next device. This process continues until all the devices are accounted for. The graph is simply an explicit representation of the formula for combining pneumatic conductance.

To gain further insight into this subject, let us compare a component $C_v$ to the strength of a single link of a chain and the system $C_{vs}$ to the strength of the entire chain. It is not an identical mathematical analogy but one that is convenient and easy to relate to. The chain's strength is dictated by the weakest link, and to be viable, it must be rated such that the maximum load limit is less than can be supported by this weakest link. So, too, the smallest component $C_v$ dictates the system's $C_{vs}$. This resultant $C_{vs}$, similarly, is also always less than the smallest component $C_v$ as is evident from the previous combination of the three devices whose $C_v$ values were 1, 2, and 3. When we combined them, their resultant was 0.857. If only 1 and 2 were combined, the answer would be 0.894. The equation which reflects this phenomenon is the addition of reciprocals and consequently applies to electricity as well. The same computations apply to electricity, for the summation of electrical conductances, as indicated earlier, except it is not involved with the square of the terms.

There is no single component in a circuit that is more significant than its neighbor. As in a chain, each link is as important as the next and each must carry its weight; if not, the entire network collapses. To improve the capacity of a chain, one must replace the weakest link and, as a corollary to this, to improve the speed of a cylinder, one must either remove or replace the smallest $C_v$ in the circuit with a larger one.

We often visit a plant in response to a complaint that the cylinder's piston is moving too slowly and a larger valve is requested to rectify the performance problem. Figure 2.2 shows, by way of analogy to chain structure, the various components that constituted the circuit of one such situation. The customer desired to cut the extend stroke time in half. It can readily be seen that increasing the valve $C_v$ (size) would render a negligible improvement to the overall system $C_{vs}$. The reason is obvious; namely, the valve, is not the weakest link. In order to improve the performance of the system, one must replace the smallest $C_v$ (weakest link). In this instance the offending link was a restrictive orifice, and once supplanted with a larger orifice the desired time was achieved. We therefore always calculate and display the $C_v$ of every component of the circuit in our survey. We are then able to quickly ferret out the offending $C_v$ (smallest) that requires replacement. It should be noted that no volume changes took place in any of the links of the chains shown in Fig. 2.2, and therefore the only variable affecting the cylinder response times was $C_{vs}$.

Now that we have an appreciation of $C_v$, let us review its fundamental importance. $C_v$ serves as a critical medium to determine the speed of an actuator. Air travels at the same speed as sound, namely, approximately 1120 feet per second (fps; ft/s) under standard conditions in the earth's atmosphere. The labyrinthine path in an air valve presents restrictions which reduce the velocity. The velocity of air through straight, and especially elbow, fittings is further impeded. Within a long straight run of a conductor, the only component which affords opportunity to acquire substantial speed, the average air speed, is reduced as a result of internal wall friction to a maximum of about 500 fps. The internal friction is a function of the surface roughness of the internal diameter and the internal diameter itself. To appreciate where it would be possible for compressed air to attain high speeds, one need only consider a single air molecule, from the constellation of air molecules contained in air, to be comparable to a racing car surging around a track. The car will attain maximum speed on the straightaway simply because there are no obstructions due to curves or other impediments.

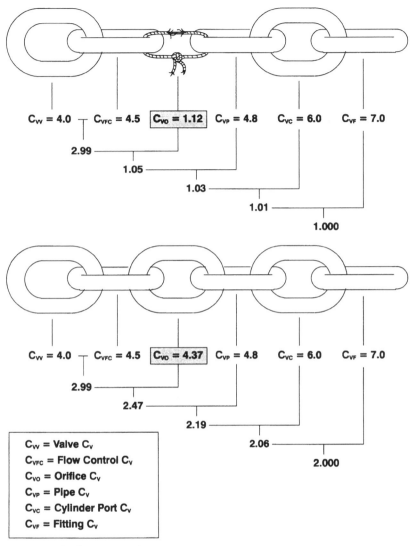

Figure 2.2  $C_v$–chain comparison.

[*Note:* Under certain high-cyclic-actuator conditions the velocity in the feeding conductor can approach sonic velocity, and steps should be taken to remedy such situations. Normally increasing the diameter of the conductor is a safe and appropriate method of solving the cavitation problems associated with high air speeds. It is common practice to use no more than 400 fps as the maximum permissible velocity to avoid any problems. We subscribe to this maximum speed only because it has been passed down through the years. Like most of these situations, it may be too conservative, and we hope future investigations will reveal documentation which will allow us to increase this maximum because there are advantages to be gained. There are also instances of highly restricting orifices (pinch valves or tiny orifice diameters) where sonic (the speed of sound) flow may be reached in the throat of the constriction. The $C_v$ of these devices will be much smaller than $C_v$ values of all the other components in the circuit and should be adjusted when reviewing all the links of the network in order to improve performance. Here, too, an appropriate solution would be to increase the diameter somewhat. As we've seen earlier, the downstream pressure $p_{2a}$ under these conditions is 0.533 of the upstream pressure $p_{1a}$, and lowering the $p_{2a}$ will not increase the flow rate.]

The air eventually reaches the actuator whose piston is considered moving extremely rapidly even if it travels as little as 10 fps. Even at this actuator speed the impact at the end of the stroke is excessive, and effective shock-absorption equipment is required to prevent premature rupture. This, however, is very slow in real time [<7 miles per hour (mph)]. The majority of actuators travel considerably slower than 10 fps. Nevertheless, a procedure is essential to determine their performance times regardless of speed in order to predict cycle time and ultimately, the vital statistic, the number of pieces of finished goods emanating from a production line. $C_v$ effectively serves as one of the vehicles in this computation. The cycle time is thus predictable for each cylinder of a machine. As we stated in Chap. 1, and which is worth repeating, if the designer's specifications for the cyclic rate of the entire machine are not met during this design stage, components and/or pressures can be immediately altered in the program until the desired results are attained. $C_v$ is a very crucial element in this process.

In the chain circuit discussed earlier (see also Fig. 2.2), the customer had a system $C_{vs}$ of 1, which rendered an extend time of 4 s. The customer desired the extend time to be 2 s, thus requiring a $C_{vs}$ of 2. We found that the valve did not have to be replaced since it was not the offending link. Simply increasing the $C_v$ of the restrictive orifice improved the system $C_{vs}$ to 2, thus reducing the extend time to the specified 2 s. Remember, the performance time of the actuator is inversely proportional to the system $C_{vs}$. Assuming an extend time of 1 s was needed. The system $C_{vs}$ would have to be 4, requiring many components to be increased, including the valve and conductor (see Fig. 2.3). Changing a conductor would bring into play different volumes due to length and diameter variations. When these volumes are combined with the adjusted $C_{vs}$, they can either improve or adversely affect the performance times. We will examine several problems dealing with the net effect of these properties on the actuator stroke times shortly.

| $C_{vs}$ | $T_e$ | $C_{vs}$ x $T_e$ |
|---|---|---|
| 1 | x    4 | =    4 |
| 2 | x    2 | =    4 |
| 4 | x    1 | =    4 |

**Figure 2.3** $C_{vs}$ versus time.

See the surveys at the rear of this chapter for the printouts of the component and total $C_v$ values pertaining to the multiviewed problem discussed in Chap. 1. Figure 2.4 shows a summary of the results.

In order to achieve 100 cpm (comparing Surveys 1-1 and 1-2 at the end of this chapter), it was necessary to select a larger conductor diameter and valve with appropriate larger fittings in the actuator and valve (increased $C_v$). It was also necessary to eliminate sharp right-angle fittings (elbows) and replace them with gentle bends (minimum 10 × ID). This aspect is elaborated on in Chap. 4. The cylinder bore was increased by one size. However, since the silencer and flow control $C_v$ values were considerably larger, even than the newly replaced valve, they virtually had no effect on the $C_{vs}$ and thus required no changes. The optimization of cylinder bores is treated in a subsequent chapter.

| Components | $C_v$'s | | | |
|---|---|---|---|---|
| | 50 CPM (#1-1) | 100 CPM (#1-2) | 100 CPM (#1-3) | 100 CPM (#1-4) |
| Actuator Fitting | 2.55 | 7.33 | 7.33 | 7.33 |
| Flow Control | 2.79/1.06 | 4.46/3.47 | — | 3.96/— |
| Main Conductor | 1.88 | 16.56 | 16.47 | 16.24 |
| Elbows | 2.33 | — | — | — |
| Silencer | 7.20 | 7.20 | 7.20 | 7.20 |
| Valve Fitting | 2.03 | 4.41 | 6.49 | 6.49 |
| Valve | 1.06 | 1.75 | 5.73 | 5.73 |
| Attained System $C_{vs}$ | 0.72/0.61 | 1.42/1.38 | 3.23/3.23 | 2.50/2.88 |
| Required System $C_{vs}$ | 0.71/0.60 | 1.40/1.35 | 3.14/3.15 | 2.42/2.83 |
| HP Required* | 3.29 | 8.80 | 3.91 | 4.20 |

SURVEY NUMBERS

#1-1   Minimum Size Components
#1-2   Least Capital Expense
#1-3   Least Energy Usage (below recommended standards)
#1-4   Least Energy Usage (within recommended standards)

* See rear of Chapter 1 for documentation.

**Figure 2.4** Component $C_v$ values.

In order to reduce the horsepower requirements (comparing Surveys 1-2 and 1-3), it was essential to increase the valve size and fitting (increased $C_v$ values) once more and eliminate the flow controls (removing $C_v$ values increases $C_{vs}$). This last alteration permitted the drop in pressure to render a sizable reduction in hp requirements. Increasing the $C_{vs}$ allows a commensurate decrease in pressure. The only drawback was operating the cylinder at 81 percent of its capacity rather than the suggested maximum of 75 percent. Notwithstanding, the low pressures of 51/11 psig can be raised slightly to 55/14 psig (Survey 1-4), to bring the 75 percent specification into line while only somewhat boosting the hp demand from 3.91 to 4.2. The $C_v$ results for these surveys (Surveys 1-1 to 1-4) are located at the end of this chapter as that is the subject matter handled in this chapter. The performance results are given in Chap. 1 (Fig. 1.6) for similar reasons.

Having discussed, explored the role of, and defined $C_v$, and shown how it can be combined if all other devices are expressed in terms of $C_v$, let us investigate what properties contribute to $C_v$ for the various components of an entire pneumatic system. The only elements to be considered, in our technique, are those which are successively pressurized and decayed each cycle. They are thus always downstream of the valve. With few exceptions, everything upstream of the valve is basically reservoirs which are examined for other criteria as they do not experience these continual large gyrations of pressure and are discussed in later chapters. Regulators are the exceptions, as they are neither reservoirs nor fixed-orifice pneumatic devices. The primary qualifications for these regulators, as well as for filters and lubricators, are whether they fulfill the necessary flow demands. The components in a pneumatic circuit that are left to be evaluated are located, and repeated for emphasis downstream of the valve. They are either fixed-orifice pneumatic devices or adjusted to specific settings, and thus their $C_v$ values are fixed for the duration of the stroke and therefore can be determined.

We had ample documentation[4] from all our tests indicating that the speed of the actuator is inversely proportional to the system $C_{vs}$ and directly related (linear with) to the exhaust system's entire volume (including conductor as well as actuator). [*Note:* The exhaust system volume is the trapped air that is decaying on the one end of the cylinder during the portion of the cycle that the other end is being pressurized (filled).] This selection technique requires that all fixed-orifice pneumatic devices considered for use in a pneumatic

---

[4]Henry Fleischer and Paul Tallant, *Practical Air Valve Sizing* (manual), Numatics, Inc., Dec. 1974.

system have reliably established flow coefficients in order to render a dependable $C_{vs}$.

To accomplish our goal of assigning a $C_v$ to every pneumatic device encountered in a circuit (required so as to permit their accumulation to render a $C_{vs}$ and thus predict performance times), it was essential to develop practical means for determining the $C_v$ of some of the elements that were lacking procedures. Most elements had formulas; for those that didn't have formulas at the outset, we established their $C_v$ values by using the proposed NFPA rig and technique.

The first item which fell into this gray area was an orifice. Slawsky et al.[5] were the three physicists (mentioned earlier) who developed the equation for combining flow factors (which subsequently were shown to be directly related to $C_v$ values) in the early 1950s. They were also responsible for developing some interesting equations dealing with gases. The contribution which aided the dual-pressure program was the equation that related $C_v$ to the diameter of an orifice $d$ expressed in inches, namely, $C_v = 18d^2$. This was limiting, as the constant 18 is specifically intended for use for a sharp-edge orifice having a coefficient of discharge $C_d$ of 0.61. For our purposes it was imperative that we cover the full range of orifices that would be encountered in the field. It thus warranted an investigation to establish assignable constants for each of the eight major types of orifice entries or exhausts commonly encountered. See Fig. 2.5 for the relationships of the various orifice discharge coefficients to their associated $C_v$ values.

The next group of devices that needed scrutinizing were angle fittings. Here, too, no method existed for expressing their flow capabilities in terms of $C_v$.

Over the years many companies have compiled extensive lists of almost every conceivable type of fitting encountered in pneumatic and hydraulic circuits and assigned values to them. We classified these values and ascribed a multiplying factor to each, denoted $K$ (See Fig. 2.6). We also developed an appropriate formula for converting the $K$ number to an equivalent conductor length. The diameter that is used in the formula is that of the conductor that is joined with the fitting. In the majority of cases the fitting diameter is equal to or greater than its mating conductor diameter. In a few instances this is not valid and can render an error in the accuracy of the performance times. This can be circumvented by knowing this condition beforehand so that it can be taken into account by using the smallest dimension in the formula for the $d$ value:

[5]Milton M. Slawsky, Martin Lutzky, and Albert E. Schmidlin, "A Method for Predicting Pressure Drops in Pneumatic Components and Systems," presented to the National Aeronautic Society, paper no. 81, April 1953.

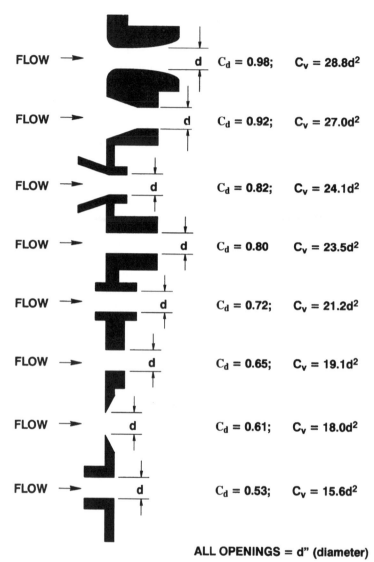

FLOW ⟶    d    $C_d = 0.98;$    $C_v = 28.8d^2$

FLOW ⟶    d    $C_d = 0.92;$    $C_v = 27.0d^2$

FLOW ⟶    d    $C_d = 0.82;$    $C_v = 24.1d^2$

FLOW ⟶    d    $C_d = 0.80$    $C_v = 23.5d^2$

FLOW ⟶    d    $C_d = 0.72;$    $C_v = 21.2d^2$

FLOW ⟶    d    $C_d = 0.65;$    $C_v = 19.1d^2$

FLOW ⟶    d    $C_d = 0.61;$    $C_v = 18.0d^2$

FLOW ⟶    d    $C_d = 0.53;$    $C_v = 15.6d^2$

**ALL OPENINGS = d" (diameter)**

**Figure 2.5**   Various orifice discharge coefficients $C_d$ and their related $C_v$.

$$L = nKd$$

where $L$ = equivalent length, expressed in feet
  $n$ = number of similar fittings in the conductor leg in question
  $K$ = multiplying factor assigned to the device
  $d$ = smallest diameter in the grouping

| COMPONENT | "K" |
|---|---|
| Globe valves, fully open | 28 |
| Angle valves, fully open | 12 |
| Gate valves, fully open | 1 |
| 3/4 open | 3 |
| 1/2 open | 13 |
| 1/4 open | 16 |
| Swing check valves, fully open | 11 |
| In line ball check valves, fully open | 12.5 |
| Butterfly valves, 6" and larger fully open | 1.65 |
| 90° standard elbow | 2.5 |
| 45° standard elbow | 1.3 |
| 90° long radius elbow | 1.5 |
| 90° street elbow | 4 |
| 45° street elbow | 2 |
| Reducer (1 size) | 1.5 |
| Enlarger (1 size) | 2 |
| Standard tee – flow through run | 1.5 |
| Standard tee – flow through branch | 5 |

**Figure 2.6** $K$ multiplying factors for various valves and fittings.

The diameter $d$ can be one of the following: the conductor coupled to the fitting, the fitting diameter, or the diameter of the aperture that the fitting threads into, expressed in inches.

The $K$ value of an integral conductor angle fitting having a bend radius of 10 times its ID or better is essentially zero. All the performance-time test data recorded was calculated to two decimal places. The performance of conductors with 10 times the ID radius bends or better required taking the readings to a minimum of three decimal places to detect any variations in results, and thus its $K$ values were considered zero. Since almost all installations dictate some bends, we recommend the use of generous integral bends (bend radii to be 10 times the conductor ID or better) instead of individual fittings wherever possible. If plastic conductors are being used, there are various devices available on the market which slip over the tubing to form the requisite bend radii; these devices are inexpensive, easy to apply, and result in a very professional-appearing installation.

Figure 2.6 is a partial list of $K$ factors assigned to the most commonly used fittings in compressed-air circuits. The information tabulated in Fig. 2.6 was gleaned from the prepared master list and represents the majority of the components applicable to pneumatic circuit applications.

Let us consider the following conductor and fitting combination to examine how all the aforementioned factors interact. Assume a conductor leg, between the valve and the cylinder, consisting of 20 ft of $\frac{3}{8}$-NPT Schedule 40 pipe and eight 90° standard elbows. Based on the equation, $C_v = 42.3a \sqrt{d/fl}$, which we will discuss shortly, the equivalent length of the fittings in terms of the conductor is calculated as follows: $n = 8$; k = 2.5; $d = 0.493$ in (the ID of $\frac{3}{8}$-NPT Schedule 40 pipe was determined to be the smallest diameter); $L = nkd = 8 \times 2.5 \times 0.493 = 10$ ft.

The eight elbows contribute an additional 50 percent to the overall length of the conductor. Unfortunately, most designers vastly underestimate their importance. As we will shortly see, this will have a dramatic consequence on the performance times of an actuator.

Slawsky et al. (see footnote 5) made another great contribution to the pneumatics field by developing the following formula (filling another gap in the technique), which expresses the length of a conductor, either real or equivalent, in terms of the essential common denominator, $C_v$:

$$C_v = 42.3a \left( \frac{d}{fl} \right)^{0.5}$$

where $C_v$ = flow capability of any actual or equivalent length of conductor
$a$ = internal area of the conductor expressed, in$^2$
$d$ = conductor diameter expressed, in
$f$ = coefficient of friction of the interior conductor surface
$l$ = conductor length (real and equivalent), in

The derivation, meaning, and role of $f$ are discussed in Chap. 5.

We now have acquired the necessary vehicle which permits us to convert any fitting to a $C_v$ via the $K$ factor and the real- and equivalent-length formulas. Applying the equivalent-length formula to the preceding problem, we have $a = 0.191$; $d = 0.493$; $f = 0.0305$; $l = 120$ in (10 ft); $C_v = 42.3a(d/fl)^{0.5} = 42.3 \times 0.191(0.493/0.0305 \times 120)^{0.5} = 2.96$.

In the preceding problem the distance between the valve and the cylinder measured only 10 ft. The additional 10 feet was required to bridge the eight elbows. All turns had to have as tight a right-angle bend, as was permissible, and the conductor had to follow the contours of the machine. The piping had to be as inconspicuous as possible so that on scanning the machine, one would be hard-pressed to discern how the air managed to get from the valve to the cylinder. All this is an indispensable part of rendering a traditional, cosmetically handsome installation. We will call this the 240-in (physical-length) survey, which in equivalent terms is 360 in (10 additional equivalent feet due to elbows). Discounting the extra capital expenditure of this strategy, let us see what is the cost in lost performance time by comparing it to a more prudent approach, which we will call the 120-in survey, which in equivalent terms is 150 in.

The new installation requires only two elbows (one in the actuator and one in the valve, equivalent to 2.5 ft or 30 in) instead of eight elbows and only 10 ft of actual conductor length. Everything else is identical. Appearancewise, it is every bit as professional-looking as the 240-in installation. We must include a volume change as well as the modified $C_{vs}$. In this particular comparison both will impact on the performance time of the actuator.

Before proceeding further, we will define several terms. The rod end of a single-rod double-acting cylinder is the end of the cylinder containing the rod. Its effective area is the bore area minus the rod area. The volume is this resultant area multiplied by the stroke. The blind end of a single-rod double-acting air cylinder is the opposite end having no internal obstructions. Its effective area is the bore area. The volume is this area multiplied by the stroke. Double-acting air cylinders are the most widely used actuators. They can accept pressure at both the rod and blind ends. Many other actuator types will be reviewed in Chap. 3.

The following information must be calculated in order to compare the performance times of the two installations:

| | |
|---|---|
| Blind-end volume of a 1.5 × 6.0-in cylinder | 10.60 in² |
| Rod-end volume of a 1.5 × 6.0-in cylinder (⅝-in rod) | 8.76 in² |
| Volume of 10 ft of conductor | 22.91 in² |
| Volume of 20 ft of conductor | 45.82 in² |
| Total system volume for 10-ft installation (retract $V_{es}$) | 33.51 in2 |
| Total system volume for 10-ft installation (extend $V_{rs}$) | 31.67 in² |
| Total system volume for 20-ft installation (retract $V_{es}$) | 56.42 in² |
| Total system volume for 20-ft installation (extend $V_{rs}$) | 54.58 in² |
| $C_v$ of one 90° actuator bend (equivalent to 14.79 in) | 8.44 |
| $C_v$ of actuator orifice | 6.32 |
| $C_v$ of actuator elbow (combination of above two) | 5.06 |
| $C_v$ of one 90° valve bend (equivalent to 14.79 in) | 8.44 |
| $C_v$ of valve orifice | 5.59 |

| | |
|---|---|
| $C_v$ of valve elbow (combination of above two) | 4.66 |
| $C_v$ of six additional elbows (equivalent to 88.74 in) | 3.44 |
| $C_v$ of 120-in conductor | 2.96 |
| $C_v$ of 240-in conductor | 2.09 |
| $C_v$ of valve | 1.75 |
| $C_{vs}$ of 120-in system consisting of actuator elbow (5.06), valve elbow (4.66), conductors (2.96), and valves (1.75) | 1.38 |
| $C_{vs}$ of 240-in system consisting of actuator elbow (5.06), valve elbow (4.66), six additional elbows (3.44), conductors (2.09), and valves (1.75) | 1.175 |

The next bit of reasoning may appear to be illogical; nevertheless, once reviewed, the determination of the cylinder's extend-stroke time, traditionally associated with, but not restricted to, the blind end of the actuator (extending the piston), uses the rod-end exhaust volume to determine its extend time. The retract-stroke time (returning the piston to its original position) uses the blind-end exhaust volume to determine its retract time. This will be elaborated on in Chap. 3.

To refresh our memory, the performance time varies directly with the exhaust volume and inversely with the $C_{vs}$ if the external moving load, cylinder bore, and extend and retract pressures remain constant. In this instance all components with the exception of conductor lengths and additional elbows were identical. The rub lies in the fact that when comparing two performance times, it is wrong to simply take only the volumes and $C_v$ values into consideration, even though this is what I stated earlier as the truth—which in retrospect is only a half-truth. We will demonstrate that there is a third and vital factor which must be dealt with. Without it the results are inaccurate.

When I was a young student, my physics instructor continually taught us half-truths so that we could acquire a rudimentary knowledge of the topic. It was an excellent method for viewing concepts and making them easy to grasp. Since the world doesn't follow perfect rules, our instructor eventually dispelled them and we understood, for by then, we were able to digest the true premises. We are engaging in the same approach here, since you have already gained a healthy awareness of the subject matter. The factor that has a great influence on the moving load is time, and if we are comparing two times, we are no longer holding the dynamic loads constant as they vary with time. The initial mass to be moved is still identical; however, the dynamic load is a function of mass and acceleration, which in turn is dependent on time. It is therefore difficult to determine a new performance time from an existing one, especially when the two times (extend and retract) are both under one second (which affects acceleration greatly) and have a spread of over 10 percent. We will discuss this in some detail in Chap. 3. For the moment let us return to the half-truth. The relationship which permits one to predict the stroke time for one system, if the stroke time is known for another system, with the qualifications discussed above, can be expressed by the following formula:

$$\text{Known time}\ \frac{\text{unknown vol.}}{\text{known vol.}}\ \frac{\text{known } C_{vs}}{\text{unknown } C_{vs}} = \text{unknown time}$$

The 240-in installation has an extend time of 0.3 s. To find the extend time for the 120-in circuit, we perform the following calculation:

$$\frac{\text{240-in ext. time 120-in ext. vol.}}{\text{240-in ext. vol.}}\ \frac{\text{240-in } C_{vs}}{\text{120-in } C_{vs}} = \text{120-in ext. time}$$

$$0.3 \times 31.67/54.58 \times 1.175/1.38 = 0.15 \text{ s}$$

This is the extend time of the actuator for the 120-in system.

Doing the same for the retract time of 0.4 s we have the following:

$$(\text{240-in ret. time})(\text{120-in ret. vol.}/\text{240-in ret. vol.})(\text{240-in } C_{vs}/\text{120-in } C_{vs})$$
$$= \text{120-in ret. time } 0.4 \times 33.51/56.42 \times 1.175/1.38 = 0.20$$

This is the retract time of the actuator for the 120-in system.

Comparison of the $C_v$ results to the computer printouts in the surveys at the end of the chapter will be identical. The attained times will not coincide because we did not take into account, in the preceding calculations, the variations in the moving load caused by the variations in time. We do not have any formulas which embrace that aspect; that is precisely one of the major reasons which precipitated our investigations. The 250,000 tests we conducted serves as the vehicle for extracting this information. As you can see, the times we arrived at were 0.21/0.30 s, as opposed to the theoretical results of 0.15/0.20 s. This is because the dynamic loads were originally 38/44 lb, as opposed to 69/68 lb at the increased speed. In using the raw data to obtain the 0.15/0.20 s, we kept the 38/44 lb of dynamic load constant, which it can't be, as it is time-dependent (the shorter the cycle time, the greater the force). If perchance the dynamic loads did in fact remain constant, then the 0.15/0.20 s would apply. But, since they were increased because of a faster time performance to 69/68 lb, the times were not quite as fast as 0.15/0.20 but increased somewhat to 0.21/0.30. Nevertheless, they were faster than the original of 0.30/0.40 s. By using the database provided in the program, we are able to fold in this variable factor and extract predictable performance-time results. A summary of the information given above appears in Fig. 2.7.

| Survey | Dynamic Loads in # | $T_e$ / $T_r$ in Seconds | $T_t$ in Seconds |
|--------|------------|-----------|-----------|
| 240" Conductor Length | 38/44 | 0.30/0.40 | 0.70 |
| 120" Conductor Length | 38/44* | 0.15/0.20 | 0.45 |
| 120" Conductor Length | 69/68** | 0.21/0.30 | 0.51 |

**Figure 2.7**  Results for two conductors of different lengths. [*Key:* single asterisk (*) indicates *theoretical value*—the dynamic-force increase was not considered as there is no readily developed formula to integrate it into the calculations; double asterisk (**) indicates *computer program*—the increased dynamic force required is included in the program. The program determines the increased propelling force required to generate the necessary dynamic force, due to the faster stroke times, and then uses the database to fold it into the computations to solve for the performance times.] (*Source: Henry Fleischer, "Why You Should Know Your $C_v$," Hydraulics and Pneumatics, Aug. 1980.*)

Returning to our original reason for going through this exercise, namely, to see the effect of removing right-angle fittings from a circuit, it is quite evident that the six added elbows with the 10 additional feet of conductor have a very detrimental affect on the actuator speed and thus should never be dismissed as unimportant additions. Bear in mind that nothing else was physically altered, yet the actual combined extend and retract times improved by 27 percent [(0.70 − 0.51)/0.51)], which is quite substantial by using the prudent approach. I am comparing the actual times of 0.30/0.40 s to 0.21/0.30 s. The dwell times remained constant, due to process requirements, and thus the cpm improved by only 23 percent, from 60.12 to 73.66.

This in no way should suggest that we have assigned a minor role to cosmetics in machine building. What we are suggesting is that it would be remiss for either us or the customers not to request information for other options. The point is that this technique recommends many alternatives, and customers should avail themselves of this offering. The most important tool for a designer is knowledge. That is exactly what we submit: many practical knowledgeable choices. Customers select the optimal circuit to satisfy their targets. Unlike previous practices where customers made selections from a position of relative ignorance, they can now make a decision from a position of knowledge.

Some further options customers may wish to explore as a result of cross-fertilization of ideas are

1. Select a conductor length between 10 and 20 ft with either long-radius bends or none, or anything between 0 and 8 sharp-angle bends as some cases may not permit the use of long-radius bends.

2. Shorten the conductor length to <10 ft.

3. Determine the degree of pressure drop—and thus air usage—by proceeding with the prudent shorter-conductor system yet maintaining the 60 cpm.

The $C_v$ method of selection for designing pneumatic systems can also be a valuable asset in troubleshooting an existing circuit. It can be used to determine whether an unsatisfactory performance of a cylinder is the result of improper sizing of the system's pneumatic devices or the design itself. The prescribed procedure would be to review the $C_v$ for each component of the system to determine or identify the weakest link. We can then enter the $C_v$ graph to remove a component (as described in a footnote on the graph) or use the formula for a new increased resultant $C_v$. If volumes are involved, they, too, can now be deducted from the original. This permits us to set up an equation linking the volumes and the $C_{vs}$, as we did earlier. Our cursory conclusions may not be accurate, but they will render rapid relative results to enable us to make decisions, and if desired, we can perform a proper audit for accurate results. We can readily determine whether the new improved performance times are adequate or some other removals, reduced lengths, or increased sizes are necessary.

This method can also be used to determine whether the desired performance times are still feasible, with the addition of ancillary pneumatic devices to an existing system, both with and without altering the adjustments or settings. (*Note:* To add further insight on the subject of $C_v$, I will compare individual $C_v$ values to various components of an automobile, i.e., the $C_v$ of a valve to the engine of a car, and $C_{vs}$ to the combination of all the parts, the complete automobile.)

Assume that we have a very spartan dune-buggy vehicle composed of only a chassis, engine, and seat. In this manner almost all the engine's power is utilized to propel the car. At times the sun is overbearing, and therefore a closure would be useful for protection against the sun's rays. This cab, however, presents its own problem of discomfort, and thus an air conditioner is mandatory. Because the driver is a lover of music, a radio and speakers are wired in as well as other creature comforts. EPA (Environmental Protection Agency) demands a catalytic converter and OSHA (Occupational Safety and Health Administration) a muffler. The associated tailpipe and exhaust system are necessary for all the interfacing. For ease of maneuvering, power steering and power brakes are added. All the added weight and accessories put a large drain on the car's performance. Originally with the benefit of almost the entire 150-hp engine, the car was able to reach 100 mph, whereas now, under identical road conditions, we barely approach 70 mph because 50 hp is diverted for auxiliary equipment, leaving available only 100 hp to propel the car.

Each time we add a $C_v$ in the form of additional hardware to the engine, we reduce the car's overall $C_{vs}$ or performance. This is similar to adding components to a valve's $C_v$, thereby reducing the available $C_{vs}$ and hence degenerating the performance times of the cylinder's extend and retract strokes.

It is worthwhile to note, and it may be obvious by now, that the single most expensive item should be the one bearing the smallest possible $C_v$, as cost is directly related to $C_v$ (the valve in the pneumatic circuit is usually the most expensive item and corresponds to the engine in the automobile). We must also realize that the $C_v$ of the valve when combined with the other elements ($C_{vs}$) must be of sufficient magnitude to meet the specified performance characteristics. This is akin to the automobile engine, where any draining apparatus you add to it will affect its efficiency, and in the final analysis it must have the necessary horsepower to meet its specified performance characteristics.

Anything that is affixed to the smallest $C_v$ reduces the $C_{vs}$ which is based on the smallest $C_v$ in the network. Again, the combination of any grouping is always smaller than the smallest $C_v$, and therefore the smallest $C_v$ is the controlling constituent.

When a small $C_v$ circuit fitting (the least expensive component in the system) is combined with a large valve $C_v$ (the most expensive device in the system), it obviously brings the mixture below the $C_v$ level of the fitting. For this combination ($C_{vs}$) to perform satisfactorily, the designer would have to interchange the two $C_v$ values, while still realizing the same resultant $C_{vs}$ generating the identical performance characteristics but at a much lower cost.

It makes more sense economically to spend a good deal less for the smaller valve and a trifle more for a larger fitting than a good deal more for a larger valve and slightly less for the fitting. One must study the combination from both $C_v$ and capital-expense viewpoints. This information is yet another benefit derived from the system to assist the designer. Cases treating this specific subject will be explored in Chap. 6.

The NFPA and the ISA have established very carefully controlled test procedures for determining $C_v$ values for valves and other fixed-orifice pneumatic devices. See Fig. 2.8 for the NFPA-suggested rig for determining the $C_v$ of any fixed-orifice device. Their proposed test standards require that the pressure drop across a device (i.e., $p_{1a} - p_{2a}$) where $p_{1a}$ is at 80 psig be no more than 0.025 of the absolute upstream pressure ($p_{1a}$), or 237 psi, and that the minimum be 1 psi. Throughout this range of pressure drops the $C_v$ of a device has an accuracy of $\pm 5$ percent. In testing of devices at system pressure

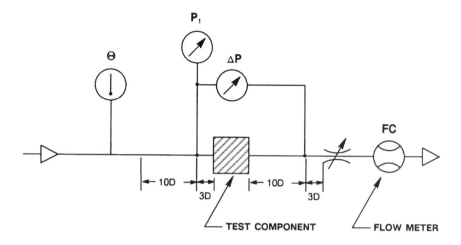

**PIPING WITH FLOW METER DOWNSTREAM**

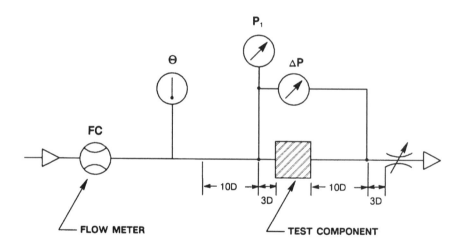

**PIPING WITH FLOW METER UPSTREAM**

**Figure 2.8**  Flow rig. [*Source: American National Standard ANSI/(NFPA) T3.21.3-1990, Flow Rig and Procedure, 1st ed., Jan. 25, 1990.*]

drops exceeding the standard limitations, the required system flow coefficient as determined by the procedure will yield $C_v$ values and flow rates with potential margins of error exceeding 20 percent. These variations are attributable in part to differences in instruments, the precision and accuracy of machined test equipment elements, and most importantly the sensitivity of air. It is essential if one desires accurate appraisals and $C_v$ determinations to make certain that the equipment is used within the parameters specified.

The rig shown in Fig. 2.8 indicates the equipment to be used to confirm the critical flow of 53 percent $(p_{2a}/p_{1a})$ and 47 percent $(\Delta p/p_{1a})$, and the flowchart in Fig. 2.9 can be used to generate the graphical means to determine the flows at different pressure combinations for a $C_v$ of 1.

We must remember that the $C_v$ value of a valve cannot of and by itself be the sole criterion for judging valve performance. This assigned $C_v$ must be used in conjunction with its port-size tap drill, the inside diameter (ID) of the conductor, and the fitting entering the valve port, whichever is the smallest.

For example, let us assume all elements of two valves to be the same except for their port sizes and both intending to mate with identical $\frac{1}{2}$-in hoses. The one with a $\frac{3}{8}$-NPT port accepting a $\frac{1}{2}$-in hose via an appropriate fitting will have a final $C_{vs}$ of 1.62, whereas the one with a $\frac{1}{4}$-NPT port, fitting, and $\frac{1}{2}$-in hose will result in a 1.4 $C_{vs}$.

---

$\frac{3}{8}$-NPT Calculations

| | |
|---|---|
| Inside diameter (ID) of $\frac{1}{2}$-in hose | 0.500 in |
| ID of $\frac{3}{8}$-NPT valve port | 0.493 in |
| Smallest ID of $\frac{1}{2}$-in, $\frac{3}{8}$-NPT hose fitting | 0.406 in |
| Controlling diameter | 0.406 in |
| $C_v$ of fitting = $23d^2$ = $23(0.406^2)$ | 3.79 |
| $C_v$ of valve | 1.79 |
| Combined $C_{vs}$ = $1/(1/3.79^2 + 1/1.79^2)$ | 1.62 |

$\frac{1}{4}$-NPT Calculations

| | |
|---|---|
| ID of $\frac{1}{2}$-in hose | 0.500 in |
| ID of $\frac{1}{4}$-NPT valve port | 0.364 in |
| Smallest ID of $\frac{1}{2}$-in, $\frac{1}{4}$-NPT hose fitting | 0.313 in |
| Controlling diameter | 0.313 in |
| $C_v$ of fitting = $23d^2$ = $23(0.313^2)$ | 2.25 |
| $C_v$ of valve | 1.79 |
| Combined $C_{vs}$ = $1/(1/2.25^2 + 1/1.79^2)$ | 1.40 |

---

This reduction in port size with commensurate reduction in conductance applies to any valve. Any device of a given design, and port size with a particular configuration and flow path, will have a specific $C_v$ as determined in accordance with the adopted NFPA test standards.

Let us evaluate another possibility where everything is identical, including all ports, except the two valves are of different makes. Will the two valves both ported $\frac{1}{2}$ NPT perform equally well in a circuit by rendering the same performance times? Only if they have the same $C_v$

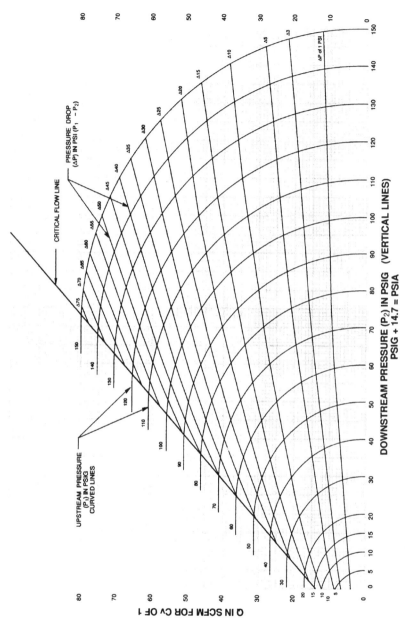

**Figure 2.9** Airflow curves for a pneumatic device with $C_v = 1.$

for that port size. Selecting a valve on the basis of port size alone is a very dangerous strategy. One must always request the $C_v$ of a valve at a particular port size in order to make a proper comparison. Knowing how to determine the $C_v$ of any fixed-orifice pneumatic device, in conjunction with a readily available method for combining $C_v$ values, provides a basic means for predicting response times for even a double-acting pneumatic cylinder which must move dissimilar loads at different operating pressures. Furthermore, one can also use it to optimize air usage, improve productivity, reduce valve and component size, minimize energy usage, or a combination of several of these and other associated objectives.

Knowing your $C_v$ and understanding how to use it has a very practical and utilitarian value which should help you in the pneumatic system design.

Following are examples demonstrating the use of the flowchart.

**Example 2.1**  To illustrate the effect that the critical backpressure ratio has on flow rate, refer to the chart (Fig. 2.9) and enter a $p_2$ downstream gauge pressure of 35.7 psig. Move vertically upward to the critical flow line and read a $p_1$ of 80 psig upstream pressure. Now, move horizontally to the left (or right) and read a maximum flow rate of 46 scfm. Reducing the downstream pressure below 35.7 psig for an upstream pressure of 80 psig will not increase the flow rate. This is because

$$\frac{p_{2a}}{p_{1a}} = \frac{35.7 + 14.7}{80 + 14.7} = 0.533$$

The maximum flow is reached when the relationship is 0.533 and the laws of physics prevent it from flowing any more.

Selecting devices to operate near sonic velocity is not recommended since considerable losses due to air disturbances can occur in this region, making it difficult to predict performance as well.

To further illustrate the determination and use of the flow coefficient, with respect to the flowchart, which is based on a $C_v$ of 1, we offer the ensuing examples. Bear in mind, however, that the chart is applicable for any $C_v$ when utilized in the following manner.

**Example 2.2**  Refer to Fig. 2.10. The object is to determine the necessary $C_{vv}$ for the valve which has to satisfy the following conditions: $Q = 80$ scfm; $p_1 = 80$ psig; $p_2 = 75$ psig; $\Gamma_1 = 72°F$ (no temperature correction is needed; if it were, you would use the formula).

Move vertically on the 75-psig $p_2$ line until you intersect the 80-psig $p_1$ curved line. Proceed horizontally to the left (or right) to a $Q$ of 21 scfm. $C_{vv}$ of the valve in question = $Q$ given/$Q$ graph:

$$C_{vv} = \frac{80}{21} = 3.81$$

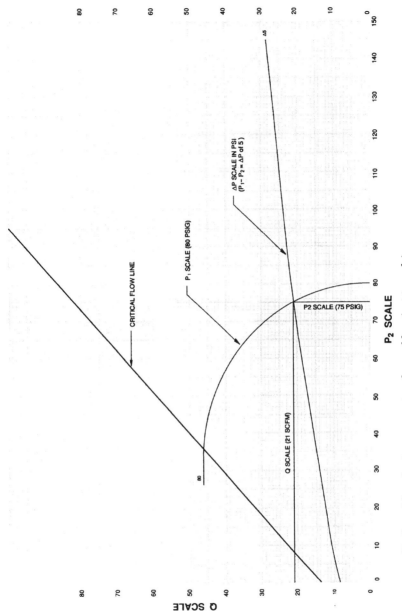

**Figure 2.10** Portion of flowchart necessary to solve problem (not to scale).

**Example 2.3**   Refer to Fig. 2.11. The object is to determine the flow rate $Q$ for the valve given: $p_1$ = 120 psig; $p_2$ = 110 psig; $C_{vv}$ = 3; $\Gamma_1$ = 64°F (no temperature correction is needed; if it were, you would use the formula). Move vertically on the 110-psig $p_2$ line until you intersect the 120-psig $p_1$ curved line. Proceed horizontally to the left (or right) to a $Q$ of 34.5 scfm. $Q$ required = $Q$ graph $\times$ $C_{vv}$ given

$$Q = 34.5 \times 3 = 103.5 \text{ scfm}$$

**Example 2.4**   Refer to Fig. 2.10. The object is to determine the $\Delta p$ across the valve under the following conditions: $Q$ = 126 scfm; $p_1$ = 80 psig; $C_{vv}$ = 6; $\Gamma_1$ = 70°F (no temperature correction is needed; if it were, you would use the formula). $Q$ given/$C_{vv}$ given renders a $Q$ for a $C_{vv}$ of 1, permitting you to enter the chart:

$$Q = \frac{126}{6} = 21 \text{ scfm}$$

for a $C_{vv}$ of 1. Move horizontally on the 21-scfm $Q$ line until you intersect the 80-psig $p_1$ curved line. The point of intersection falls on the diagonal $\Delta p$ line of 5 psi. You can make a cross-check as follows:

From the previous point of intersection, move vertically downward and read a $p_2$ of 75 psig. Therefore, $p_1 - p_2 = 80 - 75 = \Delta p = 5$ psi.

Identical results can be generated by using the flow-rate formula.

**Example 2.5**   This problem is used to illustrate the meaning and use of the terms *absolute pressure, cubic feet,* and *standard cubic feet.*

How many standard cubic feet (scf) are there in a vessel having an internal volume of 30 cubic feet (cf) and pressurized to 75 psig? (75 psig + 14.7)/14.7 = 6.1 atm. [*Hint:* To convert scf to standard cubic inches (sci), multiply scf by 1728. 6.1 atm $\times$ 30 cf (at the elevated pressure) = 183 scf (under standard atmospheric-pressure conditions), which is at 14.7 psia or 0 psig.]

Or viewing this from a different perspective, compressed air in a vessel having an original volume of 30 cf at 75 psig (89.7 psia) can expand to or will occupy a volume of 183 cf at standard atmospheric-pressure conditions (0 psig or 14.7 psia) if allowed to escape and disperse naturally into the atmosphere. Since the 183 cf is at standard conditions, it is conventionally expressed as 183 scf.

Example 2.5 is Boyle's law revisited, where $p_{1a}V_1 = p_{2a}V_2$ and

$p_{1a}$ = initial pressure conditions (89.7 psia)
$V_1$ = initial volume conditions (30 scf = 51,840 sci), expressed in sci
$p_{2a}$ = final pressure conditions (14.7 psia)
$V_2$ = final volume conditions (?), expressed in sci:

$$\frac{89.7 \times 51,840}{14.7} = V_2 = 316,330 \text{ sci}\quad\text{or}\quad 183 \text{ scf}$$

I would like to belabor this point a little longer, for there is always this lingering confusion in the minds of many, and I still feel that I have not adequately explained the distinction between the two values. We have established the fact that there is a distinction. Let us

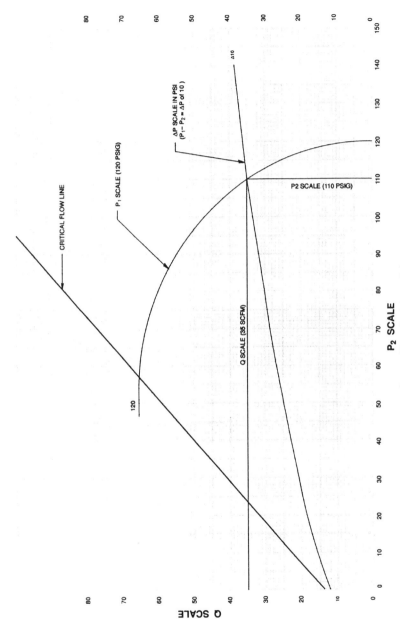

**Figure 2.11** Portion of flowchart necessary to solve problem (not to scale).

55

attempt it one more time. The weight of 183 scf is 13.91 lb (183 × 0.076). The internal volume of the original vessel had 30 cf, and thus the air in that vessel weighed 2.28 lb (30 × 0.076). We are now stuffing the 183 scf weighing 13.91 lb into a vessel which can hold only 30 scf weighing 2.28 lb at standard pressure conditions. Once we have accomplished this stuffing effect, we have increased the pressure in the tank by 6.1-fold (13.91/2.28). The weight of 183 scf always remains 13.91 lb under the standard temperature conditions, and thus the process of filling all this air into the vessel raises the pressure. We now have 6.1 times more pressure than we had originally, or 89.7 psia (6.1 × 14.7), which brings us back to 75 psig (89.7 − 14.7).

Boyle's law represents the behavior of a perfect gas where there is no change of temperature (isothermal process). The manner in which air expands and contracts in actual field conditions follows more closely a reversible adiabatic (isentropic) process where there is no transfer of heat to or away from the vessel (in our case a cylinder or a reservoir tank under certain conditions—to be discussed in a later chapter on this tank subject) but having a change in temperature. The relationship between pressure and volume would then be $p_{1a}V_1^k = p_{2a}V_2^k$. It actually makes no difference whether the pressures are expressed in the same units that the volumes are expressed in. It is important that the pressures and volumes are each expressed in the same units. I express all properties in the same units for purposes of uniformity: $k = 1.4$ for air because it is a diatomic gas (the molecule is composed of two atoms). All diatomic gases have a k value of 1.4; k is the ratio of the specific heat at constant pressure ($c_p$) to the specific heat at constant volume ($c_v$), known as the *specific-heat ratio*. [*Note:* This $c_v$ should not be confused with the $C_v$ we use for the conductance of a pneumatic device (*repeating for emphasis*.)] $c_p$ for air is 0.2415; $c_v$ for air is 0.1730; $k = c_p/c_v = 0.2415/0.1730 = 1.4$.

However, even a process of this nature does not represent actual field conditions, for it would require the gas to be contained in a vessel completely surrounded by a perfect heat insulator, where no heat would enter during expansion or escape during compression. The process that reflects the relationship between pressure and volume more closely to factory situations is called a *polytropic process*. The equation which represents this process is $p_{1a}V_1^\eta = p_{2a}V_2^\eta$, where the exponent η equals 1.35 (this is the most widely accepted exponent in use today for most circumstances; for its derivation, see Chap. 7):

$$p_{1a}V_1^{1.35} = p_{2a}V_2^{1.35}; \qquad \frac{89.7 \times 51,840^{1.35}}{14.7} = V_2^{1.35}$$

where $V_2 = 197,791$ sci and $V_2 = 114.5$ scf as compared to the isothermal answer of 183 scf and the isentropic answer of 109 scf.

| Gas | $C_p/C_v$ = k | At 60°F and 14.7 PSIA | | | Boiling Pt. at Atmos. Pr. °F | Critical Temp. °F | Critical Pressure PSIA | Critical Ratio ** γ |
| | | Specific Gravity | Molecular Weight M | Cubic ft/lb v̇ | | | | |
|---|---|---|---|---|---|---|---|---|
| Acetylene | 1.300 | 0.897 | 26.0156 | 14.534 | −116 | 96 | 910 | 0.546 |
| Air (Isentropic) | 1.395 | 1.000 | 28.9752 | 13.098 | −317 | −224 | 546 | 0.530 |
| Air (Polytropic) | 1.350* | 1.000 | 28.9752 | 13.098 | −317 | −224 | 546 | 0.537 |
| Ammonia | 1.317 | 0.587 | 17.0314 | 22.178 | −28 | 270 | 1638 | 0.543 |
| Argon | 1.667 | 1.379 | 39.9440 | 0.467 | −302 | −187 | 705 | 0.487 |
| Benzene | 1.080 | 2.694 | 78.0468 | 4.815 | 176 | 551 | 700 | 0.589 |
| Butane | 1.110 | 2.004 | 58.0780 | 6.514 | 31 | 307 | 528 | 0.583 |
| Carbon Dioxide | 1.300 | 1.519 | 44.0000 | 8.593 | −109 | 88 | 1072 | 0.546 |
| Carbon Monoxide | 1.403 | 0.966 | 28.0000 | 13.503 | −313 | −218 | 514 | 0.528 |
| Chlorine | 1.330 | 2.447 | 70.9140 | 5.333 | −30 | 291 | 118 | 0.540 |
| Ethane | 1.220 | 1.037 | 30.0468 | 12.594 | −127 | 90 | 717 | 0.561 |
| Ethyl Chloride | 1.130 | 2.226 | 64.4960 | 5.866 | 54 | 370 | 764 | 0.578 |
| Ethylene | 1.220 | 0.967 | 28.0312 | 13.495 | −155 | 50 | 747 | 0.561 |
| Flue Gas | 1.400 | --- | --- | --- | --- | --- | --- | 0.528 |
| Freon (F–12) | 1.130 | 4.173 | 120.9140 | 3.129 | −21 | 233 | 580 | 0.578 |
| Helium | 1.660 | 0.138 | 4.0020 | 94.510 | −452 | −450 | 33 | 0.488 |
| Hydrogen | 1.410 | 0.070 | 2.0156 | 188.620 | −423 | −400 | 188 | 0.527 |
| Methane | 1.316 | 0.553 | 16.0312 | 23.626 | −258 | −116 | 672 | 0.543 |
| Neon | 1.642 | 0.697 | 20.1830 | 18.784 | −410 | −380 | 389 | 0.491 |
| Nitrogen | 1.400 | 0.967 | 28.0160 | 13.460 | −320 | −232 | 492 | 0.528 |
| Oxygen | 1.398 | 1.104 | 32.0000 | 11.816 | −297 | −182 | 730 | 0.529 |
| Propane | 1.150 | 1.521 | 44.0624 | 8.587 | −48 | 204 | 632 | 0.574 |
| Sulfur Dioxide | 1.256 | 2.211 | 64.0600 | 5.901 | 14 | 315 | 1141 | 0.554 |
| Water Vapor | 1.331 | 0.622 | 18.0156 | 21.004 | 212 | 706 | 3206 | 0.540 |

Authorities differ slightly; hence above data are average results.

* Is not "k" but "η" to reflect polytropic process.

** $(2/k + 1)^{k/k-1}$

**Figure 2.12**   k value and other properties of various gases.

It is quite evident that gases, like other events occurring in the universe, do not behave in a predictable manner. Scientists are continually probing for the elusive formulas which will truly represent the phenomena of nature. This is an excellent subject worthy of exploration in order to establish some standard guidelines for use in industry, or certainly to more closely approach what is actually occurring.

*"Man cannot discover new oceans unless he is willing to lose sight of the shore."*

PROVERB

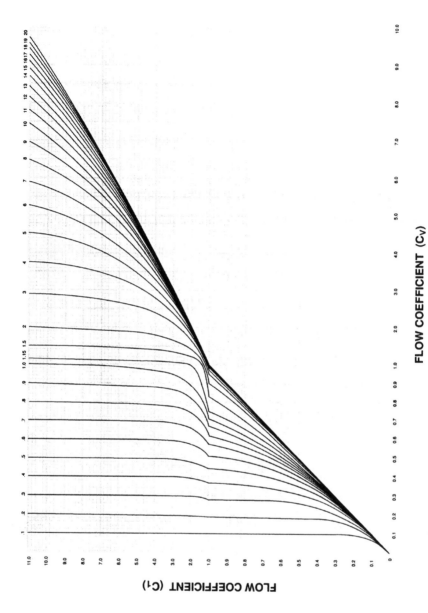

**FLOW COEFFICIENT (C$_V$)**

**Figure 2.13** Chart for combining $C_v$ values. This is the graphical representation of formulas combining conductances on p. 32. (*Source: Henry Fleischer, "Why You Should Know Your C$_v$,"* Hydraulics and Pneumatics, *Aug. 1980.*)

```
NUMATICS NUMASIZING (R) SUMMARY SHEET              Date:    04/10/95
NU301EED  Ver 3.01 (c) 1989 Numatics, Inc.        SURVEY # 1-1
===================================================================
Prepared for:              Prepared by:   Michael Liberty
Company:                   Company:       Numatics Inc.
Address:                   Address:       1450 N. Milford Rd.
City,State,Zip:            City,State,Zip: Highland, Mi. 48357
Telephone #                Telephone #    (810) 887-4111
Fax #                      Fax #          (810) 887-9190
-------------------------------------------------------------------
                                              Extend     Retract
Cv DATA PER ACTUATOR

Actuator Fitting Cv                            2.55       2.55
Flow Control Free Flow Cv from Chart           6.36       6.36
Flow Control Adjustable Cv from Chart          5.83       5.83
Flow Control Adjustable Cv Used                2.79       1.06
Quick Disconnect Cv                            N/A        N/A
Branch Conductor Cv                            N/A        N/A
Additional Cv Due to Elbows in Branch Conductor N/A       N/A
Branch Conductor Manifold Fitting Cv           N/A        N/A

Cv DATA - TOTAL SYSTEM

Actuator Fitting Cv                            2.55       2.55
Flow Control Free Flow Cv from Chart           6.36       6.36
Flow Control Adjustable Cv from Chart          5.83       5.83
Flow Control Adjustable Cv Used                2.79       1.06
Quick Disconnect Cv                            N/A        N/A
Branch Conductor Cv                            N/A        N/A
Additional Cv Due to Elbows in Branch Conductor N/A       N/A
Branch Conductor Manifold Fitting Cv           N/A        N/A
Main Conductor Cv                              1.88       1.88
Additional Cv Due to Elbows in Main Conductor  2.33       2.33
Main Conductor Manifold Fitting Cv             N/A        N/A
Silencer Cv                                    7.20       7.20
Valve Fitting Cv                               2.03       2.03
Valve Cv                                       1.06       1.06
Sandwich Regulator Cv                          N/A        N/A
Sandwich Speed Control Cv from Chart           N/A        N/A
Sandwich Speed Control Cv Used                 N/A        N/A
Sandwich Check Valve Cv (3 pos valve only)     N/A        N/A


Attained system Cv                             0.72       0.61

Required system Cv                             0.71       0.60

Flow Control Adjustable Cv Suggested           2.43       1.01
Valve Cv Suggested                             1.04       1.01
Sandwich Speed Control Cv Suggested            4.98       3.32
```

```
NUMATICS NUMASIZING (R) SUMMARY SHEET              Date:    04/10/95
NU301EED   Ver 3.01 (c) 1989 Numatics, Inc.        SURVEY # 1-2
=====================================================================
Prepared for:                  Prepared by:    Michael Liberty
Company:                       Company:        Numatics Inc.
Address:                       Address:        1450 N. Milford Rd.
City,State,Zip:                City,State,Zip: Highland, Mi. 48357
Telephone #                    Telephone #     (810) 887-4111
Fax #                          Fax #           (810) 887-9190
---------------------------------------------------------------------
                                                   Extend    Retract
Cv DATA PER ACTUATOR

Actuator Fitting Cv                                 7.33      7.33
Flow Control Free Flow Cv from Chart                6.36      6.36
Flow Control Adjustable Cv from Chart               5.83      5.83
Flow Control Adjustable Cv Used                     4.46      3.47
Quick Disconnect Cv                                 N/A       N/A
Branch Conductor Cv                                 N/A       N/A
Additional Cv Due to Elbows in Branch Conductor     N/A       N/A
Branch Conductor Manifold Fitting Cv                N/A       N/A

Cv DATA - TOTAL SYSTEM

Actuator Fitting Cv                                 7.33      7.33
Flow Control Free Flow Cv from Chart                6.36      6.36
Flow Control Adjustable Cv from Chart               5.83      5.83
Flow Control Adjustable Cv Used                     4.46      3.47
Quick Disconnect Cv                                 N/A       N/A
Branch Conductor Cv                                 N/A       N/A
Additional Cv Due to Elbows in Branch Conductor     N/A       N/A
Brancn Conductor Manifold Fitting Cv                N/A       N/A
Main Conductor Cv                                  16.56     16.56
Additional Cv Due to Elbows in Main Conductor       N/A       N/A
Main Conductor Manifold Fitting Cv                  N/A       N/A
Silencer Cv                                         7.20      7.20
Valve Fitting Cv                                    4.41      4.41
Valve Cv                                            1.75      1.75
Sandwich Regulator Cv                               N/A       N/A
Sandwich Speed Control Cv from Chart                N/A       N/A
Sandwich Speed Control Cv Used                      N/A       N/A
Sandwich Check Valve Cv (3 pos valve only)          N/A       N/A


Attained system Cv                                  1.42      1.38

Required system Cv                                  1.40      1.35

Flow Control Adjustable Cv Suggested                3.91      3.07
Valve Cv Suggested                                  1.71      1.69
Sandwich Speed Control Cv Suggested                 8.13      6.55
```

```
NUMATICS NUMASIZING (R) SUMMARY SHEET              Date:   04/10/95
NU301EED  Ver 3.01 (c) 1989 Numatics, Inc.        SURVEY # 1-3
==================================================================
Prepared for:                Prepared by:   Michael Liberty
Company:                     Company:       Numatics Inc.
Address:                     Address:       1450 N. Milford Rd.
City,State,Zip:              City,State,Zip: Highland, Mi. 48357
Telephone #                  Telephone #    (810) 887-4111
Fax #                        Fax #          (810) 887-9190
------------------------------------------------------------------
                                              Extend    Retract
Cv DATA PER ACTUATOR

Actuator Fitting Cv                            7.33      7.33
Flow Control Free Flow Cv from Chart           N/A       N/A
Flow Control Adjustable Cv from Chart          N/A       N/A
Flow Control Adjustable Cv Used                N/A       N/A
Quick Disconnect Cv                            N/A       N/A
Branch Conductor Cv                            N/A       N/A
Additional Cv Due to Elbows in Branch Conductor N/A      N/A
Branch Conductor Manifold Fitting Cv           N/A       N/A

Cv DATA - TOTAL SYSTEM

Actuator Fitting Cv                            7.33      7.33
Flow Control Free Flow Cv from Chart           N/A       N/A
Flow Control Adjustable Cv from Chart          N/A       N/A
Flow Control Adjustable Cv Used                N/A       N/A
Quick Disconnect Cv                            N/A       N/A
Branch Conductor Cv                            N/A       N/A
Additional Cv Due to Elbows in Branch Conductor N/A      N/A
Branch Conductor Manifold Fitting Cv           N/A       N/A
Main Conductor Cv                             16.47     16.47
Additional Cv Due to Elbows in Main Conductor  N/A       N/A
Main Conductor Manifold Fitting Cv             N/A       N/A
Silencer Cv                                    7.20      7.20
Valve Fitting Cv                               6.49      6.49
Valve Cv                                       5.73      5.73
Sandwich Regulator Cv                          N/A       N/A
Sandwich Speed Control Cv from Chart           N/A       N/A
Sandwich Speed Control Cv Used                 N/A       N/A
Sandwich Check Valve Cv (3 pos valve only)     N/A       N/A


Attained system Cv                             3.23      3.23

Required system Cv                             3.14      3.15

Flow Control Adjustable Cv Suggested           N/A       N/A
Valve Cv Suggested                             5.28      5.31
Sandwich Speed Control Cv Suggested           13.67     14.07
```

```
NUMATICS NUMASIZING (R) SUMMARY SHEET                    Date:   04/10/95
NU301EED   Ver 3.01 (c) 1989 Numatics, Inc.             SURVEY # 1-4 & 3-7
========================================================================
Prepared for:                    Prepared by:    Michael Liberty
Company:                         Company:        Numatics Inc.
Address:                         Address:        1450 N. Milford Rd.
City,State,Zip:                  City,State,Zip: Highland, Mi. 48357
Telephone #                      Telephone #     (810) 887-4111
Fax #                            Fax #           (810) 887-9190
------------------------------------------------------------------------
                                                    Extend     Retract
Cv DATA PER ACTUATOR

Actuator Fitting Cv                                   7.33       7.33
Flow Control Free Flow Cv from Chart                 6.36        N/A
Flow Control Adjustable Cv from Chart                5.83        N/A
Flow Control Adjustable Cv Used                      3.96        N/A
Quick Disconnect Cv                                  N/A         N/A
Branch Conductor Cv                                  N/A         N/A
Additional Cv Due to Elbows in Branch Conductor      N/A         N/A
Branch Conductor Manifold Fitting Cv                 N/A         N/A

Cv DATA - TOTAL SYSTEM

Actuator Fitting Cv                                   7.33       7.33
Flow Control Free Flow Cv from Chart                 6.36        N/A
Flow Control Adjustable Cv from Chart                5.83        N/A
Flow Control Adjustable Cv Used                      3.96        N/A
Quick Disconnect Cv                                  N/A         N/A
Branch Conductor Cv                                  N/A         N/A
Additional Cv Due to Elbows in Branch Conductor      N/A         N/A
Branch Conductor Manifold Fitting Cv                 N/A         N/A
Main Conductor Cv                                   16.24       16.24
Additional Cv Due to Elbows in Main Conductor        N/A         N/A
Main Conductor Manifold Fitting Cv                   N/A         N/A
Silencer Cv                                          7.20        7.20
Valve Fitting Cv                                     6.49        6.49
Valve Cv                                             5.73        5.73
Sandwich Regulator Cv                                N/A         N/A
Sandwich Speed Control Cv from Chart                 N/A         N/A
Sandwich Speed Control Cv Used                       N/A         N/A
Sandwich Check Valve Cv (3 pos valve only)           N/A         N/A


Attained system Cv                                   2.50        2.88

Required system Cv                                   2.42        2.83

Flow Control Adjustable Cv Suggested                 3.67        N/A
Valve Cv Suggested                                   4.93        5.35
Sandwich Speed Control Cv Suggested                  9.69       14.98
```

```
NUMATICS NUMASIZING (R) SUMMARY SHEET              Date:    04/10/95
NU301EED  Ver 3.01 (c) 1989 Numatics, Inc.        SURVEY # 240" Sol
==================================================================
Prepared for:              Prepared by:      Michael Liberty
Company:                   Company:          Numatics Inc.
Address:                   Address:          1450 N. Milford Rd.
City,State,Zip:            City,State,Zip:   Highland, Mi. 48357
Telephone #                Telephone #       (810) 887-4111
Fax #                      Fax #             (810) 887-9190
------------------------------------------------------------------
                              Avg/Tot/Oth    Extend      Retract
INITIAL CUSTOMER PARAMETERS:
Total weight of load (lbs)                    88.00      168.00
Angle of load from horizontal        0
Coefficient of Friction           0.05
Number of actuators                  1
Total load per actuator (lbs)                 38.24       44.48
Minimum line pressure (PSIG)       110
Design pressure used (PSIG)                   80.0        80.0
Shifts/day (1 shift=120,000 m/yr)  1.0
Cycles per year                7200000

ACTUATOR:
Description:  Single Rod High Flow Numatics Actuator with 3/8 NPT ports
Bore/stroke/rod            1.50" bore x 6.00" stroke x 0.625" rod
Fitting                           3/8 NPT - 3/8 NPT EL

CONDUCTOR & ASSOCIATED COMPONENTS:
Branch conductor /leg             N/A
Branch manifold fitting /leg      N/A
Branch cond equiv ftg lg /leg (in) N/A
Quick disconnect model /leg       N/A
In line flow control model /leg                NONE        NONE
Main conductor            3/8 NPT pipe 240" long with 8.0 elbow(s)
Main manifold fitting             N/A
Main cond equiv ftg lg (in)       118

VALVE ASSEMBLY & ASSOCIATED COMPONENTS:
Description    2 Pos L2 on 3/8 NPT base with ext reg
Fitting                           3/8 NPT - 3/8 NPT EL
Silencer model                    N/A

SYSTEM PERFORMANCE TIMES:
Att'n stroke time (sec)                       0.30        0.40
Required stroke time (sec)                    0.30        0.40
Stroke time @ term vel (sec)                  0.23        0.22
Att'n cyclic rate (CPM)           60.12
Required cyclic rate (CPM)        60.00
Cyclic rate @ term vel (CPM)      79.25
System delay time (sec)           0.023
Dwell time after stroke (sec)                 0.10        0.20

SYSTEM INFORMATION:
Required system Cv                            1.16        1.18
Attained system Cv                            1.18        1.18
Att'n system air flow (SCFM)                  42.5        30.4
Att'n branch air vel (400 FPS max)   N/A              N/A
Att'n main air vel (400 FPS max)              102         65
Att'n % delta p (46% max)                     19          9
% Act. capacity used (75% max)                27          38
Min pres necessary for 1d w/S.F. (PSIG)       28.9        40.6
Air per cycle (SCF)               0.41
Att'n act leakage cost/yr @ $ 0.31 /KSCF       27          6          21
Att'n operating air cost/yr @ $ 0.31 /KSCF    925         470        455
Cost /1000 cyc @ att'n times @ $ 20.00 /hr    5.68
Att'n power input total (HP)      5.48

COMMENTS:
```

```
NUMATICS NUMASIZING (R) SUMMARY SHEET                    Date:    04/10/95
NU301EED   Ver 3.01 (c) 1989 Numatics, Inc.             SURVEY # 240" Sol
==========================================================================
Prepared for:                   Prepared by:    Michael Liberty
Company:                        Company:        Numatics Inc.
Address:                        Address:        1450 N. Milford Rd.
City,State,Zip:                 City,State,Zip: Highland, Mi. 48357
Telephone #                     Telephone #     (810) 887-4111
Fax #                           Fax #           (810) 887-9190
--------------------------------------------------------------------------
                                                   Extend      Retract
Cv DATA PER ACTUATOR

Actuator Fitting Cv                                 5.06        5.06
Flow Control Free Flow Cv from Chart                N/A         N/A
Flow Control Adjustable Cv from Chart               N/A         N/A
Flow Control Adjustable Cv Used                     N/A         N/A
Quick Disconnect Cv                                 N/A         N/A
Branch Conductor Cv                                 N/A         N/A
Additional Cv Due to Elbows in Branch Conductor     N/A         N/A
Branch Conductor Manifold Fitting Cv                N/A         N/A

Cv DATA - TOTAL SYSTEM

Actuator Fitting Cv                                 5.06        5.06
Flow Control Free Flow Cv from Chart                N/A         N/A
Flow Control Adjustable Cv from Chart               N/A         N/A
Flow Control Adjustable Cv Used                     N/A         N/A
Quick Disconnect Cv                                 N/A         N/A
Branch Conductor Cv                                 N/A         N/A
Additional Cv Due to Elbows in Branch Conductor     N/A         N/A
Branch Conductor Manifold Fitting Cv                N/A         N/A
Main Conductor Cv                                   2.09        2.09
Additional Cv Due to Elbows in Main Conductor       3.44        3.44
Main Conductor Manifold Fitting Cv                  N/A         N/A
Silencer Cv                                         N/A         N/A
Valve Fitting Cv                                    4.66        4.66
Valve Cv                                            1.75        1.75
Sandwich Regulator Cv                               N/A         N/A
Sandwich Speed Control Cv from Chart                N/A         N/A
Sandwich Speed Control Cv Used                      N/A         N/A
Sandwich Check Valve Cv (3 pos valve only)          N/A         N/A


Attained system Cv                                  1.18        1.18

Required system Cv                                  1.16        1.18

Flow Control Adjustable Cv Suggested                N/A         N/A
Valve Cv Suggested                                  1.71        1.76
Sandwich Speed Control Cv Suggested                 8.27        N/A
```

```
NUMATICS NUMASIZING (R) SUMMARY SHEET              Date:   04/10/95
NU301EED  Ver 3.01 (c) 1989 Numatics, Inc.         SURVEY # 120" Sol
=================================================================
Prepared for:                   Prepared by:    Michael Liberty
Company:                        Company:        Numatics Inc.
Address:                        Address:        1450 N. Milford Rd.
City,State,Zip:                 City,State,Zip: Highland, Mi. 48357
Telephone #                     Telephone #     (810) 887-4111
Fax #                           Fax #           (810) 887-9190
-----------------------------------------------------------------
                                  Avg/Tot/Oth   Extend    Retract
INITIAL CUSTOMER PARAMETERS:
  Total weight of load (lbs)                     88.00     168.00
  Angle of load from horizontal            0
  Coefficient of Friction               0.05
  Number of actuators                      1
  Total load per actuator (lbs)                  69.27     68.46
  Minimum line pressure (PSIG)           110
  Design pressure used (PSIG)                    80.0      80.0
  Shifts/day (1 shift=120,000 m/yr)      1.0
  Cycles per year                    8837502

ACTUATOR:
  Description:  Single Rod High Flow Numatics Actuator with 3/8 NPT ports
  Bore/stroke/rod          1.50" bore x 6.00" stroke x 0.625" rod
  Fitting                        3/8 NPT - 3/8 NPT EL

CONDUCTOR & ASSOCIATED COMPONENTS:
  Branch conductor /leg                  N/A
  Branch manifold fitting /leg           N/A
  Branch cond equiv ftg lg /leg (in)     N/A
  Quick disconnect model /leg            N/A
  In line flow control model /leg                NONE      NONE
  Main conductor       3/8 NPT pipe 120" long with 2.0 elbow(s)
  Main manifold fitting                  N/A
  Main cond equiv ftg lg (in)             30

VALVE ASSEMBLY & ASSOCIATED COMPONENTS:
  Description    2 Pos L2 on 3/8 NPT base with ext reg
  Fitting                        3/8 NPT - 3/8 NPT EL
  Silencer model                         N/A

SYSTEM PERFORMANCE TIMES:
  Att'n stroke time (sec)                        0.21      0.30
  Required stroke time (sec)                     0.21      0.30
  Stroke time @ term vel (sec)                   0.12      0.11
  Att'n cyclic rate (CPM)              73.68
  Required cyclic rate (CPM)           73.65
  Cyclic rate @ term vel (CPM)        113.48
  System delay time (sec)              0.023
  Dwell time after stroke (sec)                  0.10      0.20

SYSTEM INFORMATION:
  Required system Cv                             1.37      1.38
  Attained system Cv                             1.38      1.38
  Att'n system air flow (SCFM)                   35.6      23.3
  Att'n branch air vel (400 FPS max)       N/A           N/A
  Att'n main air vel (400 FPS max)               76        47
  Att'n % delta p (46% max)                      9         3
  % Act. capacity used (75% max)                 49        59
  Min pres necessary for ld w/S.F. (PSIG)        52.3      62.5
  Air per cycle (SCF)                   0.24
  Att'n act leakage cost/yr @ $ 0.31 /KSCF   27   6        21
  Att'n operating air cost/yr @ $ 0.31 /KSCF 666 342       324
  Cost /1000 cyc @ att'n times @ $ 20.00 /hr  4.60
  Att'n power input total (HP)          3.99

COMMENTS:
```

```
NUMATICS NUMASIZING (R) SUMMARY SHEET                    Date:    04/10/95
NU301EED  Ver 3.01 (c) 1989 Numatics, Inc.              SURVEY # 120" Sol
=========================================================================
Prepared for:                  Prepared by:    Michael Liberty
Company:                       Company:        Numatics Inc.
Address:                       Address:        1450 N. Milford Rd.
City,State,Zip:                City,State,Zip: Highland, Mi. 48357
Telephone #                    Telephone #     (810) 887-4111
Fax #                          Fax #           (810) 887-9190
-------------------------------------------------------------------------
                                                     Extend    Retract
Cv DATA PER ACTUATOR

Actuator Fitting Cv                                    5.06      5.06
Flow Control Free Flow Cv from Chart                   N/A       N/A
Flow Control Adjustable Cv from Chart                  N/A       N/A
Flow Control Adjustable Cv Used                        N/A       N/A
Quick Disconnect Cv                                    N/A       N/A
Branch Conductor Cv                                    N/A       N/A
Additional Cv Due to Elbows in Branch Conductor        N/A       N/A
Branch Conductor Manifold Fitting Cv                   N/A       N/A

Cv DATA - TOTAL SYSTEM

Actuator Fitting Cv                                    5.06      5.06
Flow Control Free Flow Cv from Chart                   N/A       N/A
Flow Control Adjustable Cv from Chart                  N/A       N/A
Flow Control Adjustable Cv Used                        N/A       N/A
Quick Disconnect Cv                                    N/A       N/A
Branch Conductor Cv                                    N/A       N/A
Additional Cv Due to Elbows in Branch Conductor        N/A       N/A
Branch Conductor Manifold Fitting Cv                   N/A       N/A
Main Conductor Cv                                      2.96      2.96
Additional Cv Due to Elbows in Main Conductor          N/A       N/A
Main Conductor Manifold Fitting Cv                     N/A       N/A
Silencer Cv                                            N/A       N/A
Valve Fitting Cv                                       4.66      4.66
Valve Cv                                               1.75      1.75
Sandwich Regulator Cv                                  N/A       N/A
Sandwich Speed Control Cv from Chart                   N/A       N/A
Sandwich Speed Control Cv Used                         N/A       N/A
Sandwich Check Valve Cv (3 pos valve only)             N/A       N/A


Attained system Cv                                     1.38      1.38

Required system Cv                                     1.37      1.38

Flow Control Adjustable Cv Suggested                   N/A       N/A
Valve Cv Suggested                                    1.74      1.75
Sandwich Speed Control Cv Suggested                  16.37       N/A
```

# 3

# Actuators

We will assign a chapter to each major component or category in a pneumatic circuit. The purpose will be to scrutinize each component in the network as to how its $C_v$ is determined, and then evaluate its relevance, impact, and role in the overall scheme. We've selected the actuator to start with as it is really the place to begin even though it is the last circuit component to see the compressed air.

The calculations for a mechanical air-handling system also commence at the rear, the vents, which are the sites of the heating and cooling loads. All electrical distribution system designs originate with the outlets where the loads are located. All design considerations for a multistory structure are initiated from the roof, which is the upper terminus of the building. We start all these computations from the end so that we can total up all the loads, burdens, or their equivalents, which serve as the design foundation or the beginning of the layout phase. For example, if you were the architect of a skyscraper, you would determine snow and wind loads, weights, safety factors, and other factors to establish roof columns and structures to support the skyscraper for the top floor. Armed with this information, you would continue in an identical fashion to the floor immediately below. Specifically, you would determine the top-floor columns and supports by taking the weights and other parameters for everything above it that has been amassed thus far. You would proceed to calculate the necessary information for the floor beneath it and so on until the building foundation is reached. This concludes the design phase, which precedes and constitutes the origin of the construction stage.

So, too, as a designer, knowing the available pressure, mass to be moved, required times, volumes to be filled, and other variables, you would first compute the loads in order to arrive at the actuator sizes. From this point, in conjunction with other vital data, you would proceed to select and size, in the actual reverse physical order of their installation (very similar to the design and construction order of a tall edifice), cylinder fittings, flow controls if required, conductors, valve fittings, valves, regulators, filters, drop lines, branch lines, main lines, master headers, reservoirs, and so on and finally arrive at the very pneumatic foundation, the air compressor.

Now that we have established the actuator as the point of origin for designing, is its selection procedure much more involved than simply determining the cross-sectional area ($a$, expressed in square inches) from a required force ($F$, expressed in pounds force) and an available pressure ($p$, expressed in psig) plus some safety factor? It is not, even though it's the conventional approach.

If $a = F/p$ were the sole criterion, we would move on to the next category: actuator fittings. However, on the basis of fundamental physics and supported by all our tests, we found that the actuator is much more complex than commonly assumed. The leading critical item that complicates determination of actuator fittings is the force required of the actuator; this parameter depends on the value of the load that the actuator must overcome, which in turn hinges on time. Therein lies the rub.

We will evaluate a common case of a cylinder required to move a sliding object by examining in detail everything that is involved. The first step is to ascertain this load. The essential ingredients involved in addition to pressure are an accelerating mass, a starting and dynamic coefficient of friction, an angle of inclination, and a specified performance time that must be complied with.

The following terms are defined in our pneumatics context:

Load is the burden that is imposed on the actuator and is expressed in pounds force.

Force is what is generated by the actuator to overcome the load and is expressed in pounds force and determined by $pa$.

If the force is less than the load, it is conceivable for the load to move the actuator. When the pressure is raised to increase the force to a level equal to that of the load, there is no movement. The slightest increment in pressure above this point will bring the load to the inception of motion. From this position any additional pressure will deliver the load faster to its destination until its terminal velocity is reached. Any pressure beyond that which is necessary to reach terminal velocity is not only pointless or futile but wasteful. The exception to this premise is the need for a large force at the end of a stroke for functions such as clamping, welding, and heat sealing. Here one must compromise since the additional pressure will not propel the load any faster but is essential for a final squeeze. Under these essentially no-load conditions, the actuator is stroking through its trajectory without a moving load. Very frequently, under these circumstances, the terminal velocity is reached with a resulting impact that may create an unwanted blemish or other damage to the equipment and/or processed part. Various techniques are used to prevent these impacts and yet conclude with the necessary high pressure to assure the large final force. One common method is to use flow controls which inhibit the flow of air without sacrificing the required pressure. The drawback is that speed is affected for the entire stroke, which may be objectionable in terms of productivity. Another often employed routine is the use of a second valve for a dual-pressure-select system. A low pressure is initially introduced to advance the piston of the actuator rapidly without causing an impact. At the completion of the stroke the higher pressure necessary to generate the large end force is then introduced. Many other methods are available to the designer to adjust for extremely high productivity ($\geq$200 cpm) demanded, such as dynamic braking with one or two valves and three-position valves, which will be discussed along with showing the associated circuitry in Chap. 7 dealing with air motors, flow controls, etc.

A moving load is the only load that affects the extend and/or retract time of the actuator's piston. Therefore, a load, regardless of its size, that is produced at the termination of its stroke (as clamping, heat sealing, impact blow) has no bearing on the calculations which determine the extend- and/or retract-stroke performance times.

Let us return to the first order of business, which is to determine the composition of the extend-stroke loads. The two components of the static starting load $L_m$, which is expressed in pounds force, are the static friction load ($L_{mf}W \cos \theta$) external of the actuator, which is expressed in pounds force, and is always a positive term; and the gravitational pull ($W \sin \theta$), which is expressed in pounds force, and can either be a positive or negative term depending on whether the direction of the load is moving away from or toward the earth. The three components of the total moving load $L_d$, which is expressed in pounds force, are the accelerating load $mZ$ ($Z$ expressed in ft/s$^2$), which is expressed in pounds force and is always a positive term; the dynamic frictional load ($L_{df}W \cos \theta$) external of the actuator, which is expressed in pounds force and is always a positive term; and the gravitational pull ($W \sin \theta$), which is expressed in pounds force, and can either be a positive or negative term depending on whether the direction of the load is moving away from or toward the earth. These same determinations are made for the retract stroke loads. In our calculations we use positive and negative terms depending on the direction of movement. The positive term (moving against gravity) is the load that the actuator must overcome. The negative term (moving with the pull of gravity) is a gravity-assist load and is subtracted from the total positive actuator load as it aids the actuator. We take advantage of that phenomenon with smaller components and/or by selecting lower pressures. There are times when the negative term dominates and no pressure is demanded. This condition should be checked for and taken advantage of. A thorough investigation based on the objectives is mandatory to disclose the necessary components and pressures, which are discussed later in the chapter.

To repeat, we always solve for loads $L_m$ and $L_d$ for both the extend $T_e$ and retract stroke $T_r$. The $C_v$ method of selection that we propose is applicable for multiload (multiple $L_d$ values) conditions as well. Each portion of the stroke at which a different constant load is encountered can be treated as a distinct problem). The $pa$ portion is always designed to be greater than $L_m$ in order to overcome inertia and also to be of sufficient magnitude to move $L_d$ over the required distance within the allotted time. The results using the old techniques may still be identical to this point, for thus far these are well-established physical principles. We will assume that the same desire to obtain credible results are present with all pneumatic designers. Beyond this point the results will diverge sharply, for to my knowledge there is no other method which considers all the variables and aspects of a dynamic pneumatic system capable of rendering viable and dependable results.

Let us scrutinize the load and force aspects posed in the incline problem (Survey 1-1) in Chap. 1 in terms of the framework discussed above, which is precisely the way the computer program is configured. We will review in consecutive order the extend and retract directions for the cylinder in question. The component selection will naturally be based on the most stringent requirements.

We required a cylinder to push a 430-lb vehicle on a 20-lb carriage for a total of 450 lb up a 45° incline 3.75 in long. The retract portion required only the return of the 20-lb carriage down the same incline (gravity-assisted in this direction). We assumed the coefficients of static friction and moving friction for the carriage slide to be 0.5 and 0.3, respectively. We allowed 0.74 and 0.36 s, respectively, for the extend and the retract strokes to negotiate the 3.75-in distance. We desire to know what forces are required of a cylinder to perform the tasks. We can accomplish this by determining all the loads imposed on the cylinder. The following are the necessary terms and quantities essential to calculate $L_m$ and $L_d$ for both the extend and retract strokes:

$g$ = pull of gravity = 32.2 ft/s²

$W_e$ (extend) = weight of component in question = 450 lb

$W_r$ (retract) = weight of component in question = 20 lb

$m_e$ (extend) = mass = $W_e/g$ = 450/32.2 = 13.98 lb s²/ft

$m_r$ (retract) = mass = $W_r/g$ = 20/32.2 = 0.62 lb s²/ft

$s$ = distance or stroke required of a pneumatic cylinder = 3.75 in

$S$ = distance = 3.75/12 = 0.313 ft

$T_e$ = time (extend) = 0.74 s

$T_r$ = time (retract) = 0.36 s

$Z_e$ = acceleration (extend) = $2S/T_e^2$ = 2 × 0.313/(0.74)² = 1.14 ft/s²

$Z_r$ = acceleration (retract) = $2S/T_r^2$ = 2 × 0.313/(0.36)² = 4.82 ft/s²

$m_e Z_e$ = 13.98 × 1.14 = 15.94 lb (load component for extend acceleration component)

$m_r Z_r$ = 0.62 × 4.82 = 2.99 lb (load component for retract acceleration component)

$u_m$ = coefficient of static friction (external of the actuator) = 0.5

$u_d$ = coefficient of moving friction (external of the actuator) = 0.3

$\theta$ = angle of incline = 45°

cos $\theta$ = 0.707

sin $\theta$ = 0.707

$u_m W_e$ cos $\theta$ = 0.5 × 450 × 0.707 = 159.08 lb (load component for extend static friction)

$u_d W_e$ cos $\theta$ = 0.3 × 450 × 0.707 = 95.45 lb (load component for extend dynamic friction)

$u_m W_r$ cos $\theta$ = 0.5 × 20 × 0.707 = 7.07 lb (load component for retract static friction)

$u_d W_r$ cos $\theta$ = 0.3 × 20 × 0.707 = 4.24 lb (load component for retract dynamic friction)

$W_e$ sin $\theta$ = 450 × 0.707 = 318.15 lb (load component for extend gravitation component)

$W_r$ sin $\theta$ = 20 × 0.707 = 14.14 lb (load component for retract gravitation component)

$L_{me}$ = 159.08 + 318.15 = 477.2 lb (total extend static load)

$L_{de}$ = 15.94 + 95.45 + 318.15 = 429.6 lb (total extend dynamic load)

$L_{mr}$ = 7.07 − 14.14 = −7.1 lb (total retract static load)

$L_{dr}$ = 2.99 + 4.24 − 14.14 = −6.9 lb (total retract dynamic load)

The static internal frictional load for a cylinder is a constant multiplied by the bore diameter, which is an additional static frictional load that must be added to $L_m$. The average static internal friction constant for a cylinder is 3.8, and therefore the static frictional load is 12.4 lb (3.8 × 3.25). The dynamic internal frictional load for a cylinder is a constant multiplied by the bore diameter, which is an additional moving frictional load that must be carried by the cylinder and therefore added to $L_d$. The average dynamic internal friction constant for a cylinder is 2.3, and therefore the dynamic frictional load is 7.5 lb (2.3 × 3.25):

Grand total extend static load = 477.2 + 12.4 = 489.6 lb

Grand total retract static load = −7.1 + 12.4 = 5.3 lb

Grand total extend dynamic load = 429.6 + 7.5 = 437.1 lb

Grand total retract dynamic load = −6.9 + 7.5 = 0.6 lb

These last two figures can be verified against the data in Survey 1-1 (435.5/0.7).

For simplicity we have condensed and simplified the equation encompassing the three components which constitute the dynamic load (excluding the internal dynamic frictional cylinder load) to suit the specific dimensions generally accompanying a pneumatic survey of this nature:

$$L_d = \frac{0.00518 \, Ws}{T^2} + uW \cos \theta \pm W \sin \theta$$

where $W$ = appropriate weight in pounds (in this case 450 lb)
    $s$ = cylinder stroke in inches (in this case 3.75 in)
    $T$ = appropriate time in seconds (in this case 0.74 s)
    $u$ = coefficient of sliding friction of moving weight against surface (in this case 0.3)
    $\theta$ = angle of incline of surface (in this case 45°)
    $L_{de}$ = 1.5.94 lb + 95.44 lb + 318.15 = 429.5 lb

From the same printout information we determine that $p_e a_e = 80 \times 3.25^2 \times 3.14/4 = 663.7$ lb of force, which is more than adequate to overcome the inertial load of 489.6 lb for the extend stroke. From our broad database we find that 663.7 lb of force will move the 437.1-lb extend dynamic load 3.75 in in 0.74 s. This is specifically where the divergence occurs from the conventional approach, for this information was accessed from the collected data of the more than 250,000 test firings of all the cylinders we analyzed.

The $p_r a_r$ for the retract stroke is 600.8 lb, which obviously will present no difficulty in overcoming the inertial load of 5.3 lb. Also the

600.8-lb force, having the stated $C_{vsr}$ of 0.61, will move the dynamic load of 0.6 lb the required 3.75 in in 0.36 s, which was again excerpted from our cylinder behavior database.

We will gain some idea of the forces involved to accelerate even small loads at rapid rates by comparing various circuits and the effects of flow controls imposed on them. To review, a force of 663.7 lb was needed to move a load of 437.1 lb in 0.74 s, and by contrast a force of 600.8 lb was utilized to move a load of only 0.6 lb in 0.36 s the same distance. This was achieved predominantly by the use of flow controls restricting the flow, thus reducing the system $C_v (C_{vs})$ and, to some degree, to the retract stroke approaching terminal velocity and demanding a large force to realize it.

Now let us further consider the contrast in required forces as the stroke times diminish. For example, Survey 1-2 is the same problem as Survey 1-1 discussed above except the customer is now desirous of achieving performance times of 0.3 and 0.2 s instead of 0.74 and 0.36 s (Survey 1-1). The static loads were evidently unaffected. The accelerating loads, however, increased to 97.1 and 9.7 lb, in turn, increasing the dynamic loads to 510.7 and 0.2 lb. When factoring in the moving frictional loads of a 4-in-bore cylinder, the final tallies were 520 and 9 lb, not significantly different from before. However, to attain the desired performance times of 0.3 and 0.2 s, a 4-in bore was required having an elevated pressure of 90 psig applied at each end of the cylinder. The final forces generated were 1130 and 1060 lb to convey loads of 520 and 9 lb, respectively. These are major boosts in cylinder propelling forces, achieved again primarily by the use of flow controls. We can realize the same 0.3 and 0.2 stroke times to move the identical loads with the same cylinder, except this time we will employ the new concept of dual pressures to match the loads rather than using flow controls, and thereby we will save energy. Let us look at Survey 1-4, which uses the dual pressures of 55.2 and 14.3 psig to generate forces of only 693.4 and 168.0 lb, respectively—a stark contrast when considering we are moving essentially the same load as in the first survey with less force and doing it in less than half the time. This is the pith and marrow of the dual-pressure concept, which illustrates how to use considerably less energy than the traditional tactics to achieve the same performance times.

It is also evident from the formulas involved that the load is not constant but is time-dependent and therefore must be integrated into the calculations. As long as the time constraint is well over 1 and the mass is light, the accelerating load will be small. As soon as the required time goes below 1 s, the acceleration load increases dramatically as we are dividing by the square of the time. That is why a vehicle, even though it has a sizable mass, does not require a large force for movement if the need for acceleration is very low. The demand for a sizable engine comes into play when one insists on speed; otherwise an individual can push it with the obvious disadvantage of speed.

In the overwhelming majority of surveys conducted, where the sliding occurred on a level surface and time was of the essence, $L_d$ was greater than $L_m$. The high-speed specification produced a large accelerating load, which in turn caused $L_d$ to be the more dominant of the two.

There are many single-line formulas and short handy and accessible techniques that I have carefully reviewed. I am told there are a myriad of other simple methods available, but none to my knowledge consider all the variables. If all facets are not considered, we cannot expect to have dependable results. We now have a tested and convenient method which weighs all the ingredients, thereby negating any and all past arguments for not employing a method.

Hydraulic, electrical network, and mechanical air-handling designers, to name a few, require design criteria and concepts very similar to the pneumatic designers to appraise their work. All of them, except for pneumatics personnel, devote a significant amount of time to performing the very important function of selecting the most suitable components, perhaps because the procedures and formulas for their sizing are readily available, as are the means for selecting the optimum physical operating conditions. Nevertheless, pneumatics deserves the same careful considerations, as it is just as critical here to have the proper sizes and conditions for efficient operation. Also, there are as many funds committed and opportunities for major capital and operating savings as in the other disciplines. The reasons for neglecting and relegating it to outdated rules of thumb are no longer valid, nor should it be permissible as the technology to investigate and arrive at reliable values is obtainable and convenient to utilize.

There are several types of pneumatic actuators. The most common and widely used is the single-rod double-acting compressed-air cylinder. As such, it is the foremost user of compressed air and therefore the greatest offender of air leaks, primarily around its rod-end bushing. (*Note:* Frequently the term *actuator* is used interchangeably with the term *cylinder* only because a cylinder is the most common type of actuator that is in service today.)

The most familiar types of actuators in use in industry today are listed in random order as follows (the most widely used cylinder, as mentioned earlier, is the single-rod double-acting type, which is the one displayed in Chap. 1 for the incline problem):

*The double-rod double-acting actuator*: This is identical to the single-rod type, except it has a rod projecting from both ends of the actuator.

*The spring-return single-acting actuator:* This unit has an internal helical spring wrapped around the rod to perform minor work in the one direction requiring very little demand and uses pressure only on one end of the piston, usually to extend it, involving the major workload. Helical springs are prone to break due to fatigue and therefore must be used only in locations or applications where there are no alternatives. We recommend the following options: (1) low-pressure return air, to simulate the action of a spring, on a double-acting air cylinder or (2) a tank at constant pressure to supply the appropriate end of a double-acting air cylinder(s). This is a closed-loop circuit, and therefore no air is wasted as none is exhausted; this very closely mimics the action of a physical spring without its inherent problems.

*The rodless double-acting actuator:* This unit has a floating internal piston generally attached to an outer member. As the external member progresses along its path, it seals the moving member, preventing any connection between the internal pressurized area and the atmosphere by many ingenious zip-lock-type closures. There are several rodless units that utilize magnetic-type connections between the internal and external components that overcome the need to seal the pressurized region from the atmosphere; however, they have the obvious shortcoming of limited capability.

*The double-acting cable air cylinder:* This unit has a floating piston with an endless cable running around a pulley at the cylinder's extremities and then through a sealed port in the endcaps, terminating at the ends of the internal piston.

*The rotary-vane double-acting actuator:* This type has paddle(s) inside a sealed member which is attached to a central rotatable rod. Which side of the paddle is exposed to the pressure will depend on which direction the paddle(s) will rotate the center rod.

*Air motors:* Both unidirectional and reversible air motors are rotary actuators with no limiting stops, and thus once air is applied to one side of the paddle(s), the paddles will continue to rotate in that direction until the pressure is either relieved or applied on the opposite side of the paddle to reverse the action.

Since the single-rod double-acting air cylinder represents the bulk of the cylinders employed, it was only natural that the majority of our efforts were expended in studying them. Therefore, the vast amount of data collection and empirical testing was originally dedicated to them.

A cylinder still possesses the greatest power capability for its envelope size. It provides the most convenient and economical means of obtaining a power source, especially a remote one, in terms of both design and installation. One can readily see why cylinders are so widely used even though so little is known about them and very little attempt has been made to optimize their efficiencies. If that can be accomplished, there will be no bounds on their usage or the valves to control them.

We are all well aware, by now, that the majority of applications using air actuators have a major load in only one direction. Yet, the prevailing thinking is to utilize the same high pressure for the minor-load end as is essential for the major-load end. This is based on the supposition that the higher the pressure, the faster the cylinder will travel, ad infinitum, which we now realize is erroneous. The paradox in these dissimilar load cases is that the same productivity is achievable with a reduced pressure for the minor-load end as we have previously demonstrated, and in some cases the productivity can even be surpassed. Furthermore, because of the reduced pressure, there is also a savings in both operating and leakage costs.

It's like going downhill with the accelerator floored and because you're going too rapidly, you floor your brake as well and in the process waste energy. Take your foot off the accelerator! Reduce the pressure on the minor-load end of the cylinder! To repeat, your cylinder may not always improve its performance, but definitely in all instances savings in both cylinder operating and leakage costs will result by virtue of the reduced pressures.

Numasizing, as mentioned earlier, is not a theoretical concept, for it is based on the actual recordings of over 250,000 test firings of air cylinders ranging in bore size from $\frac{3}{8}$ to 14 in. The test cylinders were subjected to varying loads and pressures employing different conductors, valves, and fittings. The pressures to move the loads were applied in 10-psi increments. We initially started with an extend pressure of 120 psig and a retract pressure of 10 psig with 0 extend and retract loads. We kept dropping the extend pressure until the extend stroke was erratic, and noted the performance time results, including the pressure at which the terminal velocity occurred. We started again with the extend pressure at 120 psig, but this time kept the retract pressure at 20 psig and noted all the results. We continued with this procedure until our retract pressure was at 120 psig. We then reversed the process by starting the extend pressure at 10 psig and the retract pressure at 120 psig and kept dropping it in the same 10-psig increments. Eventually we repeated everything for the retract end as we did previously for the extend side. When we exhausted all the combinations without any loads, we placed a small load on the extend end of the cylinder and repeated this entire process. We continually reversed the process and gradually increased the loads, first one end, and then the other. We proceeded with these incremental load changes, continually reversing pressures. We advanced along this path, always noting when the cylinder's behavior became inconsistent and at what pressure the terminal velocity was reached. We then repeated this entire process with different valves and conductors. From this information, besides having the ability to obtain cylinder response times, we can ascertain operating costs, critical pressure ratios, pressure drops, flow rates, air usage, optimum valve and conductor sizes, horsepower requirements, etc. under an infinite number of conditions. This method therefore dispels the myth that the ability to predict the performance times of double-acting air cylinders having dissimilar loads and driven by two distinctly different pressures is highly improbable. In essence, the technique is a vehicle which permits the designer to make decisions from a position of knowledge rather than ignorance.

During our testing program we realized the often ignored fact that cylinder pistons are moving objects and thus are governed by the same laws of motion that pertain to all other moving objects. One of these laws deals with this terminal velocity we have been alluding to. *Terminal velocity* is the maximum velocity that a cylinder can reach under the prevailing conditions regardless of pressure or load. We learned that every cylinder, regardless of size or load, reaches terminal velocity at some pressure. For heavy loads (60 to 75 percent of cylinder capacity) the pressure necessary to reach terminal velocity may be beyond the capacity of the prevailing compressor. For smaller or just frictional loads, as returning tools, the pressure necessary to reach terminal velocity may be below the conventional 80 to 100 psig normally employed. All that may be necessary to return these minimal loads at terminal velocity may well be in the 40- to 50-psig range. The major-load end of the cylinder may still require the 80 to 100 psig to meet its time obligations. However, because the minor-load end may necessitate only 40 psig instead of the customary 80 to 100 psig, the demand on the compressor would be reduced, thereby consuming less energy.

A combination of such two dissimilar loads happens to be the case in the majority of applications. Thus (worth repeating for emphasis), utilizing anything over the terminal velocity pressure (with few exceptions, e.g., clamping, heat sealing, welding) is not only useless but wasteful. We are able to estimate the performance times at terminal velocity from all the testing conducted and therefore incorporate those particular details as well in the computer printouts.

Let us discuss another element uncovered in our investigations which is critical to our procedure. This is called the *exhaust pressure preload* or *load*; it is a load imposed on the cylinder's piston, delaying

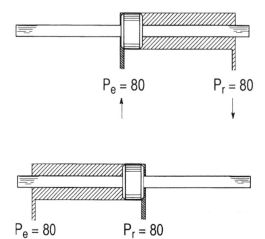

$P_e = 80$          $P_r = 80$

$P_e = 80$          $P_r = 80$

= volume to be filled

= volume to be exhausted before inception of motion

**Figure 3.1** Trapped air requiring evacuation.

its initial movement. The cause is the mass of air captured in the cylinder end adjacent to the piston (opposing its motion) and in the conductor supplying that end, as depicted in Fig. 3.1.

The trapped pressurized air shown in Fig. 3.1 must decay sufficiently before the piston can commence its extend or retract stroke, thereby imposing a delay time to lengthen the stroke time. The difference between the two pressures, one on either side of the piston, that is necessary to be reached for motion to ensue is what we term the *differential pressure* and occurs at the finale of the static state of the piston. We also observed the differential pressure during the piston's travel, in order to be familiar with its behavior, and termed it the *running differential pressure*. This is not to be confused with the delta $p$ ($\Delta p$) we spoke of earlier; that is a phenomenon associated with the dynamic aspect of the stroke which always applies and occurs on the filling end of the cylinder's piston. This can be either the extend or the retract end, depending on which end is being filled. It is a function of the initial value of this filling pressure less the lowest value, which is usually at the termination of the stroke. This occurs because, once the piston breaks loose, it moves out ahead of the incoming pressure wave, especially when there is a very negligible load involved to be moved. The incoming air has an opportunity to build back up only after the piston reaches the end of its stroke. [*Note:* Delta $p$ ($\Delta p$) is the phenomenon of the filling pressure on the same end of the cylinder's piston. *Differential pressure* is the phenomenon of the difference between the filling pressure and the exhausting pressure on opposite ends of the cylinder's piston.]

The feature of the $\Delta p$ in which we are most interested actually occurs in most cases at the end of the piston's stroke when it reaches its maximum. It is due in those cases to the pressure wave lagging behind the piston's movement. When the differential pressure increases sufficiently, it releases the piston like a slingshot as a result of the stored energy of the filled pressure. The piston races ahead of this filling pressure and continues to outpace this pressure, thus continually generating an ever-larger volume behind itself, which in turn causes the filling pressure to drop even while filling. When the piston reaches the end of the stroke, the $\Delta p$ has reached maximum strictly because of the inability of the filling pressure to keep pace with the piston's velocity. This large $\Delta p$ condition exists when the cylinder encounters fractional or only frictional loads. Conversely, when a cylinder encounters large loads and moves rather slowly, the $\Delta p$ is generally small to practically nonexistent as the pressure will keep pace with the piston's movement. Under the small load conditions it can attain critical flow, specifically reaching a $\Delta p$ of 46.7% of the filling pressure, thus reaching terminal velocity. We therefore feel very strongly that one should not levy a limitation on this $\Delta p$ of 5 or 10 psi, as that imposes an undue burden on the circuit and limits the selection of components and pressures. The individuals who developed these condensed rapid methods have elected to pursue this arbitrary assumption of a $\Delta p$ because it is precisely what they were lacking and therefore is the only avenue open to them. The new concept does not restrict the $\Delta p$; in fact, it allows $\Delta p$ to assume whatever figure is necessary to obtain the required performance times. We have encountered countless applications where the $\Delta p$ reached the maximum of 46.7 percent of the initial filling pressure without exhibiting any trace of a staccato piston action. On the contrary, under these circumstances the cylinders were prone to premature failure because they stroked so rapidly that some means of preventing impact was obligatory. The cylinders function flawlessly, and repeatability is excellent. It is well to bear in mind that the recommended cylinder force (based on $pa$) always possesses a minimum safety factor of 33 percent above the moving load. We do not use $\Delta p$ in our calculations to determine any of our components. The floating $\Delta p$ is a result we derived from our database and is used to monitor the terminal-velocity pressure. This permits us to drop to the minimum possible pressure without wasting energy. If one restricts the amount of the $\Delta p$ to an arbitrary maximum of 10 psi or anything less than maximum (it can be as much as 46.7 percent of $p_1$), it can generate a requirement for a component which can just as easily be too large as too small. The same penalties apply to the value of the pressures selected if a specific $\Delta p$ is demanded. If one obtains the correct results by any of these abbreviated methods, it is purely a matter of happenstance that the estimated $\Delta p$ corresponds to the actual $\Delta p$. See Figs. 3.4 and 3.5 later in the chapter for graphical representations of these events.

Permit me to belabor this $\Delta p$ point a little longer, as I feel it is important for the reader to fully appreciate its importance and significance. We will investigate two cases, one at each end of the spectrum, which will allow us to understand the fallacy of assigning a specific minimum figure of 5, 10, or even 15 psi to $\Delta p$. First, let us assume that we are interested in achieving a very rapid stroke time in the order of 40 or 50 ms for a 1-in stroke. The mass to be moved is small, but because of the high speed, the propelling force required of the cylinder will have to be high. Therefore, the pressure necessary to generate this propelling force, which must achieve the desired speed, will be high compared to the pressure essential to start the relatively massless piston moving. Consequently, the $\Delta p$ ($p_1 - p_2$; initial pressure − pressure at conclusion of motion at end of stroke) will, in many cases of this nature, be at or near maximum of 0.467 of $p_1$. We have here an excellent example of a piston that is rapidly driving toward its destination without any hesitation or erratic movement. If an arbitrary $\Delta p$ figure would have been imposed on the necessary components, they would have been unnecessarily oversized to compensate for the smaller allowable $\Delta p$. Yet, the $\Delta p$ would still have been the same in order to achieve the time but would be unknown to the designer. The second case will be just the opposite; in this scenario the components will have a very large mass to move as well as go at a very slow pace (3 or 4 s for a stroke of 6 in), and therefore the pressure needed to transfer the load will be very close to the pressure needed to start the piston moving and keep it in motion. Here we have a $\Delta p$ which is essentially zero. If we again impose an arbitrary figure to the $\Delta p$ of 5 or 10 psi, we could just as easily be undersized this time. The point, and it's worth repeating, is to allow the $\Delta p$ to assume whatever it takes to accomplish the task. Allow it to be a result rather than a capricious number to solve for the component sizes or pressures demanded. (*Note:* Under many conditions, because of a small load on the cylinder, the initial pressure necessary to start motion is less than the applied pressure. The piston is in motion before the full line pressure is reached. We have here a difference between the starting pressure and the available filling pressure which will be reached after the completion of the stroke. We do not use this difference, for usually when this occurs the difference continues to grow until the stroke is completed, which is the figure we use for $\Delta p$. We will discuss this aspect again a little further into the chapter.)

Let us return now to the differential-pressure subject to observe when and why it imposes a delay time onto the overall cycle time. The delay time created by the initial absence of differential pressure is the major offender of any of the delay times involved. In other words, having a very large mass to expel is due to the large exhaust pressure trapped in the end of the piston opposing motion. The lesser offender of delay time is due to seals and packings around the rod and piston, which we have already classified as static friction. The least offender of any consequence, which is considered minuscule by comparison to the exhaust pressure load, is caused by either the delay in the electromagnetic response of the solenoid of a solenoid-operated valve or the delay in the air signal of an air-piloted valve. A few definitions are in order here:

The *leading operator* of a valve is an electric solenoid. There are strictly air-piloted units and several other operators, which we will cover in Chap. 6.

The *delay mode* is composed of all the delay times.

The *motion mode* is the actual time that is spent by the piston in traversing the distance or length of the stroke.

The *stroke time* consists of the time the piston is in a delay mode plus the time it is in a motion mode and holds true for both the extend and retract segments.

The *dwell time* is a prescribed amount of time devoted to the process once the piston has concluded its stroke. It may be a necessary curing period after an extend stroke or a specific time allotted for extracting a completed part and inserting a new part after a retract stroke.

The *cycle time* consists of the extend-stroke time, the dwell time after the extend stroke, the retract-stroke time, and the dwell time beyond the retract stroke.

When a customer requests an extend or retract time of one second, we interpret that to be synonymous with a stroke time of one second (including the appropriate delay time); in that way there is no misunderstanding of the necessary inputs.

To summarize, the three elements that constitute the delay mode of the stroke time, in order of significance, are (1) the exhaust-pressure load, (2) the friction of the actuator seals and packings, and (3) the valve response time, whether it be caused by air, electromagnetism, or both.

We surveyed many cases in which the delay mode represented over 50 percent of the stroke time. There is very little we can do about further enhancing the motion mode of the cylinder's piston that hasn't already been incorporated into the inside surface of the actuator, as finish, coating, or lubrication, or into the seals and packings. We are therefore focusing our attention on the delay mode and specifically on the exhaust-pressure-load portion. It holds the greatest promise not only because it is the worst offender, but fortunately it's the one we can control. This is especially important in those cases where it represents over 50 percent of the stroke time. The use of dual pressures is an excellent method for reducing the delay mode. We discussed and demonstrated this earlier and graphically represent it below in Figs. 3.2 and 3.3.

Figure 3.2 shows the loads on the cylinder as well as the cylinder force necessary to overcome these loads. You can understand that the $L_x$ (exhaust-pressure load) and $L_f$ (friction load) are delaying the piston in its effort to commence motion. The $L_x$ is especially handicapping the motion because it is filled with a large mass of air at 80 psig that must be emptied before the piston will edge forward. The $L_e$ (external extend load) is substantial; however, the $L_r$ (external retract load) is strictly returning the tool and thus carries an insignificant load. As we can see in the upper diagram in Fig. 3.1, it will take a relatively short period of time to simply fill the extend conductor up to 80 psig compared to the time necessary to discharge the opposite end, filled at 80 psig, sufficiently to commence motion.

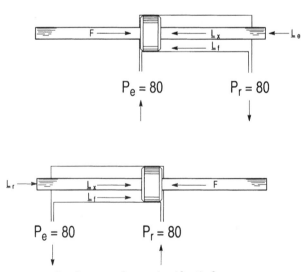

**Figure 3.2**  Loads versus force using identical pressures.

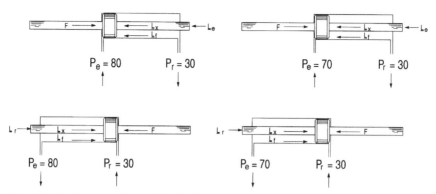

**Figure 3.3**  Loads versus force using dual pressures.

The delay time shown in Fig. 3.3 has been reduced because we were able to drop the retract pressure to 30 psig. The large initial differential allows the activation of the piston as soon as the required pressure is reached in the conductor. Interestingly, we find that we require only 70 psig for our extend pressure to achieve the desired time specification. This saved a little time for the retract-stroke time, as opposed to having to wait for a drop from 80 psig sufficient to permit retract motion.

This extend delay time, as a result of the exhaust-pressure load, is a function of how quickly we can exhaust this trapped air rather than how rapidly we can fill the small conductor cavity on the opposite end of the piston. In fact, the conductor is the largest volume to be filled, and it has the added advantage of having, essentially, an unlimited and continual supply of high-pressure air to rapidly raise it to the regulated pressure. Yet the piston can remain motionless, in most cases, until a sufficient differential pressure between the two sides of the piston has been generated to overcome the static friction and inertial load. (In fact, it is conceivable for the delay time to be infinite if no air is permitted to escape from the presumed exhausting end to generate the necessary differential to start the piston moving.) By contrast, the air on the exhaust side may be decaying unassisted, consuming time, until this differential is achieved. This delay time is obviously aggravated as the conductor length is increased as there is that much more air to be discharged. Once the piston is in motion, then and only then does the decaying pressure end of the cylinder obtain assistance from the moving piston to assist in the evacuation of the air. Here, too, if a device were to be placed on the exhausting end of the cylinder [i.e., flow control (FC)] to prevent the air from escaping, the piston would be moving very slowly, maintaining only a slight differential throughout the stroke. The $\Delta p$ would be negligible or essentially nonexistent because $p_2$ would be basically equal to $p_1$ throughout the stroke. By comparison, if the confined air initially presented no exhaust-pressure load, because it either started at a much lower pressure than its counterpart on the opposite side of the piston or was preexpelled prior to the inception of piston motion, then the exhaust pressure load would essentially be no factor, thereby having negligible influence to start the piston in motion. The $\Delta p$ under these conditions could reach a peak of 46.7 percent of filling pressure (terminal velocity). Depending on launching conditions, the differential as well as the $\Delta p$ can be almost any figure within reason.

It was problematic as to where this exhaust-pressure load should be included. Obviously it is part of $L_m$, but it also plays a role in $L_d$. We felt that we did not have to assign it to either and just assumed that it was part of a delay mode that was involved in the final performance-time results. All that was necessary to know was what the starting physical conditions (load, pressure, conductor sizes, etc.) were and then measure the elapsed stroke times. All the intervening phenomenons, although interesting, did not have to be contended with and therefore took care of themselves. As far as the $\Delta p$ is concerned, as we stated earlier, as long as the cylinder performs satisfactorily, it can vary from 0 psi to 46.7 percent of $p_1$, which is the maximum it can be.

Another interesting phenomenon that we observed was the ability of the moving piston to increase the pressure on the opposite end of the cylinder from its original starting value. This was especially evident where there was a small mechanical load to be moved and the return pressure was either very low or even completely expelled prior to inception of movement. This can be seen on the CRT (cathode-ray-tube) graphs as depicted in Figures 3.4 and 3.5.

The rod-end pressure depicted in Fig. 3.4 starts at 0 psig and builds up to approximately 15 psig by the end of the stroke. The spike (37 psig) in the blind-end pressure end at the start of the stroke is due to the incoming pressure wave initially moving faster than the piston; as the piston gains momentum and accelerates, it moves faster than the pressure wave. Another interesting facet is that the system required 37 psig to initiate motion and during the stroke the differential averaged 20 psi to maintain motion.

Reversing the conditions, as shown in Fig. 3.5, generates similar characteristics. The differences are purely in the magnitude of the spike, which in this case reaches a maximum of 30 psig and the height of the blind-end pressure buildup of only 18 psig. An observation which may or may not have any relevance is the difference in each case between the spike and pressure buildup points. It would be interesting to investigate whether this has any value and if so, whether it is predictable. One further point is the fact that the extend

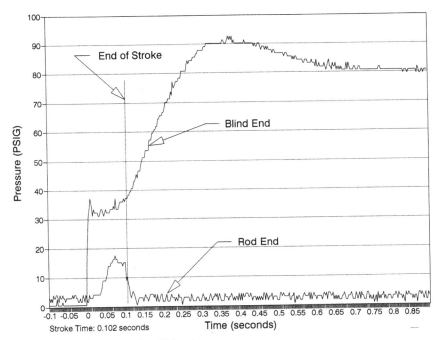

**Figure 3.4** Cylinder extend at 80/0 psig.

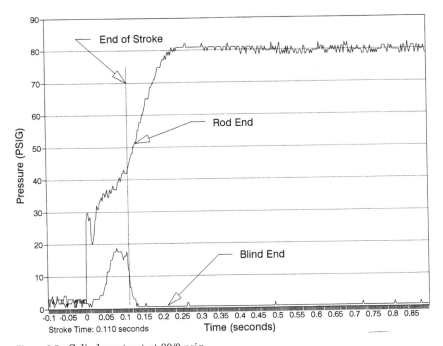

**Figure 3.5** Cylinder retract at 80/0 psig.

demanded a larger spike to launch the piston although it has a larger area. Beyond the spike, the propelling pressure is gradually building and follows the increasing exhaust-air pressure buildup.

The cause for this pressure buildup is twofold: (1) the slingshot effect of the piston moving out ahead of its pressure wave once motion is initiated as there is no or very little impeding exhaust pressure load and (2) the inability of the air to be expelled as rapidly as is necessary to maintain atmospheric pressure in that end of the cylinder, thereby slowing the piston. When high speeds are essential, it may be necessary not only to preexhaust the air from the opposite end of the cylinder but to use a large orifice and leave it continually open to the atmosphere at the emitting cylinder port end, thus eliminating the need to go through the longer and time-consuming labyrinthine path of fittings, conductor, valves, etc. This can be accomplished by using two valves, one at each end of the cylinder port without any restricting conductors, and ensuring that the $C_v$ of the ports and valves are of sufficient magnitude so as not to build up any of the aforementioned backpressure. To prevent impact and yet maintain speed, the valve which is open to the atmosphere is energized momentarily before the piston completes its stroke, thus preventing any further air from escaping and enabling the pressure to build. Thus, this minute amount of trapped air is sufficient to hesitate the piston's motion sufficiently so that when the valve is reenergized (perhaps only milliseconds later), it no longer can build up a head of steam to impact at the end of the stroke and thus gently kisses the end block. This is very similar to the dynamic braking technique (pumping) one uses when approaching a red light in one's vehicle. You approach rapidly and initially brake hard and quickly release so as not to jolt the passengers. It is no longer necessary when you rebrake to apply the same braking force as the $mZ$ (mass $\times$ acceleration) portion of the automobile has been diminished considerably by the original large braking force. In the latter part of Chap. 8, in the sections on assorted circuits, various schemes dealing with this feature are presented. It is highly improbable to predict beforehand whether a cylinder will continue to accelerate or decelerate as the piston proceeds into its stroke. It is strictly a matter of the exhaust $C_v$ which controls the ability of the exhaust air to be discharged to the atmosphere. Here once again we utilize our test data, which includes these specific situations to guarantee the resulting performance times.

By combining the two principles of terminal velocity and exhaust-pressure load, we are better able to understand the synergistic effect on cycle time and energy expenditure. At times two concurrent advantageous features can be achieved: reduction in cycle time and operating costs. Figures 3.6 and 3.7 are typical graphical representations of this notion.

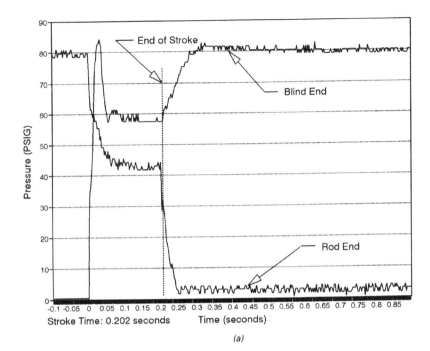

Stroke Time: 0.202 seconds          Time (seconds)

*(a)*

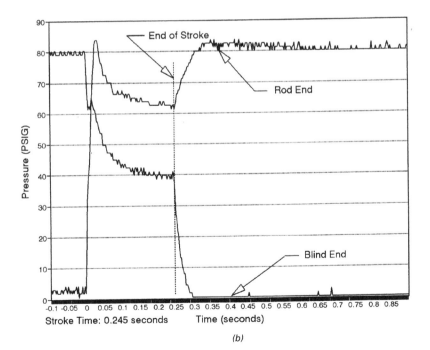

Stroke Time: 0.245 seconds          Time (seconds)

*(b)*

**Figure 3.6** *(a)* Cylinder extend at 80/80 psig; *(b)* cylinder retract at 80/80 psig.

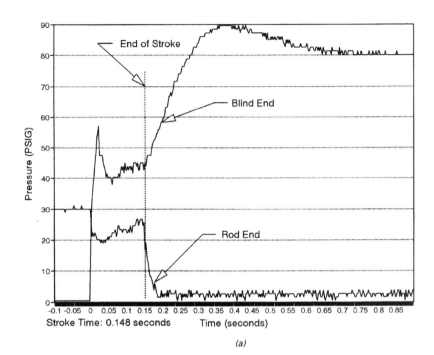

*(a)*

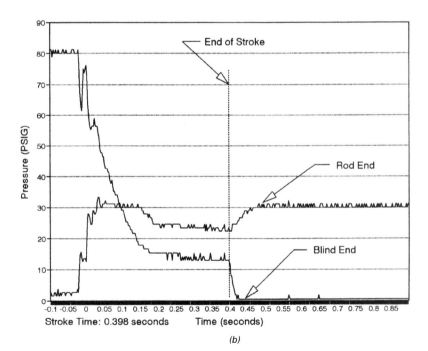

*(b)*

**Figure 3.7** (*a*) Cylinder extend at 80/30 psig; (*b*) cylinder retract at 80/30 psig.

In Fig. 3.6 one can observe the delay time, on the extend 80/80 circuit graph, before motion ensues. This is due primarily to the time elapsed while waiting for $p_x$ (the exhaust pressure on the opposite end) to drop sufficiently so as to create the necessary differential pressure that would permit the piston to break free. It was at peak fill pressure for a short time before the required differential was reached. By contrast, the piston in the 80/30 (Fig. 3.7) extend circuit commenced motion before $p_1$ even reached peak fill pressure. This was possible because of the advantage of having the vessel filled with only 30 psig, permitting the differential to be reached without the need for $p_1$ to realize the full fill pressure of 80 psig. This stroke time therefore had negligible delay, rendering better performance time. It is interesting to observe that at the end of the stroke neither the fill pressure nor the exhaust pressure reached a stable condition. The fill pressure increased to eventually attain the regulated fill pressure, and the exhaust pressure finally dropped to atmospheric conditions. Both of these situations can vary widely depending on other conditions as loads, pressures, and various restrictions. As a result of these identical external conditions, except for return pressure, the extend time at 80/30 psig (0.148 s) was faster by 0.054 s (0.202 − 0.148) than at 80/80 psig (0.202 s). The retract time at 80/30 (0.398 s) was slower in this case than at 80/80 psig (0.245 s) by 0.153 s. However, this would serve as an excellent candidate for improving cycle time for many applications exhibiting the following circumstances. After the extend stroke the part must remain in position for operations to be performed on it. While the operation is being conducted, the retract portion of the cycle can be carried out. The extend stroke would improve without the negative affect of the slower retract time because it would be conducted while the part is being processed. The net effect would be an improved cycle time.

A net cycle-time improvement can be achieved with 80/30 psig compared to 80/80 psig under the following conditions. The cylinder is vertical with a gravity-assist load replacing the lacking 50 psig on one end. We would lose nothing on the retract stroke and have an improved stroke time on the extend stroke. In this fashion we accomplish a faster time cycle and save air to boot. We will solve problems of this nature later in the chapter.

The conventional wisdom is to apply the same pressure to both ends of a cylinder even though there is a major load on only one end of the cylinder. The new opposing concept is to move the minor load with a reduced pressure which may even be enough to reach terminal velocity and thus cause no loss in stroke time. The major load will now have to contend with a much smaller exhaust-pressure load, and therefore its delay time will be shortened. The most rapid expulsion of air from any container is not to inject it into the container in the first place, and therefore it will not require its evacuation. The lower the pressure on the opposing end, the shorter the decay time to reach the proper differential pressure for the piston to start moving. The shorter decay or delay time makes for a shorter stroke time for the major-load end and when combined with the fixed stroke time of the other end, a faster cycle time follows. On the other hand, if the minor-load stroke time is increased because of a longer delay time (a greater differential pressure to overcome), there can still be a pressure reduction, which will net a faster cycle time. The rationale here is that the gain on the load end is greater than the loss on the no-load end, resulting in a shorter cycle time.

The valuable phenomenon of a gravity-assist load should be taken advantage of when it is encountered; it may represent the equivalent of 20 or ≤30 psig, and in the new scheme we immediately translate that into a commensurate reduction in pressure with its ensuing energy savings (without productivity losses). [A *gravity-assist load* is one where a weight is suspended in some fashion from the end of the cylinder (an example of this is the incline problem, in Chap. 1) aiding its piston's motion (applying to either end depending on which end is being assisted by the earth's gravitational pull). Another interesting by-product of this dual-pressure concept, which we take advantage of, is the fact that if you drop the pressure on one end to achieve the required time, it may permit the pressure to drop on the opposite end since there is a smaller exhaust-pressure load to overcome. This process is continued until the desired performance times are realized, as seen on Fig. 3.3.

The cylinder is similar to other pneumatic components in that there is no "man for all seasons"; it depends on the objective. If the objective is to maximize on productivity, it will call for a specific-size cylinder bore. If the objective is to use the minimum amount of horsepower, a cylinder of a different bore size may be called for. The target may be to use the least amount of air, which may or may not coincide with the minimum horsepower demand (there is a subtle distinction—compare Surveys 3-5 and 3-6), which would call for another bore diameter. Survey 3-5 calls for 3.66 hp and consumes $1296/year (4,320,000 scf/year) of air, whereas Survey 3-6 necessitates only 3.6 hp yet expends $1391/year (4,967,900 scf/year) of air. If the objective is to use minimum-size components in order to conserve capital, that may call for a fourth size of cylinder bore. The objective may originate from an economic concern where the least cost per 1000 units is paramount, as there may be a good deal of compressed air used in the process, which again will necessitate still another bore diameter. These are several of the major objectives which we will investigate, but there are others as demanded by conservationists, environmentalists, or other specialists to render bore sizes entirely different from those previously envisioned.

Briefly, as the bore size is raised, the area increases, as does the force, thus improving the ability to move the load which is responsible for reducing the stroke time. By the same token, as the area increases, so does the volume, with the internal mass of air to be exhausted thus responsible for increasing the stroke time. Let us start with a minimum bore size required to just advance the load. As the diameter increases, the force multiplies at a faster rate than does the mass to be expelled (due to the expanded volume), thereby continually improving the stroke time. This proceeds until the bore reaches a peak, where the combination of the increased area and the greater mass of air to be expelled renders the fastest stroke time. Beyond this point the trend inverts and continually descends. For any particular load and pressure, there is only one cylinder bore which reaches this pinnacle to render the maximum cycles per minute. Generally that point is when the most stringent load is approximately 50 percent of the cylinder's force capability (capacity).

Figures 3.8 and 3.9 are summary charts of the results of the evaluations of various objectives with different-size cylinders having all parameters identical for each objective, such as load, valve, conductor, port sizes, and pressures, except for the cylinder bore diameters to see their effect on the cpm (Fig. 3.8). The summary tabulation in Fig. 3.9 listed pressures of different values necessary to drive the cylinders but kept the cpm the same. This clearly demonstrates how the various sizes fulfill different objectives as well as even having discrete alternatives with the same bore diameter.

The objective here was to determine the cylinder bore rendering the best productivity under identical design pressures (80/80); this is a variation of the incline problem in Chap. 1:

1. All compressor pressures are set to kick out at 100 psig.

2. All cylinder pressures are regulated to 80/80 psig.

The 4-in bore (Fig. 3.8) proved to be the most productive (Survey 3-2), with a load 63 percent of capacity. It was not the cylinder having

| Survey # | Bore | Maximum CPM Attain | % Cylinder Capacity | HP | Operating Cost/yr | Cost/ 1000 pcs |
|---|---|---|---|---|---|---|
| 3–1 | 3.25" | 135.04 | 81 | 7.43 | $2,636 | $2.55 |
| 3–2 | 4.00" | 150.84 | 63 | 11.99 | $4,252 | $2.33 |
| 3–3 | 5.00" | 139.16 | 42 | 16.74 | $5,934 | $2.57 |

**Figure 3.8**  Cylinder performance using different bores.

| Survey # | Bore | S.F. | Set Pressure (PSIG) | % Cylinder Capacity | HP | Operating Cost/yr | Cost/ 1000 pcs |
|---|---|---|---|---|---|---|---|
| 3–4 | 3.25" | 24% | 110 | 75 | 3.85 | $1,339 | $3.39 |
| 3–5 | 3.25" | 17% | 100 | 75 | 3.66 | $1,296 | $3.39 |
| 3–6 | 4.00" | 26% | 75 | 75 | 3.60 | $1,391 | $3.39 |
| 3–7 | 4.00" | 45% | 100 | 75 | 4.20 | $1,490 | $3.40 |
| 3–8 | 4.00" | 20% | 100 | 52 | 8.10 | $2,872 | $3.43 |
| 3–9 | 5.00" | 25% | 55 | 64 | 4.33 | $1,747 | $3.41 |
| 3–10 | 5.00" | 58% | 100 | 64 | 5.91 | $2,097 | $3.42 |

**Figure 3.9**  Cylinder performance using different bores and pressures.

a value closest to the 50 percent rule of thumb. As you can see, we've already found an exception. This is not a hard-and-fast rule; it depends on loads, available standard size bores, and corresponding required pressures for both ends of the cylinder, but it certainly can permit one to judge if the result is within range. The complete printouts are given in Surveys 3-1 to 3-20 at the end of this chapter.

The objective here is to determine a combination of pressures and bore sizes that would render the least operating cost for a specific 100-cpm cyclic rate; this is the same problem as in Chap. 1 with the new proviso of adhering to the 100-cpm specification.

The 3.25-in-bore (Fig. 3.9) costs the least to operate even though it required the compressor to be set at a cut-in pressure of 110 psig. It was set at this pressure in order to fulfill the recommended safety factor above the operating pressure (20 percent). If it is not possible for the compressor to satisfy this higher pressure, the customer may elect to remain with 100 psig, which renders a safety factor of only 17 percent. The operating cost at this point would only be $1296, and the required hp would only be 3.66. Finally, if the customer is intent on abiding by the recommendations and cannot increase the compressor pressure, the 4-in bore would be the logical suggested cylinder size. It would run up the cost, but the hp would be reduced, as discussed earlier.

The 4- and 5-in cylinders did not necessitate any more than 75 and 55 psig, respectively, for compressor settings. These may not be possible as there may be other cylinders requiring higher compressor settings, and therefore the compressor would be set to accommodate all the actuators on the floor. This would mean that the 3.25-in (if acceptable for operation at 100 psig) cylinder would appear to be even more economical. The reason for this is that for every 2-psig drop in compressor pressure setting there is an approximate reduction of 1 percent in brake hp required to operate the compressor. Since there is a

10-psi drop, it carries a 5 percent reduction in brake hp (bhp) of 0.19 hp (0.05 × 3.85). This is exactly what the results indicate, a drop from 3.85 to 3.66 (compare Surveys 3-4 and 3-5). However, such exact substantiation across the board should not be expected. The 4-in bore carries a reduction in bhp of 14 percent with a pressure reduction of 25 psi (compare Surveys 3-6 and 3-7 as both are using dual pressures but different compressor settings; Survey 3-8 is a flow-control approach). The 5-in bore carries a bhp reduction of 27 percent with a 45-psi reduction in pressure (compare Surveys 3-9 and 3-10). See the graphs of the Dow Chemical Company studies (see Fig. 3.11 at the end of this chapter) indicating these conditions with different compressor types to appreciate the magnitude of the savings possible.

The 4-in bore would be used if one is primarily interested in utilizing the least hp as already stated. The 3.25-in bore would be used if one is interested in the least capital expense. The 5-in bore would be used if one is interested in the minimum pressure required. The facilities engineer may be forced to struggle with an ailing compressor or a supply having inadequate capacity. Insufficient financial resources may be responsible for preventing supplementation or replacement of the existing installation. The cost per 1000 units does not vary significantly; however, for those who manufacture in the hundreds of millions, this may be a pertinent consideration and therefore we include that information as well.

Assume the end user has elected to proceed with the dual-purpose concept, for all the inherent advantages discussed, leaving us with Surveys 3-5, 3-6, and 3-9 to compare. Even here it is evident that there is no single choice to satisfy all objects. For example, as the cylinder diameter increases, the cost per 1000 units and operating costs consistently increase, but the compressor hp needed is at optimum with the 4-in bore. As stated above, if pressure is a question, it's wisest to go with the largest bore, but the capital expense is greatest.

One should not conclude from this limited investigation that a smaller cylinder using higher pressures will always render lower operating costs. Each case must be handled on its own merits and requirements.

There is no one ideal cylinder bore size to use; as you can readily see, it depends on your objective. The cylinder stroke, on the other hand, should be viewed with a critical eye from only one reference point—make it only as long as required. Every inch you add will only incur needless and wasteful operating costs. All the supporting documentation for the following data are presented in Surveys 3-1 to 3-20.

1. The $C_v$ of a cylinder is really the $C_v$ of its port and is simply a function of the inside diameter (ID) of the smallest device entering or

smallest internal diameter of the cylinder end block. It may be the tapped drill size in the actuator port, the smallest dimension of a fitting (used to mate a conductor which may or may not have an integral thread matched to the threaded port of the actuator) or the ID of a conductor. The smallest of these diameters is represented by the letter $d$ (expressed in inches). The formula for the $C_v$ of the cylinder port is approximately $23d^2$. The constant 23 can vary by $\pm 10$ percent depending on how large and how well the right angle is configured in the actuator.

2. In most cases there are two dissimilar loads, warranting two different pressures, and thus candidacy for the dual-pressure concept to save energy without loss of productivity.

3. If a cylinder size is chosen which requires a pressure greater than the compressor's peak capability in order to fulfill its 75 percent of rated cylinder capacity requirement, the next-larger cylinder bore size is recommended (see Survey 3-1).

4. A 20 percent differential between the minimum compressor kick-in pressure and the maximum regulated design pressure available to the actuator are always recommended (see Survey 3-5 at rear).

5. The recommended pressure should always be at least 33 percent greater than that which is essential to move the load. If the selected pressure is such that it can move the load within the allotted time but is less than 33 percent, we suggest the pressure be boosted to the minimum and then introduce a flow control to bring the faster time in line to the specified level (see Surveys 1-3 and 1-4). If, on the other hand, the minimum pressure required to move the load within the allotted time is such that it cannot be reached by the compressor, in order to satisfy the 33 percent safety factor, a larger actuator is recommended in conjunction with flow control(s). This was stated above by viewing it from the perspective of the 75 percent of cylinder capacity position. This is usually the case when a large force is required, not so much to raise or move a load, but to accelerate it rapidly.

6. A frequently asked question is, "How can one save energy by reducing the regulated pressures to the actuators, yet leaving the compressor pressure untouched?" First, let us review why reducing the compressor pressure will save energy. The reason is that it takes less effort (less bhp) for a compressor motor to drive a compressor to compress air to a lower pressure than it does to a higher pressure (Fig. 3.11) and thus requires less kilowattage from the utility. This is similar to pumping up bicycle tires, where it is considerably easier to bring them up to 50 psig than to 80 psig. The compressor motor experiences the same increased effort required as does the individual pumping up the tires.

To explain the savings experienced by just reducing the pressure to the actuators without a commensurate reduction in the compressor pressure, we must first revert to a little basic chemistry. We will first derive the weight of air, as that is pivotal to the explanation.

The following table indicates the major constituents of atmospheric air:

| Constituent | MW | Content, vol% | | Total |
|---|---|---|---|---|
| Nitrogen ($N_2$) | 28.02 | $\times$ | 78.084 | = 21.88 |
| Oxygen ($O_2$) | 32.00 | $\times$ | 20.946 | = 6.71 |
| Argon (Ar) | 39.94 | $\times$ | 0.934 | = 0.37 |
| Carbon dioxide ($CO_2$) | 44.00 | $\times$ | 0.033 + trace gases | = 0.02 |
| | | Molecular weight (MW) of air ($M_a$) | | = 28.98 |

Universal gas constant $(R) = 1544$

Specific gas constant of air $(R_a) = R/M_a = 1544/28.96 = 53.3$

Absolute pressure $(P) = 14.7$ psia or $14.7 \times 144$ in$^2$/ft$^2 = 2116$ pounds per square foot absolute (psfa)

Volume $(V) = 1$ standard cubic foot (scf)

Absolute temperature $(\Gamma) = 68°F + 460 = 528°R$

Weight of air $(w)$ in pcf at standard conditions $= PV/R_a\Gamma$

$w = (2116 \times 1)/(53.3 \times 538) = 0.076$ pcf at standard sea-level conditions of 14.7 psia atmospheric pressure and 68°F temperature

Another means of verifying the universal gas constant $(R)$ is as follows:

$J = 778.26$ ft-lb/Btu (mechanical equivalent of heat)

$c_p = 0.2415$ (discussed in Chap. 2; arrived at empirically)

$c_v = 0.173$ (discussed in Chap. 2; arrived at empirically)

For a well-written treatise on this subject, see Hausmann and Slack.[1] Also, the molecular weight of air is

$$M_a = 28.98$$

---

[1]E. Hausmann and E. Slack, *Physics,* 2d ed., Van Nostrand, New York, 1940, Chap. XVII (special emphasis on pp. 284, 285).

and the formula for deriving $R$ is

$$R = MJ(c_p - c_v)$$

Then $R = (28.98 \times 778.26)(0.2415 - 0.173) = 1544$ (confirms preceding result).

Now that we have established that one cubic foot of air at standard conditions weighs 0.076 lb, let us factor it into the cost equation. We will compare the difference in cost and hp of two 4-in-bore cylinders, each with identical requirements but different associated components and pressures. One uses two flow controls and pressures of 80 psig at each end to obtain the 100 cpm, while the other uses regulators to achieve the necessary dual pressures to acquire the same 100 cpm. (The cylinder required slight pressure increases to conform to recommended standards. The elevated pressures improved the extend time necessitating a flow control to bring it back into specification.) The important point is that the compressor pressure is identical in both cases: 100 psig kick-in pressure.

(*Note:* Many compressors are of the type that store compressed air in a reservoir. There is a pressure switch on the reservoir that monitors its pressure. When the pressure in the reservoir drops to the designated setpoint of the pressure switch, it either turns on a small compressor or switches a larger compressor from an idling mode to a compressing mode. When the compressor has recharged the reservoir to the high-pressure cutoff point, the small compressor shuts off or the larger compressor reverts back into an idling mode. There are screw-type compressors which run continuously and may not have reservoirs; however, they achieve similar results of alternately idling and compressing by cutting back on the intake, which depends on the compressed-air demand and thus increases or decreases the electrical load. The term *kick-in* describes the action of the compressor going into its compressing mode and is a function of the pressure switch; the term *kick-out* implies that the compressor has concluded its compressing mode by satisfying the elevated pressure because it charged up the reservoir sufficiently and is shifting into its idling or shut-off mode.)

One of the 4-in bore cylinders that we are comparing is the one listed in Fig. 3.9 as Survey 3-7 and already solved for in Chap. 1. The solution for the other cylinder, listed in Fig. 3.9 as Survey 3-8, is using 80 psig at each end of the cylinder.

The highlights of these solutions are as follows: The total operating cost and hp for the case using a single-pressure source was $2856 (operating cost of $2747 + leakage cost of $109) and 8.05 hp expended (7.74 hp to supply operating needs and 0.31 hp for leakage losses), whereas the dual-pressure application amounted to only $1490 (operating cost of $1451 + leakage cost of $39) and 4.20 hp expended (4.09 hp to supply operating requirements and 0.11 hp for leakage losses).

We will consider a 20-cf reservoir (approximately 150 gal; 7.48 gal/ft$^3$; see Chap. 9, section on tanks for various aspects of sizing of this reservoir) supplied by as yet an unknown-size compressor which kicks in at 100 psig (114.7 psia) and kicks out at 125 psig (139.7 psia). The available air for usage, expressed in standard cubic feet, to the system once the compressor kicks out and before it kicks in, is determined as follows. The difference between the high-point setting (kick-in) and the low-point setting (kick-out) of the compressor, called the *cycling range,* is divided by 14.7 and the result is multiplied by the tank volume: (25/14.7)(20) = 34 scf and then

$$34 \text{ scf} \times 0.076 \text{ lb/scf} = 2.58 \text{ lb} ******$$

We will now calculate the mass weight of air used under the two options to determine how much more air is extracted from the reservoir or surge tank by one cylinder combination over the other. Let us *first* consider the dual-pressure case of 55.2 psig (69.9 psia) and 14.2 psig (28.9 psia).

This does not mean that one should attempt to set the regulators to read these exact pressures, as that would be highly improbable with standard gauges. One should arrive at the performance times by utilizing an elapsed-time indicator, if accuracy is warranted. The standard commercial pressure regulators and gauges are not sufficiently accurate or precise to be set and read close to the suggested pressures. However, one can be certain that the actual pressures will be reasonably close to the ones recommended. All our tests were conducted with apparatus and gauges traceable to the National Institute of Standards and Technology (NIST):[2]

$$\text{Sweep volume of extend end} = (4)^2 \times \frac{3.14}{4} \times 3.75 = 47.12 \text{ in}^3$$

$$\text{Sweep volume of retract end} = [(4)^2 - (1)^2]\frac{3.14}{4} \times 3.75 = 44.18 \text{ in}^3$$

$$\text{Volume of conductor} = (0.625)^2\frac{3.14}{4} \times 18 = 5.52 \text{ in}^3$$

---

[2]Formerly known as the National Bureau of Standards (NBS).

Total volume extend $= 47.12 + 5.52 = 52.64$ in$^3$

Total volume retract $= 44.18 + 5.52 = 49.70$ in$^3$

Converting to standard cubic feet, we have

$$\text{Extend } \frac{(52.64)(69.9/14.7)}{1728} = 0.145 \text{ scf}$$

$$\text{Retract } \frac{(49.70)(28.9/14.7)}{1728} = 0.057 \text{ scf}$$

Total for one cycle $= 0.202$ scf $\times$ 0.076 lb/scf $= 0.01531$ lb

For 24,000,000 cycles per year, that becomes 367,200 lb/year and at $0.395/100 lb (cost based on the compressor operating at a kick-in pressure of 100 psig—see mathematics below), that amounts to $1450 (printout reads $1451—variance due to rounding):

Total leakage/cycle $= 0.0054$ scf $\times$ 0.076 lb/scf $= 0.0004$ lb

For 24,000,000 cycles per year, that becomes 9600 lb/year and at $0.395/100 lb, that amounts to $38 (printout is $39):

Total scf/cycle $= 0.2074$ (0.202 + 0.0054);
total lb/cycle $= 0.0157$ (0.0153 + 0.0004) ******

We will now make all the determinations for the other case where a single pressure of 80 psig (94.7 psia) was used for each end of the cylinder in conjunction with flow controls to arrive at the identical required times. I might add, for emphasis again, that this is the more widely accepted tactic used in the field today. Converting to standard cubic feet, we obtain

$$\text{Extend } \frac{(52.64)(94.7/14.7)}{1728} = 0.1962 \text{ scf}$$

$$\text{Retract } \frac{(49.70)(94.7/14.7)}{1748} = 0.1853 \text{ scf}$$

Total for one cycle $= 0.3815$ scf $\times$ 0.076 lb/scf $= 0.029$ lb

For 24,000,000 cycles per year, that becomes 696,000 lb/year, and at $0.395/100 lb that amounts to $2749 (computer printout $2764 variance due to rounding):

Total leakage/cycle $= 0.0151$ scf $\times$ 0.076 lb/scf $= 0.00115$ lb

For 24,000,000 cycles/year, that becomes 27,600 lb/year, and at $0.395/100 lb, that amounts to $109:

Total scf/cycle = 0.3966;    total lb/cycle = 0.0301 ******

[*Note:* The operating air cost is $0.30/1000 scf based on a compressor cycling between 100 and 125 psig, which in turn includes a utility rate which is based on a current average cost of $0.07/kWh. This translates into $0.395/100 lb (based on 0.076 lb/scf), $0.30/1000 scf or $0.30/76 lb (weight of 1000 scf), which amounts to $0.395/100 lb.]

The range of the majority of sources for the utility portion of the total operating cost of a compressor hovers between 55 and 65 percent.[3,4] For very small compressors (<25 hp) which go into an idling or off mode, the 65 percent figure can reach 75 percent. Our calculations for the utility portion fluctuate from 58 to 65 percent. The horsepower arrived at in our calculations always includes the cylinder leakage, and therefore this broad band exists depending whether the customer used single or dual pressures. We limit the air source to large efficient multistage installations of 100 hp or greater. Obviously there are some geographic pockets which stray outside these utility-cost windows. The operating cost along with its derivation will be handled in full in Chap. 7, dealing with the sizing and other perspectives of compressors and tanks.

Let us measure the results in the light of this information. Our first evaluation will be based on the origin of compressed air emanating from a large source, and therefore the hp determined is the entire burden on the installation. If you were a facilities engineer, you would then measure the effect of this added obligation on your facility. Subsequently we will view this from a dedicated compressor(s) supplying the requirements for this installation:

Utility cost = hp $\times$ 0.746 kW/hp $\times$ hours of operation $\times$ cost/kWh

The utility cost of the prudent approach operating two shifts or 4000 h can be calculated as follows. First, review Survey 3-7 to obtain power input of 4.2 hp:

$$4.2 \times 0.746 \times 4000 \times \$0.07 = \$877$$

---

[3]*Compressed Air and Gas Handbook,* 4th ed., Compressed Air and Gas Institute, 1973, New York. (The text uses 65% as their estimate for the utility portion of the entire compressed air cost.)

[4]We specifically polled several utilities in the Michigan and Ohio area; the utility portion of the total air cost ranged from 60 to 66 percent, with few exceptions.

The average range of utility cost per total operating cost ratio is 55 to 65 percent and for small units, is 75 percent. Then

$$\$877/\$1470 = 59\%$$

To obtain the utility cost of the customary approach operating two shifts or 4000 h, review Survey 3-8 to obtain power input of 8.1 hp:

$$8.1 \times 0.746 \times 4000 \times \$0.07 = \$1692$$

$$\$1692/\$2872 = 59\%$$

The leakage rate and costs mentioned earlier are a function of the loss of compressed air around the actuator seals and packings. Obviously the older the member, the worse the seepage of air. The area predominantly responsible for the major loss of air is around the rod-end bushing. It is well to remember that whenever there is an equivalent orifice, whether the piston is in motion or in a delay or dwell mode, accompanied by a differential pressure, air will course from the higher to the lower pressure level. All our tests were carried out with cylinders having accrued approximately 10,000 cycles with normal factory air and therefore prone to some leakage.

We extracted 0.1892 scf (0.3966 − 0.2074) or 0.0144 lb (0.0301 − 0.0157) less air per cycle with the dual-pressure system than we did with the common or conventional approach, which amounts to approximately \$1365 (0.0144 × 24 × $10^6$ × \$0.395/100 lb) savings per year [variance from computer printout of \$1382 (\$2872 − \$1490)].

Now let us weigh the effects assuming that a dedicated compressor(s) is (are) supplying the needs for each circuit. The questions raised that need answering are

1. How much longer compressor idling time would be gained with circuit A (55/14 psig) over circuit B (80/80 psig)?

2. How much longer compressing time would be required of circuit B over A?

The reservoir has 2.58 lb of air to dispense before it calls on the compressor to recharge it. At 100 cpm the cycle time is 0.6 second per cycle. If we draw 0.0157 lb per cycle (in circuit A), we can operate for 164 cycles prior to recharging or 98 s of compressor idling or off time. Whereas, if we draw 0.0301 lb per cycle (in circuit B) we can experience only 85 cycles prior to recharging, or 51 s of compressor idling or off time. Let us select a compressor size in order to continue with our calculations. The compressor selection process, along with its associated surge tank, will be handled in greater detail in Chap. 7. There are specific ranges that govern the selection of a compressor, and we will briefly discuss one here that will allow us to continue. The specific ratio we are interested in at this moment is the relationship between the off time or idling-mode time and the on time or compressing-mode time, which should lie between 2 and 3:1. In that way we allow the compressor to idle sufficiently without overtaxing or overheating the unit and at the same time prevent from idling too long, as that, too, is wasteful, even though current compressors are quite efficient and draw only about 10 percent of the power that is used in the compressing mode. We will select a compressor(s) to satisfy the needs for the 0.0301-lb/cycle demand and then compare the costs and operation with the same unit(s) for the 0.0157 lb/cycle demand. We will then select a smaller compressor(s) specifically suited for the 0.0157-lb/cycle demand and compare the new results with the same demand using the larger compressor(s).

[*Note:* Compressors are selected on the basis of their output, i.e., the scfm they produce. We will derive formulas further in the text as to how much scfm per horsepower is delivered by the average compressor today at the various operating ranges. For all our calculations, a compressor operating between 100 and 125 psig delivers approximately 5 scfm/hp in the multistage 100-hp range and beyond. It improves as you venture into greater hp ranges, and by the same token the smaller-capacity units progressively decrease in output. The hp ranges that we recommend in our surveys are governed by output efficiencies based on >100 hp and are drawn from a central facility. The hp that is calculated and stated in Surveys 3-1 to 3-20 is therefore the total drain on the system on a continuous basis. We can then sum up all our needs to arrive at a total. We then add some percentage for future expansion. The last item on the agenda is to multiply this by 3 or 4 for the grand total to arrive at a size that would render a 2 to 3:1 off/on time.]

We have divided compressors, for simplicity, into two categories: those above 100 hp and those below 100 hp. All the suggestions we recommend as well as the costs are based on the efficiencies of multistage 100-hp compressors and larger. Obviously, as stated earlier, the efficiency crawls up gradually with size, but for our purposes at this stage it is beneficial to consider only two classes. The smaller-size group (<100 hp) has a 20 percent higher cost of air, due to a corresponding lower compressor efficiency of 20 percent. Thus, the required 4.2 hp and 8.1 hp for our two comparisons (when dealing with small dedicated compressors) become 5.04 and 9.72 hp, respectively. The operating costs at $0.30/1000 scf are, respectively, $1490 and $2872 and at $0.36/1000 scf (20 percent higher), they become $1788 and $3446, respectively. It should be kept in mind that the 100-hp dividing point is not sacrosanct. Obviously a 75-hp unit is not 20 percent less efficient than a 100-hp unit, just as a 200-hp unit may be more efficient than a 100-hp compressor. The graduations are modest in each direction.

We will use the worst-case scenario, which transpires just as the tank has dropped to 100 psig and is calling for the compressor to kick in, and simultaneously the demand for compressed air is telegraphed:

Demand = 0.3966 scf/cycle × 100 cpm = 39.66 scfm (3.01 lb/min)

The 2:1 ratio is for a compressor that can deliver 120 scfm (39.66 × 3). To satisfy the 2:1 ratio, a compressor must deliver three times its demand so that two thirds of the time it would be off and one third of the time it would be on.

Two 15-hp units will deliver about 120 scfm and are of the type that shut off at the end of the compressing mode rather than go into an idling mode. They are also wired to operate sequentially and incrementally as dictated by floor demands:

120 scfm = 2.00 scfs;    2.00 × 0.6 = 1.2 scf/cycle (0.09 lb/cycle)

The circuit at 80/80 expends 0.3966 scf/cycle (0.03 lb/cycle). The net gain in lb/cycle during the compressing mode is

$$0.090 - 0.03 = 0.06 \text{ lb/cycle}$$

We must replenish 2.58 lb; therefore, it would require

$$2.58/0.06 = 43 \text{ cycles} \quad \text{or} \quad 25.8 \text{ s}$$

The off/on ratio of the 30-hp tandem units for this 80/80 circuit is

$$(120 - 39.66):39.66 = 2.0:1$$

One total compressor cycle time is 51 + 25.8 = 76.8 s.

Check: 51:25.8 = 2.0:1

$$51/76.8 = 0.66 \text{ of } 4000 \text{ h (2 shifts of 2000 h/year)} \quad \text{or} \quad 2640 \text{ h}$$

in a nonoperating mode at no power and

$$25.8/76.8 = 0.34 \text{ of } 4000 \text{ h or } 1360 \text{ h}$$

of compressing mode at full power and

$$30 \text{ hp} = 22.4 \text{ kW (30} \times 0.746 \text{ kW/hp)}$$

22.4 kW × $0.07/kWh × 1360 = $2132 utility compressing cost ******

The total utility cost is $2132, ****** which is 62 percent (2132/3427) of the overall cost of air of $3427 [2856 × 1.2 (20% higher)].

The circuit at 55/14 expends 0.2074 scf/cycle (0.0158 lb/cycle). For 100 cpm the demand is 20.74 scfm (1.58 lb/min). The net gain in pounds per cycle during the 30-hp compressing mode is

$$0.09 - 0.0158 = 0.0742 \text{ lb/cycle}$$

We must replenish 2.58 lb; therefore it would require

$$2.58/0.0742 = 34.8 \text{ cycles or } 20.9 \text{ s}$$

The off/on ratio of the 30-hp unit for the 55/14 circuit is (120 − 20.9)/20.9 = 4.7:1. One total compressor cycle time is 98 + 20.9 = 118.9 s.

$$\text{Check: } 98/20.9 = 4.7:1$$

$$98/118.9 = 82.4\% \text{ of } 5000 \text{ h} \quad \text{or} \quad 3296 \text{ h}$$

in a nonoperating mode at no power and

$$20.9/118.9 = 17.6\% \text{ of } 4000 \text{ h} \quad \text{or} \quad 704 \text{ h}$$

of compressing mode at full power and

$$30 \text{ hp} = 22.4 \text{ kW} (30 \times 0.746 \text{ kW/hp})$$

$$22.4 \times 0.07 \times 704 = \$1102 \text{ utility compressing cost } ******$$

The total utility cost is \$1102, ****** which is 62 percent (1102/1788) of the overall cost of air of \$1788 [\$1490 × 1.2 (20% higher)].

Actually, in reviewing the 55/14 approach we find that it is necessary to utilize only one 15-hp compressor to be within the approximate off/on-time ratio of 2 to 3:1. Since the demand is only 20 scfm and a 15-hp compressor can deliver 60 scfm within the required operating range, it would appear, in terms of an initial capital expense, to be more beneficial to employ only one compressor. In assessing the circuit on a utility-cost basis to determine whether it is more or less favorable than the 4.7:1 ratio, we will find that there is no difference from simply a mathematical outlook as long as the tank size does not vary. The 30-hp compressor will use twice the energy in half the time to charge up the tank to the same pressure. Unfortunately, it isn't quite that simple. There is a starting current involved with its surge, there is the stopping and starting element to contend with, power factors come into play, and not allowing a sufficient interval of time between on cycles (off/on ratio) and a host of other items should be carefully investigated with one's compressor suppliers. Because of the power factor and starting current, it may be wiser to allow the compressor motor to go into an idling mode rather than having it come to a complete halt, which requires a large starting current to overcome inertia. Moreover, the compressor manufacturer may recommend a longer off/on ratio, which would result in lower operating costs due to improved life and all the above. The purchasing decision should not be hastily arrived at, and an economic feasibility study should be undertaken, as is the case with all the other fluid-dynamic components. Also

1. Compressor size governs the off/on ratio.

2. Tank size governs the duration of the off and on times but does not modify their relationship.

3. The compressor should idle for approximately 2 min before going into a compressing mode of about 1 min. If the idling mode is much below 2 min, the tank size should be increased. Again, these suggestions should be meticulously reviewed with the manufacturer. We refer to this as the "two-minute rule."

Let us examine the utilitarian value of a substantial gravity-assist load, on one end of a cylinder, by comparing the single pressure to the dual-pressure approach for (1) the reduction of required hp, (2) the reduction of operating costs, and (3) the increase in cpm, to name just a few vital properties that are impacted. This problem again is a fairly standard application for an air cylinder. It is necessary to vertically raise an 800-lb load 12 in, discharge it, and return empty ready to receive the next 800-lb load. The weight of the elevator is 1200 lb; therefore, the extend load is 2000 lb and the retract load is $-$ 1200 lb. The requisite extend/retract (extend and retract) times are 2.00/1.50 s. The dwell times are 1.8/2.7 s, for a total cycle time of 8 s (7.50 cpm). Before we zero in on the various methods used to arrive at the designated times, let us compare the maximum cyclic rates possible at 80/80 (Survey 3-12), 80/5 (Survey 3-13), and 80/0 (Survey 3-14) with all conditions being equal except the retract pressures. In comparing the results (in Surveys 3-12 to 3-14) of 80/80, 80/5, and 80/0, it is quite evident that increasing the retract pressure does not improve the cyclic rate; on the contrary, it worsens it. This is because the large retract gravity-assist load of 1200 lb enabled the terminal velocity to be reached without any retract pressure at all. Therefore, increasing the retract pressure above 0 psig does not enhance the retract time, but it does prolong the extend time because of the additional exhaust load that the increased pressure placed on the extend end. Even though terminal velocity was reached without any retract pressure at all, some company standards dictate a minimal pressure of 5 psig. The maximum cyclic rate at 80/5 was 10.03, whereas the higher retract pressure of 80/80 achieved only 9.28. The value that a large gravity-assist load can play, if there is a method available to take advantage of it, is dramatic. The hp differences and the operating costs are just as dramatic. At 80/80 the input hp required is 9.35 and the cost is $3316, whereas at 80/5 the input hp is 6.04, with an accompanying air cost of only $2142.

Let us now return to the original question that was posed: whether a considerable gravity-assist load can have an appreciable effect on hp, operating costs, and cpm when applying the dual-pressure method. Survey 3-11 (80/80) necessitates 7.69 hp with the aid of two flow controls, whereas Survey 3-15 (55/5) calls for only 3.57 hp. The contrasting operating costs are just as spectacular, $2726 to $1265. In this instance there was no need for productivity comparisons as the customer required a cyclic rate of 7.5 and desired the optimum selections of components and pressures to achieve that end.

Another frequently posed question is whether it is wiser to use a smaller cylinder at a higher pressure or a larger cylinder at a lower pressure to move the same loads in the identical times. This is similar to the surveys listed in Fig. 3.9, and discussed earlier in the chapter, where the results indicated that it was wiser to select a smaller cylinder at a higher operating pressure. The subtle difference is that we have a very large gravity-assist load here compared to the earlier problem. Therefore, the added issue is whether the same deductions will apply here. The only thing we can categorically state is that it depends on the circumstances, for each problem must be solved for individually, and there are no hard-and-fast rules. For example, if the compressor pressure must remain at 100 psig, for a variety of reasons, then the 7-in bore (Survey 3-17) at the higher pressure (71/5) would be the odds-on favorite as it would require only 3.3 hp, whereas the 8-in bore (Survey 3-15) at the lower pressure (55/5) would require 3.57 hp. On the other hand, if the compressor pressure can be set to suit the applications, then the situation is reversed; specifically, the 7-in bore (Survey 3-18) at 71/5 requires 3.12 hp, whereas the 8-in bore (Survey 3-16) at 55/5 requires only 2.95 hp. Again, we walk away with the conclusion, as we have in the past, that there are no universal laws, as each case must be solved on its own merits. The operating costs at the 100 psig compressor pressure are $1171 (Survey 3-17) for the 7-in bore and $1265 (Survey 3-15) for the 8-in bore following very closely the hp results. The operating costs at the set compressor pressures reverse the hp trend; in other words, it costs more to operate the 8-in bore ($1138; Survey 3-16) than it does the 7-in bore ($1131; Survey 3-18), even though the hp requirements were less for the 8-in bore. Again the results indicate that it is mandatory to fully explore all the parameters before rendering a decision.

The next set of surveys will explore another often perplexing dilemma: whether one should select a single cylinder, two cylinders, or even three cylinders to raise a vertical load, all things being equal. We will use as our basis the 7-in-bore example (Survey 3-18) operating with a 90-psig compressor pressure regulated down to 71/5, which is about 78 percent of its capacity and generating 7.5 cpm. The next solution (Survey 3-19) also operates with the compressor set at 90 psig but regulated down to 70/5 feeding two 5-in-bore cylinders also at about 78 percent of each of their cylinder capacities generating the same 7.5 cpm. In the last solution (Survey 3-20) the compressor is set at 100 psig and regulated down to 73/5 to supply three 4-in-bore cylinders (each with a 73 percent capacity) moving the same load 7.5 cpm. All three solutions require the same valve to operate the systems. The hp requirements were 3.12 for the single 7-in bore, 3.24 for the two 5-in bores, and 3.54 for the three 4-in bores. The total operating costs in this instance tracked the horsepower; the 7-in bore was $1131, the 5-in bores were $1174, and the 4-in bores were $1256. Even if the 7-in- and 5-in-bore cylinders were operating with a compressor set at 100 psig, the results would continue to favor the 7-in unit. The benefits would not be as great, but would nevertheless be there. The 7-in actuator would require 3.3 hp, and the 5-in unit would require 3.43 hp, still less than the 3.54 hp necessary for the 4-in units. The operating savings are less but also continue to support the 7-in bore. The operating cost of the 7-in unit with the 100-psig compressor pressure is now up to $1171; and the 5-in cylinders up to $1214, but both less than the $1256 generated by the 4-in cylinders. If the design does not warrant multiple supports, it would behoove the designer to use a single 7-in bore in terms of both hp and operating cost, but only in this specific instance. The other aspects to investigate are the cost of the cylinders ($562 for one 7-in-bore cylinder, $707 for two 5-in-bore cylinders, and $859 for three 4-in-bore cylinders), the necessary structure required for the elevator depending on the number of cylinders, whether it's for a single machine for an end user or for an OEM, the estimated life, etc. These combined elements will then foster a creditable economic-feasibility study. To do any justice to the study, it is essential to have access to the variety of information that the dual-pressure method supplies.

Let us briefly summarize some of the vital points that we have learned. The total force the cylinder generates must be slightly greater than the total moving load to launch the piston. The force equals pressure times the face area. These apply equally to the extend and retract strokes, depending on which end is being filled and which is being exhausted. The difference between the filling pressure and the exhaust pressure at any given moment is called the *differential pressure*. Once the piston is in motion, the $\Delta p$ is the difference

| Survey # | Bore & Quantity | Set Pressure (PSIG) | Regulator Cyl. Press. (PSIG) | HP | Operating Cost/yr | CPM |
|---|---|---|---|---|---|---|
| 3–11 | 8 x 1 | 100 | 80/80 | 7.69 | $2,726 | 7.50 |
| 3–12 | 8 x 1 | 100 | 80/80 | 9.35 | $3,316 | 9.28 |
| 3–13 | 8 x 1 | 100 | 80/5 | 6.04 | $2,142 | 10.03 |
| 3–14 | 8 x 1 | 100 | 80/0 | 5.17 | $1,832 | 10.24 |
| 3–15 | 8 x 1 | 100 | 55/5 | 3.57 | $1,265 | 7.50 |
| 3–16 | 8 x 1 | 70 | 55/5 | 2.95 | $1,138 | 7.50 |
| 3–17 | 7 x 1 | 100 | 71/5 | 3.30 | $1,171 | 7.50 |
| 3–18 | 7 x 1 | 90 | 71/5 | 3.12 | $1,131 | 7.50 |
| 3–19 | 5 x 2 | 100 | 70/5 | 3.24 | $1,174 | 7.50 |
| 3–20 | 4 x 3 | 100 | 73/5 | 3.54 | $1,256 | 7.50 |

**Figure 3.10**    Cylinder performance using different bores, pressures, and quantities.

between the highest and lowest reading of the filling pressure during the stroke. It is strictly a function of the end which is being filled. The total moving load is composed of the accelerating load, the dynamic frictional load of the weight being moved as well as that of the cylinder, the gravitational load, and the exhaust-pressure load. At any given moment during the stroke the exhaust load equals the exhaust pressure, at that instant, times its face area. Determination of the exhaust-pressure load and the total force at any instance is unnecessary when using the selection method presented in the preceding paragraphs because the performance data employed includes these two elements as well as any of the delays due to the static loads.

Figure 3.10 summarizes Surveys 3-11 to 3-20.

We spoke earlier of compressor hp operating costs and how they relate to pressures and flow. Another yardstick is widely used today by plant operating people that expresses the dollar cost per hp-year, which warrants some discussion so as to be conversant with the subject.

We have been using an average utility cost of $0.07/kWh, which amounts to $0.052/hph (0.07 × 0.746 kW/hp). Since there are 8760 h per year (running continuously for purposes of deriving this $/hpy figure), the cost per hpy is $456 (0.052 × 8760). This figure is exactly twice what *Factory Magazine*[5] was quoting in 1976, when the average cost of electricity was $0.035/kWh.

---

[5]*Factory Magazine,* Nov. 1976, stated that the cost per horsepower per year was $230. ($0.035 × 0.746 × 8760) at the then-prevailing utility rate per killowatthour of $0.035.

To round out this review, let us take a look at the cost of air based on $0.07/kWh and determine what 1000 scf amounts to and what percentage of the total the utility portion is:

$0.07/kWh × 0.746 = $0.052/hph   or   $0.00087/hpm    (hp-month)

Assume that we obtain on an average from efficient 100-hp compressors delivering 100 to 125 psig a flow of 5 scf/hpm, which calculates to $0.000174/scf (0.00087/5) and for 1000 scf, the tally is $0.174. When we use $0.30/1000 scf for the total cost of air, which is based on and arrived at from a rate for electricity of $0.07/kWh, we obtain the percentage of utility to total cost to be 58 percent. This is within the operating percentage we have stated.

We are now ready to proceed to the next category of components, so let us journey upstream from the actuator to encounter fittings.

*"All that is necessary for the triumph of evil is that good men do nothing."*
EDMUND BURKE, BRITISH STATESMAN, ORATOR, AND WRITER, 1729–1797

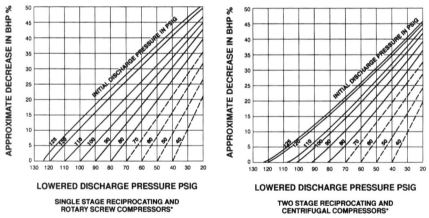

**Figure 3.11** How lowered discharge pressures affect brake-horsepower requirements. (*Source: Dow Chemical Co., Freeport, Tex.*)

```
NUMATICS NUMASIZING (R) SUMMARY SHEET                  Date:    04/10/95
NU301EED  Ver 3.01 (c) 1989 Numatics, Inc.            SURVEY # 3-1
=========================================================================
Prepared for:                   Prepared by:    Michael Liberty
Company:                        Company:        Numatics Inc.
Address:                        Address:        1450 N. Milford Rd.
City,State,Zip:                 City,State,Zip: Highland, Mi. 48357
Telephone #                     Telephone #     (810) 887-4111
Fax #                           Fax #           (810) 887-9190
-------------------------------------------------------------------------
                                     Avg/Tot/Oth    Extend      Retract
INITIAL CUSTOMER PARAMETERS:
Total weight of load (lbs)                          450.00      -20.00
Angle of load from horizontal          45
Coefficient of Friction              0.30
Number of actuators                     1
Total load per actuator (lbs)                       540.59       71.77
Minimum line pressure (PSIG)          100
Design pressure used (PSIG)                          80.0        80.0
Shifts/day (1 shift=120,000 m/yr)     2.0
Cycles per year                  32515021

ACTUATOR:
Description:   Single Rod High Flow Numatics Actuator with 1/2 NPT ports
Bore/stroke/rod            3.25" bore x 3.75" stroke x 1.000" rod
Fitting                    5/8 NPT - 1/2 NPT STR

CONDUCTOR & ASSOCIATED COMPONENTS:
Branch conductor /leg                 N/A
Branch manifold fitting /leg          N/A
Branch cond equiv ftg lg /leg (in)    N/A
Quick disconnect model /leg           N/A
In line flow control model /leg                     NONE        NONE
Main conductor             5/8" rubber hose 18" long with 0.0 elbow(s)
Main manifold fitting                 N/A
Main cond equiv ftg lg (in)             0

VALVE ASSEMBLY & ASSOCIATED COMPONENTS:
Description    2 Pos Mk 55 on 1/2 NPT base with ext reg
Fitting                    5/8 NPT - 1/2 NPT STR
Silencer model             M4 (1/2 NPT)

SYSTEM PERFORMANCE TIMES:
Att'n stroke time (sec)                             0.27        0.07
Required stroke time (sec)                          0.27        0.07
Stroke time @ term vel (sec)                        0.05        0.05
Att'n cyclic rate (CPM)             135.04
Required cyclic rate (CPM)          135.48
Cyclic rate @ term vel (CPM)        292.13
System delay time (sec)              0.023
Dwell time after stroke (sec)                       0.00        0.10

SYSTEM INFORMATION:
Required system Cv                                  3.15        2.97
Attained system Cv                                  3.23        3.23
Att'n system air flow (SCFM)                        30.2       102.8
Att'n branch air vel (400 FPS max)       N/A                 N/A
Att'n main air vel (400 FPS max)                    37         144
Att'n % delta p (46% max)                            1          14
% Act. capacity used (75% max)                      81  ?       12
Min pres necessary for ld w/S.F. (PSIG)            86.9        12.7
Air per cycle (SCF)                   0.26
Att'n act leakage cost/yr @ $ 0.30 /KSCF             87          39          48
Att'n operating air cost/yr @ $ 0.30 /KSCF         2549        1328        1221
Cost /1000 cyc @ att'n times @ $ 20.00 /hr         2.55
Att'n power input total (HP)         7.43

COMMENTS:
```

```
NUMATICS NUMASIZING (R) SUMMARY SHEET              Date:   04/10/95
NU301EED  Ver 3.01 (c) 1989 Numatics, Inc.        SURVEY # 3-2
=================================================================
Prepared for:                  Prepared by:     Michael Liberty
Company:                       Company:         Numatics Inc.
Address:                       Address:         1450 N. Milford Rd.
City,State,Zip:                City,State,Zip:  Highland, Mi. 48357
Telephone #                    Telephone #      (810) 887-4111
Fax #                          Fax #            (810) 887-9190
-----------------------------------------------------------------
                                        Avg/Tot/Oth   Extend    Retract
INITIAL CUSTOMER PARAMETERS:
Total weight of load (lbs)                            450.00    -20.00
Angle of load from horizontal               45
Coefficient of Friction                   0.30
Number of actuators                          1
Total load per actuator (lbs)                        636.24     42.43
Minimum line pressure (PSIG)               100
Design pressure used (PSIG)                           80.0      80.0
Shifts/day (1 shift=120,000 m/yr)          2.0
Cycles per year                       36244340

ACTUATOR:
Description:   Single Rod High Flow Numatics Actuator with 1/2 NPT ports
Bore/stroke/rod             4.00" bore x 3.75" stroke x 1.000" rod
Fitting                     5/8 NPT - 1/2 NPT STR

CONDUCTOR & ASSOCIATED COMPONENTS:
Branch conductor /leg                   N/A
Branch manifold fitting /leg            N/A
Branch cond equiv ftg lg /leg (in)      N/A
Quick disconnect model /leg             N/A
In line flow control model /leg                       NONE       NONE
Main conductor              5/8" rubber hose 18" long with 0.0 elbow(s)
Main manifold fitting                   N/A
Main cond equiv ftg lg (in)               0

VALVE ASSEMBLY & ASSOCIATED COMPONENTS:
Description    2 Pos Mk 55 on 1/2 NPT base with ext reg
Fitting                     5/8 NPT - 1/2 NPT STR
Silencer model              M4 (1/2 NPT)

SYSTEM PERFORMANCE TIMES:
Att'n stroke time (sec)                                0.20       0.09
Required stroke time (sec)                             0.20       0.09
Stroke time @ term vel (sec)                           0.08       0.07
Att'n cyclic rate (CPM)                  150.84
Required cyclic rate (CPM)               151.02
Cyclic rate @ term vel (CPM)             236.78
System delay time (sec)                    0.023
Dwell time after stroke (sec)                          0.00       0.10

SYSTEM INFORMATION:
Required system Cv                                     3.15       3.00
Attained system Cv                                     3.23       3.23
Att'n system air flow (SCFM)                          58.1      117.1
Att'n main air vel (400 FPS max)              N/A              N/A
Att'n branch air vel (400 FPS max)                     73        175
Att'n main air vel (400 FPS max)                        4         19
% Act. capacity used (75% max)                         63          5
Min pres necessary for ld w/S.F. (PSIG)               67.5       4.8
Air per cycle (SCF)                        0.38
Att'n act leakage cost/yr @ $ 0.30 /KSCF    108         40         67
Att'n operating air cost/yr @ $ 0.30 /KSCF 4144       2132       2012
Cost /1000 cyc @ att'n times @ $ 20.00 /hr  2.33
Att'n power input total (HP)              11.99

COMMENTS:
```

```
NUMATICS NUMASIZING (R) SUMMARY SHEET                    Date:    04/10/95
NU301EED  Ver 3.01 (c) 1989 Numatics, Inc.              SURVEY # 3-3
==========================================================================
Prepared for:                    Prepared by:     Michael Liberty
Company:                         Company:         Numatics Inc.
Address:                         Address:         1450 N. Milford Rd.
City,State,Zip:                  City,State,Zip:  Highland, Mi. 48357
Telephone #                      Telephone #      (810) 887-4111
Fax #                            Fax #            (810) 887-9190
--------------------------------------------------------------------------
                                      Avg/Tot/Oth    Extend      Retract
INITIAL CUSTOMER PARAMETERS:
Total weight of load (lbs)                          450.00       -20.00
Angle of load from horizontal             45
Coefficient of Friction                   0.30
Number of actuators                       1
Total load per actuator (lbs)                       655.33        23.03
Minimum line pressure (PSIG)              100
Design pressure used (PSIG)                          80.0         80.0
Shifts/day (1 shift=120,000 m/yr)         2.0
Cycles per year                           33526902

ACTUATOR:
Description:    Single Rod High Flow Numatics Actuator with 1/2 NPT ports
Bore/stroke/rod             5.00" bore x 3.75" stroke x 1.000" rod
Fitting                     5/8 NPT - 1/2 NPT STR

CONDUCTOR & ASSOCIATED COMPONENTS:
Branch conductor /leg                  N/A
Branch manifold fitting /leg           N/A
Branch cond equiv ftg lg /leg (in)     N/A
Quick disconnect model /leg            N/A
In line flow control model /leg                     NONE          NONE
Main conductor              5/8" rubber hose 18" long with 0.0 elbow(s)
Main manifold fitting                  N/A
Main cond equiv ftg lg (in)            0

VALVE ASSEMBLY & ASSOCIATED COMPONENTS:
Description    2 Pos Mk 55 on 1/2 NPT base with ext reg
Fitting                                5/8 NPT - 1/2 NPT STR
Silencer model                         M4 (1/2 NPT)

SYSTEM PERFORMANCE TIMES:
Att'n stroke time (sec)                              0.20          0.14
Required stroke time (sec)                           0.19          0.13
Stroke time @ term vel (sec)                         0.12          0.11
Att'n cyclic rate (CPM)                139.16
Required cyclic rate (CPM)             139.70
Cyclic rate @ term vel (CPM)           180.26
System delay time (sec)                0.023
Dwell time after stroke (sec)                        0.00          0.10

SYSTEM INFORMATION:
Required system Cv                                   3.13          3.09
Attained system Cv                                   3.23          3.23
Att'n system air flow (SCFM)                         90.4         125.9
Att'n branch air vel (400 FPS max)        N/A           N/A
Att'n main air vel (400 FPS max)                    122           199
Att'n % delta p (46% max)                            10            23
% Act. capacity used (75% max)                       42             2
Min pres necessary for 1d w/S.F. (PSIG)             44.5           1.6
Air per cycle (SCF)                    0.58
Att'n act leakage cost/yr @ $ 0.30 /KSCF            45            86
Att'n operating air cost/yr @ $ 0.30 /KSCF   131   5803          2957          2847
Cost /1000 cyc @ att'n times @ $ 20.00 /hr   2.57
Att'n power input total (HP)           16.74

COMMENTS:
```

```
NUMATICS NUMASIZING (R) SUMMARY SHEET                  Date:   04/10/95
NU301EED  Ver 3.01 (c) 1989 Numatics, Inc.            SURVEY # 3-4
=====================================================================
Prepared for:                        Prepared by:   Michael Liberty
Company:                             Company:       Numatics Inc.
Address:                             Address:       1450 N. Milford Rd.
City,State,Zip:                      City,State,Zip: Highland, Mi. 48357
Telephone #                          Telephone #    (810) 887-4111
Fax #                                Fax #          (810) 887-9190
---------------------------------------------------------------------
                                   Avg/Tot/Oth    Extend    Retract
INITIAL CUSTOMER PARAMETERS:
Total weight of load (lbs)                         450.00    -20.00
Angle of load from horizontal           45
Coefficient of Friction               0.30
Number of actuators                      1
Total load per actuator (lbs)                      518.26      7.29
Minimum line pressure (PSIG)           110
Design pressure used (PSIG)                         83.3      10.2
Shifts/day (1 shift=120,000 m/yr)      2.0
Cycles per year                    24000000

ACTUATOR:
Description:   Single Rod High Flow Numatics Actuator with 1/2 NPT ports
Bore/stroke/rod            3.25" bore x 3.75" stroke x 1.000" rod
Fitting                    5/8 NPT - 1/2 NPT STR

CONDUCTOR & ASSOCIATED COMPONENTS:
Branch conductor /leg                   N/A
Branch manifold fitting /leg            N/A
Branch cond equiv ftg lg /leg (in)      N/A
Quick disconnect model /leg             N/A
In line flow control model /leg                    4FC3B       NONE
Main conductor             5/8" rubber hose 18" long with 0.0 elbow(s)
Main manifold fitting                   N/A
Main cond equiv ftg lg (in)              0

VALVE ASSEMBLY & ASSOCIATED COMPONENTS:
Description    2 Pos Mk 55 on 1/2 NPT base with ext reg
Fitting                    5/8 NPT - 1/2 NPT STR
Silencer model             M4 (1/2 NPT)

SYSTEM PERFORMANCE TIMES:
Att'n stroke time (sec)                            0.30        0.20
Required stroke time (sec)                         0.30        0.20
Stroke time @ term vel (sec)                       0.13        0.06
Att'n cyclic rate (CPM)               100.00
Required cyclic rate (CPM)            100.00
Cyclic rate @ term vel (CPM)          207.70
System delay time (sec)                0.023
Dwell time after stroke (sec)                      0.00        0.10

SYSTEM INFORMATION:
Required system Cv                                 1.29        2.85
Attained system Cv                                 1.34        2.88
Att'n system air flow (SCFM)                       28.7         9.7
Att'n branch air vel (400 FPS max)      N/A        N/A
Att'n main air vel (400 FPS max)                    36          46
Att'n % delta p (46% max)                            5           2
% Act. capacity used (75% max)                      75          10
Min pres necessary for 1d w/S.F. (PSIG)            83.3        1.3
Air per cycle (SCF)                    0.17
Att'n act leakage cost/yr @ $ 0.31 /KSCF    42                   8
Att'n operating air cost/yr @ $ 0.31 /KSCF 1297               1051
Cost /1000 cyc @ att'n times @ $ 20.00 /hr  3.39                246
Att'n power input total (HP)           3.85

COMMENTS:
```

```
NUMATICS NUMASIZING (R) SUMMARY SHEET              Date:    04/10/95
NU301EED  Ver 3.01 (c) 1989 Numatics, Inc.        SURVEY # 3-5
==================================================================
Prepared for:                    Prepared by:   Michael Liberty
Company:                         Company:       Numatics Inc.
Address:                         Address:       1450 N. Milford Rd.
City,State,Zip:                  City,State,Zip: Highland, Mi. 48357
Telephone #                      Telephone #    (810) 887-4111
Fax #                            Fax #          (810) 887-9190
------------------------------------------------------------------
                                 Avg/Tot/Oth    Extend      Retract
INITIAL CUSTOMER PARAMETERS:
Total weight of load (lbs)                      450.00      -20.00
Angle of load from horizontal        45
Coefficient of Friction            0.30
Number of actuators                   1
Total load per actuator (lbs)                   518.26       7.29
Minimum line pressure (PSIG)        100
Design pressure used (PSIG)                     83.3 ?      10.2
Shifts/day (1 shift=120,000 m/yr)   2.0
Cycles per year                24000000

ACTUATOR:
Description:   Single Rod High Flow Numatics Actuator with 1/2 NPT ports
Bore/stroke/rod              3.25" bore x 3.75" stroke x 1.000" rod
Fitting                      5/8 NPT - 1/2 NPT STR

CONDUCTOR & ASSOCIATED COMPONENTS:
Branch conductor /leg                N/A
Branch manifold fitting /leg         N/A
Branch cond equiv ftg lg /leg (in)   N/A
Quick disconnect model /leg          N/A
In line flow control model /leg               4FC3B        NONE
Main conductor               5/8" rubber hose 18" long with 0.0 elbow(s)
Main manifold fitting                N/A
Main cond equiv ftg lg (in)           0

VALVE ASSEMBLY & ASSOCIATED COMPONENTS:
Description    2 Pos Mk 55 on 1/2 NPT base with ext req
Fitting                      5/8 NPT - 1/2 NPT STR
Silencer model               M4 (1/2 NPT)

SYSTEM PERFORMANCE TIMES:
Att'n stroke time (sec)                         0.30        0.20
Required stroke time (sec)                      0.30        0.20
Stroke time @ term vel (sec)                    0.13        0.06
Att'n cyclic rate (CPM)            100.00
Required cyclic rate (CPM)         100.00
Cyclic rate @ term vel (CPM)       207.70
System delay time (sec)             0.023
Dwell time after stroke (sec)                   0.00        0.10

SYSTEM INFORMATION:
Required system Cv                              1.29        2.85
Attained system Cv                             1.34        2.88
Att'n system air flow (SCFM)                   28.7         9.7
Att'n branch air vel (400 FPS max)    N/A               N/A
Att'n main air vel (400 FPS max)               36          46
Att'n % delta p (46% max)                       5           2
% Act. capacity used (75% max)                 75          10
Min pres necessary for 1d w/S.F. (PSIG)        83.3        1.3
Air per cycle (SCF)                 0.17
Att'n act leakage cost/yr @ $ 0.30 /KSCF        41          33          8
Att'n operating air cost/yr @ $ 0.30 /KSCF    1255        1018        238
Cost /1000 cyc @ att'n times @ $ 20.00 /hr    3.39
Att'n power input total (HP)        3.66

COMMENTS:
```

```
NUMATICS NUMASIZING (R) SUMMARY SHEET                    Date:    04/10/95
NU301EED  Ver 3.01 (c) 1989 Numatics, Inc.              SURVEY # 3-6
=========================================================================
Prepared for:                      Prepared by:    Michael Liberty
Company:                           Company:        Numatics Inc.
Address:                           Address:        1450 N. Milford Rd.
City,State,Zip:                    City,State,Zip: Highland, Mi. 48357
Telephone #                        Telephone #     (810) 887-4111
Fax #                              Fax #           (810) 887-9190
-------------------------------------------------------------------------
                                       Avg/Tot/Oth    Extend    Retract
INITIAL CUSTOMER PARAMETERS:
Total weight of load (lbs)                           450.00     -20.00
Angle of load from horizontal              45
Coefficient of Friction                  0.30
Number of actuators                         1
Total load per actuator (lbs)                        519.98      9.01
Minimum line pressure (PSIG)               75
Design pressure used (PSIG)                           55.2      14.2
Shifts/day (1 shift=120,000 m/yr)         2.0
Cycles per year                      24000000

ACTUATOR:
Description:   Single Rod High Flow Numatics Actuator with 1/2 NPT ports
Bore/stroke/rod           4.00" bore x 3.75" stroke x 1.000" rod
Fitting                                  5/8 NPT - 1/2 NPT STR

CONDUCTOR & ASSOCIATED COMPONENTS:
Branch conductor /leg                    N/A
Branch manifold fitting /leg             N/A
Branch cond equiv ftg lg /leg (in)       N/A
Quick disconnect model /leg              N/A
In line flow control model /leg                       4FC3B      NONE
Main conductor            5/8" rubber hose 18" long with 0.0 elbow(s)
Main manifold fitting                    N/A
Main cond equiv ftg lg (in)                0

VALVE ASSEMBLY & ASSOCIATED COMPONENTS:
Description    2 Pos Mk 55 on 1/2 NPT base with ext reg
Fitting                                  5/8 NPT - 1/2 NPT STR
Silencer model                           M4 (1/2 NPT)

SYSTEM PERFORMANCE TIMES:
Att'n stroke time (sec)                                0.30       0.20
Required stroke time (sec)                             0.30       0.20
Stroke time @ term vel (sec)                           0.10       0.08
Att'n cyclic rate (CPM)                    99.94
Required cyclic rate (CPM)                100.00
Cyclic rate @ term vel (CPM)              210.07
System delay time (sec)                   0.023
Dwell time after stroke (sec)                          0.00       0.10

SYSTEM INFORMATION:
Required system Cv                                     2.42       2.83
Attained system Cv                                     2.50       2.88
Att'n system air flow (SCFM)                           29.3      16.7
Att'n branch air vel (400 FPS max)       N/A                    N/A
Att'n main air vel (400 FPS max)                        50        70
Att'n % delta p (46% max)                                3         4
% Act. capacity used (75% max)                          75         5
Min pres necessary for 1d w/S.F. (PSIG)                55.2       1.0
Air per cycle (SCF)                       0.20
Att'n act leakage cost/yr @ $ 0.28 /KSCF   37          25        12
Att'n operating air cost/yr @ $ 0.28 /KSCF 1354        974       380
Cost /1000 cyc @ att'n times @ $ 20.00 /hr 3.39
Att'n power input total (HP)              3.60

COMMENTS:
```

```
NUMATICS NUMASIZING (R) SUMMARY SHEET                    Date:    04/10/95
NU301EED  Ver 3.01 (c) 1989 Numatics, Inc.              SURVEY # 1-4 & 3-7
===============================================================================
Prepared for:                         Prepared by:    Michael Liberty
Company:                              Company:        Numatics Inc.
Address:                             Address:        1450 N. Milford Rd.
City,State,Zip:                      City,State,Zip: Highland, Mi. 48357
Telephone #                          Telephone #     (810) 887-4111
Fax #                                Fax #           (810) 887-9190
-------------------------------------------------------------------------------
INITIAL CUSTOMER PARAMETERS:          Avg/Tot/Oth    Extend      Retract
Total weight of load (lbs)                          450.00      -20.00
Angle of load from horizontal             45
Coefficient of Friction                  0.30
Number of actuators                        1
Total load per actuator (lbs)                       519.98       9.01
Minimum line pressure (PSIG)             100
Design pressure used (PSIG)                          55.2        14.2
Shifts/day (1 shift=120,000 m/yr)        2.0
Cycles per year                       24000000

ACTUATOR:
Description:  Single Rod High Flow Numatics Actuator with 1/2 NPT ports
Bore/stroke/rod            4.00" bore x 3.75" stroke x 1.000" rod
Fitting                             5/8" - 1/2 NPT STR

CONDUCTOR & ASSOCIATED COMPONENTS:
Branch conductor /leg                    N/A
Branch manifold fitting /leg             N/A
Branch cond equiv ftg lg /leg (in)       N/A
Quick disconnect model /leg              N/A
In line flow control model /leg                      4FC3B       NONE
Main conductor             5/8" rubber hose 18" long with 0.0 elbow(s)
Main manifold fitting                    N/A
Main cond equiv ftg lg (in)                0

VALVE ASSEMBLY & ASSOCIATED COMPONENTS:
Description    2 Pos Mk 55 on 1/2 NPT base with ext req
Fitting                             5/8" - 1/2 NPT STR
Silencer model                      M4 (1/2 NPT)

SYSTEM PERFORMANCE TIMES:
Att'n stroke time (sec)                              0.30        0.20
Required stroke time (sec)                           0.30        0.20
Stroke time @ term vel (sec)                         0.10        0.08
Att'n cyclic rate (CPM)
Required cyclic rate (CPM)               99.94
Cyclic rate @ term vel (CPM)            100.00
System delay time (sec)                 210.08
Dwell time after stroke (sec)             0.023
                                                     0.00        0.10
SYSTEM INFORMATION:
Required system Cv                                    2.42        2.83
Attained system Cv                                   2.50        2.88
Att'n system air flow (SCFM)                         29.3        16.7
Att'n branch air vel (400 FPS max)       N/A                 N/A
Att'n main air vel (400 FPS max)
Att'n % delta p (46% max)                            50          70
% Act. capacity used (75% max)                        3           4
Min pres necessary for 1d w/S.F. (PSIG)             75           5
Air per cycle (SCF)                                 55.2        1.0
Att'n act leakage cost/yr @ $ 0.30 /KSCF  0.20
Att'n operating air cost/yr @ $ 0.30 /KSCF  39       27         12
Cost /1000 cyc @ att'n times @ $ 20.00 /hr 1451     1044        407
Att'n power input total (HP)             3.40
                                         4.20
COMMENTS:
IDENTICAL TO 1-3 EXCEPT USED RECOMMENDED MIN PR OF 55 PSIG W/ONE FC
```

```
NUMATICS NUMASIZING (R) SUMMARY SHEET                    Date:   04/10/95
NU301EED  Ver 3.01 (c) 1989 Numatics, Inc.             SURVEY # 3-8
========================================================================
Prepared for:                    Prepared by:    Michael Liberty
Company:                         Company:        Numatics Inc.
Address:                         Address:        1450 N. Milford Rd.
City,State,Zip:                  City,State,Zip: Highland, Mi. 48357
Telephone #                      Telephone #     (810) 887-4111
Fax #                            Fax #           (810) 887-9190
------------------------------------------------------------------------
                                   Avg/Tot/Oth    Extend    Retract
INITIAL CUSTOMER PARAMETERS:
Total weight of load (lbs)                        450.00    -20.00
Angle of load from horizontal           45
Coefficient of Friction               0.30
Number of actuators                      1
Total load per actuator (lbs)                     519.98     9.01
Minimum line pressure (PSIG)           100
Design pressure used (PSIG)                        80.0      80.0
Shifts/day (1 shift=120,000 m/yr)      2.0
Cycles per year                   24000000

ACTUATOR:
Description:  Single Rod High Flow Numatics Actuator with 1/2 NPT ports
Bore/stroke/rod           4.00" bore x 3.75" stroke x 1.000" rod
Fitting                   5/8 NPT - 1/2 NPT STR

CONDUCTOR & ASSOCIATED COMPONENTS:
Branch conductor /leg                   N/A
Branch manifold fitting /leg            N/A
Branch cond equiv ftg lg /leg (in)      N/A
Quick disconnect model /leg             N/A
In line flow control model /leg                   4FC3B      4FC3B
Main conductor            5/8" rubber hose 18" long with 0.0 elbow(s)
Main manifold fitting                   N/A
Main cond equiv ftg lg (in)              0

VALVE ASSEMBLY & ASSOCIATED COMPONENTS:
Description    2 Pos Mk 55 on 1/2 NPT base with ext reg
Fitting                   5/8 NPT - 1/2 NPT STR
Silencer model            M4 (1/2 NPT)

SYSTEM PERFORMANCE TIMES:
Att'n stroke time (sec)                            0.30       0.20
Required stroke time (sec)                         0.30       0.20
Stroke time @ term vel (sec)                       0.15       0.17
Att'n cyclic rate (CPM)                100.60
Required cyclic rate (CPM)             100.00
Cyclic rate @ term vel (CPM)           142.00
System delay time (sec)                  0.023
Dwell time after stroke (sec)                      0.00       0.10

SYSTEM INFORMATION:
Required system Cv                                 1.60       1.37
Attained system Cv                                 1.66       1.43
Att'n system air flow (SCFM)                      39.7       55.7
Att'n branch air vel (400 FPS max)      N/A               N/A
Att'n main air vel (400 FPS max)                   52         88
Att'n % delta p (46% max)                           7         23
% Act. capacity used (75% max)                     52          1
Min pres necessary for ld w/S.F. (PSIG)           55.2        1.0
Air per cycle (SCF)                     0.38
Att'n act leakage cost/yr @ $ 0.30 /KSCF  108      39         69
Att'n operating air cost/yr @ $ 0.30 /KSCF 2764  1422       1342
Cost /1000 cyc @ att'n times @ $ 20.00 /hr 3.43
Att'n power input total (HP)            8.10

COMMENTS:
Kept pressures at 80/80 and throttled down the flow controls until
performance times met desired specifications.
```

```
NUMATICS NUMASIZING (R) SUMMARY SHEET              Date:    04/10/95
NU301EED  Ver 3.01 (c) 1989 Numatics, Inc.        SURVEY # 3-9
===================================================================
Prepared for:                     Prepared by:    Michael Liberty
Company:                          Company:        Numatics Inc.
Address:                          Address:        1450 N. Milford Rd.
City,State,Zip:                   City,State,Zip: Highland, Mi. 48357
Telephone #                       Telephone #     (810) 887-4111
Fax #                             Fax #           (810) 887-9190
-------------------------------------------------------------------
                                  Avg/Tot/Oth    Extend     Retract
INITIAL CUSTOMER PARAMETERS:
Total weight of load (lbs)                        450.00     -20.00
Angle of load from horizontal          45
Coefficient of Friction              0.30
Number of actuators                     1
Total load per actuator (lbs)                     522.28      11.31
Minimum line pressure (PSIG)           55
Design pressure used (PSIG)                        41.5       21.8
Shifts/day (1 shift=120,000 m/yr)     2.0
Cycles per year                  24000000

ACTUATOR:
Description:  Single Rod High Flow Numatics Actuator with 1/2 NPT ports
Bore/stroke/rod          5.00" bore x 3.75" stroke x 1.000" rod
Fitting                  5/8 NPT - 1/2 NPT STR

CONDUCTOR & ASSOCIATED COMPONENTS:
Branch conductor /leg             N/A
Branch manifold fitting /leg      N/A
Branch cond equiv ftg lg /leg (in) N/A
Quick disconnect model /leg       N/A
In line flow control model /leg                   NONE       NONE
Main conductor           5/8" rubber hose 18" long with 0.0 elbow(s)
Main manifold fitting             N/A
Main cond equiv ftg lg (in)         0

VALVE ASSEMBLY & ASSOCIATED COMPONENTS:
Description    2 Pos Mk 55 on 1/2 NPT base with ext req
Fitting                  5/8 NPT - 1/2 NPT STR
Silencer model           M4 (1/2 NPT)

SYSTEM PERFORMANCE TIMES:
Att'n stroke time (sec)                            0.30       0.20
Required stroke time (sec)                         0.30       0.20
Stroke time @ term vel (sec)                       0.12       0.11
Att'n cyclic rate (CPM)              100.00
Required cyclic rate (CPM)           100.00
Cyclic rate @ term vel (CPM)         180.26
System delay time (sec)               0.023
Dwell time after stroke (sec)                      0.00       0.10

SYSTEM INFORMATION:
Required system Cv                                 3.17       3.10
Attained system Cv                                 3.23       3.23
Att'n system air flow (SCFM)                       34.9       33.1
Att'n branch air vel (400 FPS max)    N/A          N/A
Att'n main air vel (400 FPS max)                    74        114
Att'n % delta p (46% max)                            4          9
% Act. capacity used (75% max)                      64          3
Min pres necessary for ld w/S.F. (PSIG)            35.5        0.8
Air per cycle (SCF)                   0.28
Att'n act leakage cost/yr @ $ 0.25 /KSCF    39       21         18
Att'n operating air cost/yr @ $ 0.25 /KSCF 1708    1051        657
Cost /1000 cyc @ att'n times @ $ 20.00 /hr  3.41
Att'n power input total (HP)          4.33

COMMENTS:
```

```
NUMATICS NUMASIZING (R) SUMMARY SHEET                      Date:    04/10/95
NU301EED   Ver 3.01 (c) 1989 Numatics, Inc.               SURVEY # 3-10
==============================================================================
Prepared for:                        Prepared by:   Michael Liberty
Company:                             Company:       Numatics Inc.
Address:                             Address:       1450 N. Milford Rd.
City,State,Zip:                      City,State,Zip: Highland, Mi. 48357
Telephone #                          Telephone #    (810) 887-4111
Fax #                                Fax #          (810) 887-9190
------------------------------------------------------------------------------
                                         Avg/Tot/Oth   Extend      Retract
INITIAL CUSTOMER PARAMETERS:
Total weight of load (lbs)                            450.00       -20.00
Angle of load from horizontal              45
Coefficient of Friction                  0.30
Number of actuators                         1
Total load per actuator (lbs)                        522.28        11.31
Minimum line pressure (PSIG)              100
Design pressure used (PSIG)                           41.5         21.8
Shifts/day (1 shift=120,000 m/yr)         2.0
Cycles per year                      24000000

ACTUATOR:
Description:   Single Rod High Flow Numatics Actuator with 1/2 NPT ports
Bore/stroke/rod            5.00" bore x 3.75" stroke x 1.000" rod
Fitting                    5/8 NPT - 1/2 NPT STR

CONDUCTOR & ASSOCIATED COMPONENTS:
Branch conductor /leg                    N/A
Branch manifold fitting /leg             N/A
Branch cond equiv ftg lg /leg (in)       N/A
Quick disconnect model /leg              N/A
In line flow control model /leg                       NONE         NONE
Main conductor            5/8" rubber hose 18" long with 0.0 elbow(s)
Main manifold fitting                    N/A
Main cond equiv ftg lg (in)                0

VALVE ASSEMBLY & ASSOCIATED COMPONENTS:
Description       2 Pos Mk 55 on 1/2 NPT base with ext req
Fitting                                  5/8 NPT - 1/2 NPT STR
Silencer model                           M4 (1/2 NPT)

SYSTEM PERFORMANCE TIMES:
Att'n stroke time (sec)                               0.30         0.20
Required stroke time (sec)                            0.30         0.20
Stroke time @ term vel (sec)                          0.12         0.11
Att'n cyclic rate (CPM)               100.00
Required cyclic rate (CPM)            100.00
Cyclic rate @ term vel (CPM)          180.26
System delay time (sec)                0.023
Dwell time after stroke (sec)                         0.00         0.10

SYSTEM INFORMATION:
Required system Cv                                    3.17         3.10
Attained system Cv                                    3.23         3.23
Att'n system air flow (SCFM)                          34.9         33.1
Att'n branch air vel (400 FPS max)       N/A
Att'n main air vel (400 FPS max)                       74          114
% Act. capacity used (75% max)                          4            9
Att'n % delta p (46% max)                              64            3
Min pres necessary for ld w/S.F. (PSIG)              35.5          0.8
Air per cycle (SCF)                      0.28
Att'n act leakage cost/yr @ $ 0.30 /KSCF   47          26           21
Att'n operating air cost/yr @ $ 0.30 /KSCF 2050      1262          788
Cost /1000 cyc @ att'n times @ $ 20.00 /hr 3.42
Att'n power input total (HP)             5.91

COMMENTS:
```

```
NUMATICS NUMASIZING (R) SUMMARY SHEET              Date:    04/10/95
NU301EED  Ver 3.01 (c) 1989 Numatics, Inc.        SURVEY # 3-11
==================================================================
Prepared for:                    Prepared by:    Michael Liberty
Company:                         Company:        Numatics Inc.
Address:                         Address:        1450 N. Milford Rd.
City,State,Zip:                  City,State,Zip: Highland, Mi. 48357
Telephone #                      Telephone #     (810) 887-4111
Fax #                            Fax #           (810) 887-9190
------------------------------------------------------------------
                                 Avg/Tot/Oth    Extend     Retract
INITIAL CUSTOMER PARAMETERS:
  Total weight of load (lbs)                     2000.00   -1200.00
  Angle of load from horizontal        90
  Coefficient of Friction            0.00
  Number of actuators                   1
  Total load per actuator (lbs)                  2049.48   -1148.45
  Minimum line pressure (PSIG)        100
  Design pressure used (PSIG)                      80.0       80.0
  Shifts/day (1 shift=120,000 m/yr)   2.0
  Cycles per year                 1800000

ACTUATOR:
  Description:    Single Rod High Flow Numatics Actuator with 3/4 NPT ports
  Bore/stroke/rod          8.00" bore x 12.00" stroke x 2.000" rod
  Fitting                  1" - 3/4 NPT STR

CONDUCTOR & ASSOCIATED COMPONENTS:
  Branch conductor /leg                  N/A
  Branch manifold fitting /leg           N/A
  Branch cond equiv ftg lg /leg (in)     N/A
  Quick disconnect model /leg            N/A
  In line flow control model /leg                 5FC3B      5FC3B
  Main conductor           1" rubber hose 48" long with 1.0 elbow(s)
  Main manifold fitting                  N/A
  Main cond equiv ftg lg (in)             42

VALVE ASSEMBLY & ASSOCIATED COMPONENTS:
  Description     2 Pos Mk 55 on 3/4 NPT base with ext reg
  Fitting                  1" - 3/4 NPT EL
  Silencer model           M5 (3/4 NPT)

SYSTEM PERFORMANCE TIMES:
  Att'n stroke time (sec)                          2.00       2.00
  Required stroke time (sec)                       2.00       1.50
  Stroke time @ term vel (sec)                     1.09       1.50
  Att'n cyclic rate (CPM)              7.50
  Required cyclic rate (CPM)           7.50
  Cyclic rate @ term vel (CPM)         8.47
  System delay time (sec)            0.023
  Dwell time after stroke (sec)                    1.80       2.70

SYSTEM INFORMATION:
  Required system Cv                               2.87       1.95
  Attained system Cv                               2.85       1.95
  Att'n system air flow (SCFM)                     71.8       89.9
  Att'n branch air vel (400 FPS max)      N/A              N/A
  Att'n main air vel (400 FPS max)                   37         79
  Att'n % delta p (46% max)                           8         46 ?
  % Act. capacity used (75% max)                     51        -30
  Min pres necessary for ld w/S.F. (PSIG)          54.4      -32.5
  Air per cycle (SCF)                  4.64
  Att'n act leakage cost/yr @ $ 0.30 /KSCF          75        145
  Att'n operating air cost/yr @ $ 0.30 /KSCF       2506     1291       1215
  Cost /1000 cyc @ att'n times @ $ 0.00 /hr  1.51
  Att'n power input total (HP)         7.69

COMMENTS:
  Conventional approach using FC's & single pressure source. Observe the
  retract delta p result.
```

```
NUMATICS NUMASIZING (R) SUMMARY SHEET                    Date:   04/10/95
NU301EED  Ver 3.01 (c) 1989 Numatics, Inc.              SURVEY # 3-12
=========================================================================
Prepared for:                    Prepared by:     Michael Liberty
Company:                         Company:         Numatics Inc.
Address:                         Address:         1450 N. Milford Rd.
City,State,Zip:                  City,State,Zip:  Highland, Mi. 48357
Telephone #                      Telephone #      (810) 887-4111
Fax #                            Fax #            (810) 887-9190
-------------------------------------------------------------------------
                                        Avg/Tot/Oth   Extend     Retract
INITIAL CUSTOMER PARAMETERS:
  Total weight of load (lbs)                        2000.00    -1200.00
  Angle of load from horizontal          90
  Coefficient of Friction              0.00
  Number of actuators                     1
  Total load per actuator (lbs)                    2090.97    -1010.73
  Minimum line pressure (PSIG)          100
  Design pressure used (PSIG)                        80.0       80.0
  Shifts/day (1 shift=120,000 m/yr)     2.0
  Cycles per year                   2225797

ACTUATOR:
  Description:   Single Rod High Flow Numatics Actuator with 3/4 NPT ports
  Bore/stroke/rod          8.00" bore x 12.00" stroke x 2.000" rod
  Fitting                  1" - 3/4 NPT STR

CONDUCTOR & ASSOCIATED COMPONENTS:
  Branch conductor /leg                     N/A
  Branch manifold fitting /leg              N/A
  Branch cond equiv ftg lg /leg (in)        N/A
  Quick disconnect model /leg               N/A
  In line flow control model /leg                   NONE          NONE
  Main conductor           1" rubber hose 48" long with 1.0 elbow(s)
  Main manifold fitting                     N/A
  Main cond equiv ftg lg (in)                42

VALVE ASSEMBLY & ASSOCIATED COMPONENTS:
  Description     2 Pos Mk 55 on 3/4 NPT base with ext reg
  Fitting                              1" - 3/4 NPT EL
  Silencer model                       M5 (3/4 NPT)

SYSTEM PERFORMANCE TIMES:
  Att'n stroke time (sec)                            1.31       0.66
  Required stroke time (sec)                         1.31       0.66
  Stroke time @ term vel (sec)                       0.70       0.66
  Att'n cyclic rate (CPM)                  9.28
  Required cyclic rate (CPM)               9.27
  Cyclic rate @ term vel (CPM)            10.24
  System delay time (sec)                 0.023
  Dwell time after stroke (sec)                      1.80       2.70

SYSTEM INFORMATION:
  Required system Cv                                 4.48       4.42
  Attained system Cv                                 4.42       4.42
  Att'n system air flow (SCFM)                     109.5      204.5
  Att'n branch air vel (400 FPS max)       N/A               N/A
  Att'n main air vel (400 FPS max)                    56        180
  Att'n % delta p (46% max)                            8         46  ?
  % Act. capacity used (75% max)                      52        -27
  Min pres necessary for ld w/S.F. (PSIG)           55.5      -28.6
  Air per cycle (SCF)                     4.64
  Att'n act leakage cost/yr @ $ 0.30 /KSCF 219        76        143
  Att'n operating air cost/yr @ $ 0.30 /KSCF 3097   1596       1502
  Cost /1000 cyc @ att'n times @ $ 0.00 /hr 1.49
  Att'n power input total (HP)             9.35

COMMENTS:
  Best time possible at 80/80 w/o Flow Controls, otherwise identical to 3-11.
```

```
NUMATICS NUMASIZING (R) SUMMARY SHEET          Date:    04/10/95
NU301EED  Ver 3.01 (c) 1989 Numatics, Inc.     SURVEY # 3-13
==============================================================
Prepared for:               Prepared by:    Michael Liberty
Company:                    Company:        Numatics Inc.
Address:                    Address:        1450 N. Milford Rd.
City,State,Zip:             City,State,Zip: Highland, Mi. 48357
Telephone #                 Telephone #     (810) 887-4111
Fax #                       Fax #           (810) 887-9190
--------------------------------------------------------------
                                Avg/Tot/Oth   Extend    Retract
INITIAL CUSTOMER PARAMETERS:
Total weight of load (lbs)                   2000.00   -1200.00
Angle of load from horizontal        90
Coefficient of Friction            0.00
Number of actuators                   1
Total load per actuator (lbs)                2201.62   -1010.73
Minimum line pressure (PSIG)        100
Design pressure used (PSIG)                    80.0       5.0
Shifts/day (1 shift=120,000 m/yr)   2.0
Cycles per year                 2406237

ACTUATOR:
Description:  Single Rod High Flow Numatics Actuator with 3/4 NPT ports
Bore/stroke/rod            8.00" bore x 12.00" stroke x 2.000" rod
Fitting                    1" - 3/4 NPT STR

CONDUCTOR & ASSOCIATED COMPONENTS:
Branch conductor /leg               N/A
Branch manifold fitting /leg        N/A
Branch cond equiv ftg lg /leg (in)  N/A
Quick disconnect model /leg                   NONE       NONE
In line flow control model /leg
Main conductor          1" rubber hose 48" long with 1.0 elbow(s)
Main manifold fitting               N/A
Main cond equiv ftg lg (in)          42

VALVE ASSEMBLY & ASSOCIATED COMPONENTS:
Description    2 Pos Mk 55 on 3/4 NPT base with ext reg
Fitting                             1" - 3/4 NPT EL
Silencer model                      M5 (3/4 NPT)

SYSTEM PERFORMANCE TIMES:
Att'n stroke time (sec)                        0.82       0.66
Required stroke time (sec)                     0.82       0.66
Stroke time @ term vel (sec)                   0.70       0.66
Att'n cyclic rate (CPM)            10.03
Required cyclic rate (CPM)         10.03
Cyclic rate @ term vel (CPM)       10.24
System delay time (sec)            0.023
Dwell time after stroke (sec)                  1.80       2.70

SYSTEM INFORMATION:
Required system Cv                             4.52       4.42
Attained system Cv                             4.42       4.42
Att'n system air flow (SCFM)                  173.9      42.5
Att'n branch air vel (400 FPS max)   N/A               N/A
Att'n main air vel (400 FPS max)               108        180
% Act. capacity used (75% max)                  24         46  ?
% Act. delta p (46% max)                        55       -429
Min pres necessary for ld w/S.F. (PSIG)       58.4      -28.6
Air per cycle (SCF)                 2.86
Att'n act leakage cost/yr @ $ 0.30 /KSCF        79         69         10
Att'n operating air cost/yr @ $ 0.30 /KSCF    2063       1725        338
Cost /1000 cyc @ att'n times @ $ 0.00 /hr     0.89
Att'n power input total (HP)        6.04

COMMENTS:
Best time possible at 80/5 w/o Flow Controls, otherwise identical to 3-12.
```

```
NUMATICS NUMASIZING (R) SUMMARY SHEET                    Date:   04/10/95
NU301EED  Ver 3.01 (c) 1989 Numatics, Inc.              SURVEY # 3-14
===============================================================================
Prepared for:                    Prepared by:     Michael Liberty
Company:                         Company:         Numatics Inc.
Address:                         Address:         1450 N. Milford Rd.
City,State,Zip:                  City,State,Zip:  Highland, Mi. 48357
Telephone #                      Telephone #      (810) 887-4111
Fax #                            Fax #            (810) 887-9190
-------------------------------------------------------------------------------
                                        Avg/Tot/Oth    Extend      Retract
INITIAL CUSTOMER PARAMETERS:
Total weight of load (lbs)                          2000.00     -1200.00
Angle of load from horizontal              90
Coefficient of Friction                  0.00
Number of actuators                         1
Total load per actuator (lbs)                      2215.81      -947.99
Minimum line pressure (PSIG)              100
Design pressure used (PSIG)                          80.0         0.0
Shifts/day (1 shift=120,000 m/yr)         2.0
Cycles per year                       2457910

ACTUATOR:
Description:   Single Rod High Flow Numatics Actuator with 3/4 NPT ports
Bore/stroke/rod          8.00" bore x 12.00" stroke x 2.000" rod
Fitting                  1" - 3/4 NPT STR

CONDUCTOR & ASSOCIATED COMPONENTS:
Branch conductor /leg                    N/A
Branch manifold fitting /leg             N/A
Branch cond equiv ftg lg /leg (in)       N/A
Quick disconnect model /leg              N/A
In line flow control model /leg                        NONE         NONE
Main conductor           1" rubber hose 48" long with 1.0 elbow(s)
Main manifold fitting                    N/A
Main cond equiv ftg lg (in)               42

VALVE ASSEMBLY & ASSOCIATED COMPONENTS:
Description     2 Pos Mk 55 on 3/4 NPT base with ext req
Fitting                  1" - 3/4 NPT EL
Silencer model           M5 (3/4 NPT)

SYSTEM PERFORMANCE TIMES:
Att'n stroke time (sec)                                0.79         0.57
Required stroke time (sec)                             0.79         0.57
Stroke time @ term vel (sec)                           0.70         0.00 ?
Att'n cyclic rate (CPM)                  10.24
Required cyclic rate (CPM)               10.24
Cyclic rate @ term vel (CPM)             11.54
System delay time (sec)                  0.023
Dwell time after stroke (sec)                          1.80         2.70

SYSTEM INFORMATION:
Required system Cv                                     4.52         4.57
Attained system Cv                                     4.42         4.42
Att'n system air flow (SCFM)             180.8                      0.0
Att'n branch air vel (400 FPS max)                N/A          N/A
Att'n main air vel (400 FPS max)                       117            0
Att'n % delta p (46% max)                              26            0
% Act. capacity used (75% max)                         55     -2011705
Min pres necessary for ld w/S.F. (PSIG)               58.8        -26.8
Air per cycle (SCF)                      2.39
Att'n act leakage cost/yr @ $ 0.30 /KSCF  70           70            0
Att'n operating air cost/yr @ $ 0.30 /KSCF 1762      1762            0
Cost /1000 cyc @ att'n times @ $ 0.00 /hr 0.75
Att'n power input total (HP)             5.17

COMMENTS:
Best time possible at 80/0 w/o Flow Controls, otherwise identical to 3-13.
```

```
NUMATICS NUMASIZING (R) SUMMARY SHEET                Date:    04/10/95
NU301EED  Ver 3.01 (c) 1989 Numatics, Inc.           SURVEY # 3-15
==================================================================
Prepared for:                 Prepared by:   Michael Liberty
Company:                      Company:       Numatics Inc.
Address:                      Address:       1450 N. Milford Rd.
City,State,Zip:               City,State,Zip: Highland, Mi. 48357
Telephone #                   Telephone #    (810) 887-4111
Fax #                         Fax #          (810) 887-9190
------------------------------------------------------------------
                                      Avg/Tot/Oth   Extend    Retract
INITIAL CUSTOMER PARAMETERS:
Total weight of load (lbs)                         2000.00  -1200.00
Angle of load from horizontal            90
Coefficient of Friction                0.00
Number of actuators                       1
Total load per actuator (lbs)                      2049.48  -1148.45
Minimum line pressure (PSIG)            100
Design pressure used (PSIG)                          55.1       5.0
Shifts/day (1 shift=120,000 m/yr)       2.0
Cycles per year                     1800000

ACTUATOR:
Description:   Single Rod High Flow Numatics Actuator with 3/4 NPT ports
Bore/stroke/rod          8.00" bore x 12.00" stroke x 2.000" rod
Fitting                               1" - 3/4 NPT STR

CONDUCTOR & ASSOCIATED COMPONENTS:
Branch conductor /leg                    N/A
Branch manifold fitting /leg             N/A
Branch cond equiv ftg lg /leg (in)       N/A
Quick disconnect model /leg              N/A
In line flow control model /leg                    NONE      5FC3B
Main conductor           1" rubber hose 48" long with 1.0 elbow(s)
Main manifold fitting                    N/A
Main cond equiv ftg lg (in)              42

VALVE ASSEMBLY & ASSOCIATED COMPONENTS:
Description     2 Pos Mk 55 on 3/4 NPT base with ext req
Fitting                               1" - 3/4 NPT EL
Silencer model                        M5 (3/4 NPT)

SYSTEM PERFORMANCE TIMES:
Att'n stroke time (sec)                             2.00      1.50
Required stroke time (sec)                          2.00      1.50
Stroke time @ term vel (sec)                        0.80      1.50
Att'n cyclic rate (CPM)                  7.50
Required cyclic rate (CPM)               7.50
Cyclic rate @ term vel (CPM)             8.82
System delay time (sec)                 0.023
Dwell time after stroke (sec)                       1.80      2.70

SYSTEM INFORMATION:
Required system Cv                                  3.90      1.95
Attained system Cv                                  3.87      1.95
Att'n system air flow (SCFM)             52.9                18.7
Att'n branch air vel (400 FPS max)       N/A      N/A
Att'n main air vel (400 FPS max)                    35        79
Att'n % delta p (46% max)                           4         46 ?
% Act. capacity used (75% max)                      74       -487
Min pres necessary for ld w/S.F. (PSIG)  54.4               -32.5
Air per cycle (SCF)                      2.23
Att'n act leakage cost/yr @ $ 0.30 /KSCF  61               9
Att'n operating air cost/yr @ $ 0.30 /KSCF  1204    951     253
Cost /1000 cyc @ att'n times @ $ 0.00 /hr  0.70
Att'n power input total (HP)             3.57

COMMENTS:
Dual pressure approach. Observe that even with a min pressure of 5 PSIG we
are still at terminal velocity pressure.
```

```
NUMATICS NUMASIZING (R) SUMMARY SHEET                    Date:    04/10/95
NU301EED   Ver 3.01 (c) 1989 Numatics, Inc.             SURVEY # 3-16
========================================================================
Prepared for:                      Prepared by:    Michael Liberty
Company:                           Company:        Numatics Inc.
Address:                           Address:        1450 N. Milford Rd.
City,State,Zip:                    City,State,Zip: Highland, Mi. 48357
Telephone #                        Telephone #     (810) 887-4111
Fax #                              Fax #           (810) 887-9190
------------------------------------------------------------------------
                                     Avg/Tot/Oth   Extend      Retract
INITIAL CUSTOMER PARAMETERS:
Total weight of load (lbs)                         2000.00    -1200.00
Angle of load from horizontal           90
Coefficient of Friction                0.00
Number of actuators                       1
Total load per actuator (lbs)                      2049.48    -1148.45
Minimum line pressure (PSIG)            70
Design pressure used (PSIG)                          55.1        5.0
Shifts/day (1 shift=120,000 m/yr)      2.0
Cycles per year                     1800000

ACTUATOR:
Description:    Single Rod High Flow Numatics Actuator with 3/4 NPT ports
Bore/stroke/rod                8.00" bore x 12.00" stroke x 2.000" rod
Fitting                        1" - 3/4 NPT STR

CONDUCTOR & ASSOCIATED COMPONENTS:
Branch conductor /leg                   N/A
Branch manifold fitting /leg            N/A
Branch cond equiv ftg lg /leg (in)      N/A
Quick disconnect model /leg             N/A
In line flow control model /leg                      NONE       5FC3B
Main conductor                 1" rubber hose 48" long with 1.0 elbow(s)
Main manifold fitting                   N/A
Main cond equiv ftg lg (in)              42

VALVE ASSEMBLY & ASSOCIATED COMPONENTS:
Description    2 Pos Mk 55 on 3/4 NPT base with ext reg
Fitting                        1" - 3/4 NPT EL
Silencer model                 M5 (3/4 NPT)

SYSTEM PERFORMANCE TIMES:
Att'n stroke time (sec)                              2.00        1.50
Required stroke time (sec)                           2.00        1.50
Stroke time @ term vel (sec)                         0.80        1.50
Att'n cyclic rate (CPM)                 7.50
Required cyclic rate (CPM)              7.50
Cyclic rate @ term vel (CPM)            8.82
System delay time (sec)                0.023
Dwell time after stroke (sec)                        1.80        2.70

SYSTEM INFORMATION:
Required system Cv                                   3.90        1.95
Attained system Cv                                   3.87        1.95
Att'n system air flow (SCFM)                         52.9        18.7
Att'n branch air vel (400 FPS max)      N/A                  N/A
Att'n main air vel (400 FPS max)                      35         79
% Act. capacity used (75% max)                         4         46  ?
Min pres necessary for ld w/S.F. (PSIG)               74       -487
Air per cycle (SCF)                     2.23         54.4      -32.5
Att'n act leakage cost/yr @ $ 0.27 /KSCF 55           47          8
Att'n operating air cost/yr @ $ 0.27 /KSCF 1083      856        227
Cost /1000 cyc @ att'n times @ $ 0.00 /hr 0.63
Att'n power input total (HP)            2.95

COMMENTS:
With compressor pressure reduced to 70 PSIG, but still maintaining a slightly
over 20% S.F. above 55 PSIG operating pressure.
```

```
NUMATICS NUMASIZING (R) SUMMARY SHEET                Date:    04/10/95
NU301EED  Ver 3.01 (c) 1989 Numatics, Inc.          SURVEY # 3-17
=====================================================================
Prepared for:                    Prepared by:   Michael Liberty
Company:                         Company:       Numatics Inc.
Address:                         Address:       1450 N. Milford Rd.
City,State,Zip:                  City,State,Zip: Highland, Mi. 48357
Telephone #                      Telephone #    (810) 887-4111
Fax #                            Fax #          (810) 887-9190
---------------------------------------------------------------------
                                 Avg/Tot/Oth    Extend      Retract
INITIAL CUSTOMER PARAMETERS:
Total weight of load (lbs)                      2000.00    -1200.00
Angle of load from horizontal         90
Coefficient of Friction             0.00
Number of actuators                    1
Total load per actuator (lbs)                   2047.18    -1150.75
Minimum line pressure (PSIG)         100
Design pressure used (PSIG)                       71.0        5.0
Shifts/day (1 shift=120,000 m/yr)    2.0
Cycles per year                  1800000

ACTUATOR:
Description:   Single Rod High Flow Numatics Actuator with 3/4 NPT ports
Bore/stroke/rod          7.00" bore x 12.00" stroke x 2.000" rod
Fitting                          1" - 3/4 NPT STR

CONDUCTOR & ASSOCIATED COMPONENTS:
Branch conductor /leg            N/A
Branch manifold fitting /leg     N/A
Branch cond equiv ftg lg /leg (in) N/A
Quick disconnect model /leg      N/A
In line flow control model /leg                 5FC3B       5FC3B
Main conductor                   1" rubber hose 48" long with 1.0 elbow(s)
Main manifold fitting            N/A
Main cond equiv ftg lg (in)       42

VALVE ASSEMBLY & ASSOCIATED COMPONENTS:
Description    2 Pos Mk 55 on 3/4 NPT base with ext req
Fitting                          1" - 3/4 NPT EL
Silencer model                   M5 (3/4 NPT)

SYSTEM PERFORMANCE TIMES:
Att'n stroke time (sec)                          2.00        1.50
Required stroke time (sec)                       2.00        1.50
Stroke time @ term vel (sec)                     0.89        1.50
Att'n cyclic rate (CPM)             7.50
Required cyclic rate (CPM)          7.50
Cyclic rate @ term vel (CPM)        8.71
System delay time (sec)            0.023
Dwell time after stroke (sec)                    1.80        2.70

SYSTEM INFORMATION:
Required system Cv                               2.74        1.49
Attained system Cv                               2.74        1.49
Att'n system air flow (SCFM)                    50.6        14.3
Att'n branch air vel (400 FPS max)    N/A                   N/A
Att'n main air vel (400 FPS max)                  28          60
Att'n % delta p (46% max)                          5          46  ?
% Act. capacity used (75% max)                    75        -651
Min pres necessary for 1d w/S.F. (PSIG)         70.9       -43.4
Air per cycle (SCF)                2.04
Att'n act leakage cost/yr @ $ 0.30 /KSCF          67           8
Att'n operating air cost/yr @ $ 0.30 /KSCF      1104         193
Cost /1000 cyc @ att'n times @ $ 0.00 /hr       0.65
Att'n power input total (HP)       3.30

COMMENTS:
Used a smaller cylinder with higher pressures than in previous survey # 3-16
```

```
NUMATICS NUMASIZING (R) SUMMARY SHEET                    Date:   04/10/95
NU301EED   Ver 3.01 (c) 1989 Numatics, Inc.             SURVEY # 3-18
========================================================================
Prepared for:                      Prepared by:    Michael Liberty
Company:                           Company:        Numatics Inc.
Address:                           Address:        1450 N. Milford Rd.
City,State,Zip:                    City,State,Zip: Highland, Mi. 48357
Telephone #                        Telephone #     (810) 887-4111
Fax #                              Fax #           (810) 887-9190
------------------------------------------------------------------------
                                    Avg/Tot/Oth    Extend      Retract
INITIAL CUSTOMER PARAMETERS:
Total weight of load (lbs)                         2000.00    -1200.00
Angle of load from horizontal            90
Coefficient of Friction                0.00
Number of actuators                       1
Total load per actuator (lbs)                      2047.18    -1150.75
Minimum line pressure (PSIG)             90
Design pressure used (PSIG)                          71.0        5.0
Shifts/day (1 shift=120,000 m/yr)       2.0
Cycles per year                      1800000

ACTUATOR:
Description:    Single Rod High Flow Numatics Actuator with 3/4 NPT ports
Bore/stroke/rod            7.00" bore x 12.00" stroke x 2.000" rod
Fitting                    1" - 3/4 NPT STR

CONDUCTOR & ASSOCIATED COMPONENTS:
Branch conductor /leg                   N/A
Branch manifold fitting /leg            N/A
Branch cond equiv ftg lg /leg (in)      N/A
Quick disconnect model /leg             N/A
In line flow control model /leg                    5FC3B        5FC3B
Main conductor             1" rubber hose 48" long with 1.0 elbow(s)
Main manifold fitting                   N/A
Main cond equiv ftg lg (in)              42

VALVE ASSEMBLY & ASSOCIATED COMPONENTS:
Description     2 Pos Mk 55 on 3/4 NPT base with ext req
Fitting                    1" - 3/4 NPT EL
Silencer model             M5 (3/4 NPT)

SYSTEM PERFORMANCE TIMES:
Att'n stroke time (sec)                            2.00         1.50
Required stroke time (sec)                         2.00         1.50
Stroke time @ term vel (sec)                       0.89         1.50
Att'n cyclic rate (CPM)                 7.50
Required cyclic rate (CPM)              7.50
Cyclic rate @ term vel (CPM)            8.71
System delay time (sec)                0.023
Dwell time after stroke (sec)                      1.80         2.70

SYSTEM INFORMATION:
Required system Cv                                 2.74         1.49
Attained system Cv                                 2.72         1.49
Att'n system air flow (SCFM)                       50.6        14.3
Att'n branch air vel (400 FPS max)      N/A                N/A
Att'n main air vel (400 FPS max)                    28           60
Att'n % delta p (46% max)                            5           46  ?
% Act. capacity used (75% max)                      75         -651
Min pres necessary for 1d w/S.F. (PSIG)            70.9       -43.4
Air per cycle (SCF)                     2.04
Att'n act leakage cost/yr @ $ 0.29 /KSCF  64        56            8
Att'n operating air cost/yr @ $ 0.29 /KSCF 1067    880          187
Cost /1000 cyc @ att'n times @ $ 0.00 /hr 0.63
Att'n power input total (HP)            3.12

COMMENTS:
Results with compressor reduced to 90 PSIG but still maintaining a
20% S.F. above 71 PSIG, otherwise identical to survey # 3-17.
```

```
NUMATICS NUMASIZING (R) SUMMARY SHEET                    Date:    04/10/95
NU301EED  Ver 3.01 (c) 1989 Numatics, Inc.              SURVEY # 3-19
=========================================================================
Prepared for:                      Prepared by:    Michael Liberty
Company:                           Company:        Numatics Inc.
Address:                           Address:        1450 N. Milford Rd.
City,State,Zip:                    City,State,Zip: Highland, Mi. 48357
Telephone #                        Telephone #     (810) 887-4111
Fax #                              Fax #           (810) 887-9190
-------------------------------------------------------------------------
                                   Avg/Tot/Oth     Extend       Retract
INITIAL CUSTOMER PARAMETERS:
 Total weight of load (lbs)                        2000.00     -1200.00
 Angle of load from horizontal          90
 Coefficient of Friction              0.00
 Number of actuators                     2
 Total load per actuator (lbs)                     1027.04      -571.92
 Minimum line pressure (PSIG)           90
 Design pressure used (PSIG)                         70.0         5.0
 Shifts/day (1 shift=120,000 m/yr)     2.0
 Cycles per year                   1800000

ACTUATOR:
 Description:    Single Rod High Flow Numatics Actuator with 1/2 NPT ports
 Bore/stroke/rod         5.00" bore x 12.00" stroke x 1.500" rod
 Fitting                             3/4" - 1/2 NPT STR

CONDUCTOR & ASSOCIATED COMPONENTS:
 Branch conductor /leg        3/4" rubber hose 36" long with 0.0 elbow(s)
 Branch manifold fitting /leg        3/4" - 1/2 NPT STR
 Branch cond equiv ftg lg /leg (in)  N/A
 Quick disconnect model /leg         N/A
 In line flow control model /leg                 4FC3B        4FC3B
 Main conductor               1" rubber hose 12" long with 1.0 elbow(s)
 Main manifold fitting                1" - 3/4 NPT STR
 Main cond equiv ftg lg (in)         42

VALVE ASSEMBLY & ASSOCIATED COMPONENTS:
 Description     2 Pos Mk 55 on 3/4 NPT base with ext req
 Fitting                             1" - 3/4 NPT EL
 Silencer model                      M5 (3/4 NPT)

SYSTEM PERFORMANCE TIMES:
 Att'n stroke time (sec)                            2.00         1.50
 Required stroke time (sec)                         2.00         1.50
 Stroke time @ term vel (sec)                       0.90         1.50
 Att'n cyclic rate (CPM)                  7.50
 Required cyclic rate (CPM)               7.50
 Cyclic rate @ term vel (CPM)             8.70
 System delay time (sec)                 0.023
 Dwell time after stroke (sec)                      1.80         2.70

SYSTEM INFORMATION:
 Required system Cv                                 2.79         1.52
 Attained system Cv                                 2.77         1.52
 Att'n system air flow (SCFM)                       51.4        14.6
 Att'n branch air vel (400 FPS max)                   26          55
 Att'n main air vel (400 FPS max)                     29          62
 Att'n % delta p (46% max)                             5          46   ?
 % Act. capacity used (75% max)                       75        -640
 Min pres necessary for 1d w/S.F. (PSIG)            69.7       -42.7
 Air per cycle (SCF)                     2.07
 Att'n act leakage cost/yr @ $ 0.29 /KSCF             91          79          12
 Att'n operating air cost/yr @ $ 0.29 /KSCF        1083         892         190
 Cost /1000 cyc @ att'n times @ $ 0.00 /hr         0.65
 Att'n power input total (HP)            3.24

COMMENTS:
 Using two 5" bore cylinders in place of one 7" bore cylinder, still able to
 maintain a 90 PSIG compressor pressure as operating pressure is 70 PSIG.
```

```
NUMATICS NUMASIZING (R) SUMMARY SHEET                    Date:   04/10/95
NU301EED  Ver 3.01 (c) 1989 Numatics, Inc.              SURVEY # 3-20
========================================================================
Prepared for:                    Prepared by:    Michael Liberty
Company:                         Company:        Numatics Inc.
Address:                         Address:        1450 N. Milford Rd.
City,State,Zip:                  City,State,Zip: Highland, Mi. 48357
Telephone #                      Telephone #     (810) 887-4111
Fax #                            Fax #           (810) 887-9190
------------------------------------------------------------------------
                                     Avg/Tot/Oth    Extend      Retract
INITIAL CUSTOMER PARAMETERS:
Total weight of load (lbs)                         2000.00    -1200.00
Angle of load from horizontal          90
Coefficient of Friction              0.00
Number of actuators                     3
Total load per actuator (lbs)                       686.23    -379.75
Minimum line pressure (PSIG)          100
Design pressure used (PSIG)                          73.0        5.0
Shifts/day (1 shift=120,000 m/yr)     2.0
Cycles per year                   1800000

ACTUATOR:
Description:  Single Rod High Flow Numatics Actuator with 1/2 NPT ports
Bore/stroke/rod              4.00" bore x 12.00" stroke x 1.500" rod
Fitting                      3/4" - 1/2 NPT STR

CONDUCTOR & ASSOCIATED COMPONENTS:
Branch conductor /leg      3/4" rubber hose 36" long with 0.0 elbow(s)
Branch manifold fitting /leg         3/4" - 1/2 NPT STR
Branch cond equiv ftg lg /leg (in)   N/A
Quick disconnect model /leg          N/A
In line flow control model /leg               4FC3B       4FC3B
Main conductor             1" rubber hose 12" long with 1.0 elbow(s)
Main manifold fitting                1" - 3/4 NPT STR
Main cond equiv ftg lg (in)          42

VALVE ASSEMBLY & ASSOCIATED COMPONENTS:
Description    2 Pos Mk 55 on 3/4 NPT base with ext reg
Fitting                              1" - 3/4 NPT EL
Silencer model                       M5 (3/4 NPT)

SYSTEM PERFORMANCE TIMES:
Att'n stroke time (sec)                            2.00        1.50
Required stroke time (sec)                         2.00        1.50
Stroke time @ term vel (sec)                       0.96        1.50
Att'n cyclic rate (CPM)               7.50
Required cyclic rate (CPM)            7.50
Cyclic rate @ term vel (CPM)          8.63
System delay time (sec)             0.023
Dwell time after stroke (sec)                      1.80        2.70

SYSTEM INFORMATION:
Required system Cv                                  2.60        1.44
Attained system Cv                                 2.58        1.44
Att'n system air flow (SCFM)          52.8                     13.8
Att'n branch air vel (400 FPS max)      17                       35
Att'n main air vel (400 FPS max)        29                       58
Att'n % delta p (46% max)                6                       46  ?
% Act. capacity used (75% max)          75                     -703
Min pres necessary for 1d w/S.F. (PSIG)           72.8       -46.9
Air per cycle (SCF)                   2.10
Att'n act leakage cost/yr @ $ 0.30 /KSCF   119     103         16
Att'n operating air cost/yr @ $ 0.30 /KSCF 1137    950        187
Cost /1000 cyc @ att'n times @ $ 0.00 /hr  0.70
Att'n power input total (HP)               3.54

COMMENTS:
Using three 4" bore cylinders in place of two 5" bore cylinders, had to
increase compressor pressure to 100 PSIG to maintain 20% S.F. above 73 PSIG.
```

# 4

# Fittings

As we proceed from the actuator, the next link in the chain that confronts us is the inconspicuous fitting. The fitting has a $C_v$, as does every other component, and consequently it must be determined so that it can take its rightful place alongside its neighboring links. Depending on the fitting and the method of calculation, its $C_v$ can be ascertained directly or expressed as an equivalent length and then converted to $C_v$.

Fortunately, there are some application engineers in the fluid-power community who appreciate the significance of fittings in a pneumatic circuit but unfortunately fall short because there is no known method to arrive at fitting values in order to include them into their calculations, and thus even though the fitting influence is appreciated it can't be incorporated. Most, however, disregard fittings and their importance entirely or consider them so minuscule as to have a negligible effect on the overall performance stroke times of actuators. Either view is a poor stance to take, for it turns a blind eye to a vital element in the network. You will notice in the group of cited cases (Survey 4-1 to 4-1$d$ at the end of the chapter) how a valve size had to be increased several times to compensate for the added resistance the fittings created when they were included in the calculations. The relevance of fittings cannot be ignored. The assembled fixture with the initial smaller valve was unable to satisfy the performance requirements once the elbow fittings were incorporated into the computations. The horsepower usage necessitated greater input, as did the costs to operate the fixture with the initial valve choice, as much greater pressures were required to compensate for the added resistance of the elbows. The productivity along with the associated efficiency was unattainable with the original pressures and valve size recommended when the fittings were incorporated into the calculations. The only reason that readily comes to mind for fittings being unintentionally omitted and rationalized away as having minuscule or no affect is that the prevailing approaches have no means of integrating their worth into the system equation.

This should no longer be the case, as it is not only feasible but relatively simple to include fittings into the scheme today. As we've observed in Chap. 2, fittings can be expressed in terms of equivalent lengths of conductor. I believe all pneumatic designers would agree that conductor lengths play a vital role in the performance time of actuators, and since fittings are equivalent conductor lengths (often exceeding the actual length because of their extensive use in a circuit to achieve a cosmetically handsome installation), they should be accorded the same representation. Thus the questions that should arise and deserve answers, are "Why do sharp-angle fittings generate extra resistance (expressed as so much added conductor length), thus playing havoc with the flow of fluids, and how best can we reduce the problems they create?" We learned earlier that a fluid has mass and can be either a liquid or a gas. Air is made up of a combination of gases and therefore falls into this category and thus has mass. We derived it in a previous chapter, and found it to be approximately 0.076 lb/ft$^3$ (pcf) at standard conditions. Since electricity does not have mass, its flow is therefore not hampered by hairpin turns within its conductors in the same sense that compressed air is in its respective conductors. In a pneumatic conductor air travels at about the speed of an automobile on an expressway and since it has mass, it behaves in a similar fashion. What are the consequences of a car attempting to negotiate a sharp-right-angle turn traveling at an assumed speed of 60 miles per hour (mph)? The aftermath is obvious; the vehicle will careen and eventually be wiped out before completing the turn. Since air is composed of many molecules, we can regard each individual one to be analogous to a little auto, and thus as each desires to negotiate the turn the auto gets wiped out in the process because it continually impacts the wall. This creates a disturbance, blocking the flow of oncoming molecules, not too unlike a pileup on an expressway. This interference to air-molecule movement creates a resistance or backpressure preventing the operation of newly arriving molecules. The smaller or tighter the bend radius of the right-angle turn, the worse the behavior. For the solution to this specific condition, let us take a page out of the *Civil Engineer's Handbook* to see how they deal with an equivalent problem on highways. The text suggests a very generous bend on the expressway to remedy this precise circumstance. In fact, on an expressway even if one travels at 75 mph, all that is entailed is to steer the auto, without the need to slow it down. This is realized because the curve of the bend radius is so gentle (large). All circuits in fluid dynamics dictate and utilize bends, as conductors must negotiate around corners, must pass through walls and other obstacles, and must bridge two ports that are hardly ever in proper alignment. Therefore, it would be just as beneficial to apply the large-bend-radius concept here as it would on highways. The least bend radius we suggest is 10 times the inside diameter (10 × ID) of the conductor, so that the effect on cylinder performance times will be evident only in the third decimal place. If one uses a 20 × ID bend radius the first indication of any significant variation in extend or retract time of cylinders would be apparent in the fourth decimal place. [*Note:* Fluid dynamics is composed of two major categories: (1) pneumatics, which deals with gases; and (2) hydraulics, which deals with liquids.]

I would like to comment on an interesting observation I made regarding the use of hoses. One benefit of using hose is that it has a built-in method of assuring a bend radius of 15 to 20 times its ID. This is because the hose's wall thickness is relatively thick compared to its ID. Consequently, in order to prevent kinking, one cannot generate a curve smaller than 15 to 20 times the ID of the hose. However, many pipefitters and their colleagues, in an attempt to dress up the installation will cut the hose and replace the gentle bend with a sharp-right-angle fitting, thus unintentionally losing that built-in large-radius advantage. The large radius is capable of reducing the resistance, thereby increasing the $C_v$.

At this point it is appropriate to mention two additional types of fitting:

1. *Quick disconnect:* A *quick disconnect* in a line is used for precisely that, to quickly uncouple a tool or cylinder for the purpose of rapidly exchanging it for another so as to reduce setup time. There are three types of quick disconnects: straight (STR), one-way shutoff (OWS), and two-way shutoff (TWS). All the conventional disconnects are added resistances in the conductor; however, the TWS is the most damaging to the actuator performance times because of the labyrinth of air passages due to all the internal sharp bends. The economic consideration that should be appraised is whether the short gain in setup time is worth the prolonged loss in long-term productivity. Setup time should not be the sole yardstick for inclusion of quick disconnects into a pneumatic circuit. There are quick disconnects on the market today which resolved the restrictive flow paths of the traditional units. They have essentially the same internal diameter as the conductor while they are flowing air and also serve as positive-pressure shutoffs when disconnected. You (the readers) should familiarize yourselves with all types of quick disconnects in fittings design or operation and should not avoid using them because of the perceived throttling nature of all units.

2. *Swivel right-angle fitting:* Conceptually the design of this fitting is marvelous for it allows unlimited freedom of movement within a confined space. If time and/or space is not of the utmost concern, one should not hesitate to use this device. However, the penalty one pays in productivity is great as the nature of the design imposes many restrictions on flow. Use of swivel right-angle fittings should therefore be very carefully weighed, and here, too, the necessary calculations can and should be made, to both include and exclude these fittings in the design for proper comparisons. Unfortunately, in this case I am not familiar with any new developments that could potentially resolve this problem.

The first case we will explore (alluded to earlier) is one similar to that discussed in Chap. 2 which used many standard elbows to bridge the various portions of a conductor stretching from a valve to a cylinder. In this instance we will investigate it more completely so as to indicate its widespread effect on many of the circuit performance results rather than restrict it only to the effect on the conductor length and its ensuing $C_v$ reduction.

The specific results are as follows. Survey 4-1 indicates that a valve having a $C_v$ of 0.83 (Mk 8) would have no difficulty in accomplishing the desired performance-time results if the elbows in the circuit were totally ignored or large bend radii were used throughout. Survey 4-1*a* indicates that it is not possible for this valve to meet its commitments if the elbows are included in the calculations. Survey 4-1*b* indicates that it would be possible for this valve to satisfy the specifications only if it had 95 psig available to it. This would mean increasing the minimum compressor pressure, or cut-in pressure, to 120 psig to maintain the necessary 20 percent spread between the minimum pressure obtainable and the maximum pressure to be used. The need for this minimum considered safety spread of 20 percent is based on the premise that large variations occur within a plant for sundry reasons and consequently the minimum compressor pressure level should be of sufficient magnitude to consistently deliver the designed-for pressure. We have a minimum pressure of 100 psig, and according to good plant practice, one should use a maximum of 80 psig for a design pressure. Utilizing 95 psig as the design pressure under these conditions leaves only a 5 percent spread, which is inadvisable as it doesn't leave enough slack for a myriad of plant conditions.

It is interesting to note that the 95/95-psig selection meets the criteria for total cycle time only, for if the end user insisted on adhering to each stroke time, then 160/160 psig (Survey 4-1*c*) would be necessary in conjunction with flow controls. Obviously 160 psig is not a practical approach, and other alternatives should be sought and are, in fact, available. The important point is that if elbows are not considered, the 160/160-psig approach is what would have been necessary to achieve the performance-time specifications. No one therefore should casually dismiss the effects of elbows on circuit performance. Survey 4-1$d$ demonstrates that a Mk 25 having a $C_v$ of 2.05 is required to fulfill the essential requirements if all the elbows were included into the calculations (a Mk 15 having a $C_v$ of 1.56 would still be incapable of meeting the required performance times) and the pressures were not permitted to stray beyond the 80-psig safety limit. Survey 4-1$e$ is identical to Survey 4-1 in every respect, including the fact that elbows were excluded and not neglected from the calculations because in their place we used bends having bend radii of 20 times the tubing ID (the results are thus identical). Survey 4-1$f$ replaces the flow controls (single-pressure concept) of Survey 4-1$e$ with dual pressures to again indicate the value of this approach over the conventional single-pressure strategy.

Figure 4.1 tabulates the pertinent information for each survey, and the respective computer printouts of these surveys (4-1 to 4-1$f$) are, as stated previously, at the end of the chapter.

Calculations follow from Fig. 4.1:

1. 2.37 hp $\times$ 16 h $\times$ 0.746 kW/hp = 28.29 kWh/day     (Survey 4-1)

For Survey 4-1$a$ to produce the same number of pieces per day as Survey 4-1, it would have to operate 10.5 percent longer [(74.3 − 67.2)/67.2] as it can achieve only 67.2 cpm compared to 74.3 cpm.

2.16 hp $\times$ 16(1.105) $\times$ 0.746 kW/hp = 28.51 kWh/day     (Survey 4-1$a$)

More power is expended in the latter case, even though the same amount of air is consumed per cycle, because the compressor is required to operate for $\geq$10 percent longer to achieve the same number of cycles, thus allowing compressed air to leak over this longer span of time.

2. The operating cost is obviously identical; it is $778 for Survey 4-1 and for Survey 4-1$a$ it is $704 $\times$ 74.3/67.2 = $778. However, the leakage for Survey 4-1 is $62, whereas that for Survey 4-1$a$ is

$$\$62 \times 74.3/67.2 = \$68.5$$

thus making the totals for each:

$$\$778 + \$62 = \$840 \qquad \text{(Survey 4-1)}$$
$$\$778 + \$68.5 = \$846.5 \qquad \text{(Survey 4-1}a\text{)}$$

| Survey # | 90° Elbow Fittings Included in Calculations | Valve $C_v$ Used | Pressure Used PSIG | Cyclic Rate CPM | Air Cost/Year $ | HP Req'd | Eff. % | Cost/1000 PCS $ | Remarks |
|---|---|---|---|---|---|---|---|---|---|
| 1 | No | 0.83 | 80/80 | 74.3 | 840.00 | 2.37 | 6.5 | 4.54 | Presumably meets all performance time criteria.* |
| 1a | Yes | 0.83 | 80/80 | 67.2 | 766.00** | 2.16** | 6.5 | 5.01 | Does not meet all performance time criteria. |
| 1b | Yes | 0.83 | 95/95 | 75.0 | 1051.00 | 3.07 | 5.1 | 4.50 | Meets only total performance time criteria. |
| 1c | Yes | 0.83 | 160/160 | 74.7 | 2041.00 | 6.55 | 2.4 | 4.57 | Meets all performance time criteria. |
| 1d | Yes | 0.83 | 80/80 | 74.3 | 841.00 | 2.37 | 6.5 | 4.53 | Meets all performance time criteria. |
| 1e | Yes*** | 0.83 | 80/80 | 74.3 | 840.00 | 2.37 | 6.5 | 4.54 | Meets all performance time criteria. |
| 1f | Yes | 0.83 | 75/68 | 75.0 | 768.00 | 2.17 | 7.2 | 4.49 | Meets all performance time criteria. |

**Figure 4.1** Effects of fittings and flow controls on cylinder performance. [Key: single asterisk (*) indicates that this conductor has 11 sharp 90° elbow fittings but considered to be inconsequential and therefore is not included in the calculations. Double asterisk (**) indicates that, since the cyclic rate does not meet the required 75 cpm, the 2.16 hp required as well as the operating cost and efficiency are misleading as the unit would have to operate longer to attain the same quantity produced (approximately 10.6 percent longer). Thus a more valid yardstick would be to compare the horsepower-hours per day or the more commonly used kilowatthours per day and then recalculate the total operating cost on the new basis. Triple asterisks (***) indicate that long radius bends are used having bend radii of 20 times the tubing ID thereby essentially negating their effect on the actuator performance. Therefore, the results are identical to those of Survey 4-1.]

Again, the reason is, as before, that there is a 10.5 percent longer leakage time. A check on this additional sum can be made by comparing the $68.5 to the $62.0, which amounts to 10.5 percent more <(68.5 − 62.0)/62>.

3. Efficiency calculations:

$\Lambda_e$ = Load to extend = 228.5 lb

$S$ = Stroke in feet = 0.25; $s$ = stroke in inches = 3

$\Lambda_r$ = Load to retract = 46.32 lb

$T_t$ = Cycle time in seconds = (60 s/min)/74.3 cpm = 0.81 s for Survey 4-1 and (60 s/min)/67.2 cpm = 0.89 s for Survey 4-1$a$

The following constant 550 refers to the fact that 1 hp = 550 ft lb/s

$$\text{Output hp} = \frac{(\Lambda_e S)+(\Lambda_r S)}{T_t \times 550}$$

$$\text{Output hp for Survey 4-1} = \frac{(228.45 \times 0.25)+(46.32 \times 0.25)}{0.81 \times 550} = 0.154 \text{ hp}$$

$$\text{Output hp for Survey 4-1}a = \frac{(228.45 \times 0.25)+(46.32 \times 0.25)}{0.89 \times 550} = 0.140 \text{ hp}$$

Total input hp for Survey 4-1 = 2.37 hp

Total input hp for Survey 4-1$a$ = 2.16 hp

$$\text{Efficiency} = \frac{\text{output hp}}{\text{input hp}} \times 100$$

$$\text{Efficiency for Survey 4-1} = \frac{0.154}{2.37} \times 100 = 6.5\%$$

$$\text{Efficiency for Survey 4-1}a = \frac{0.140}{2.16} \times 100 = 6.5\%$$

The efficiencies should be identical since the operating hp is proportional to the amount of air consumed per cycle and the leakage is constant per cycle.

It is interesting to note that all the sharp 90° elbows and the additional conductor length to bridge the elbows are used in the name of cosmetically enhancing the machine to improve its salability. To view a machine where the technician has ensured that the conductors closely follow the contour of the machine framework, with tight right-angle fittings hidden in the recesses of the frame to mask their appearance, undoubtedly makes for a very handsome installation, but the end user pays a heavy penalty for this beauty. There are a multiplicity of disadvantages one must consider and then weigh against the major advantage of attractiveness, such as

1. The additional length to bridge the elbows as well as the elbows themselves, increasing the initial capital expenditure and the labor to install them.

2. The elbows creating an equivalent longer conductor length affecting performance.

3. The additional conductor volume affecting performance.

4. The additional continual operating cost for the greater mass of air that must be expended to fill and evacuate the increased volume (due to the additional conductor length) with each and every stroke of the cylinder.

5. Larger components to overcome the handicap of smaller $C_v$ values due to longer actual and equivalent line lengths.

There are currently other ways of improving the salability without compromising on image, professionalism, rigidity, or strength. There are many devices on the market that permit the installer of pneumatic appliances to negotiate turns and twists without hiding them yet achieving sleek appearance via smart long radius bends, thus forgoing all the pitfalls mentioned above. In addition, one can enhance the salability by preaching lower capital expense, higher productivity, and greater energy efficiency without the need to apologize for appearance.

The pneumatic designer should be concerned not only with the number of bends in a conductor leg but also, just as crucially, whether there are any restrictions in the line or appliances in the form of reduced fitting IDs compared to their mating conductor or appliance port IDs. Restricting straight fittings can be just as harmful to the performance of actuators as unrestricted fittings, and most certainly restricted right-angle fittings. Obviously restricted right-angle fittings are disastrous, for now you have the combination of two troublesome conditions.

As we learned earlier, the $C_v$ of an orifice is approximately $23d^2$, which applies to the bulk of the conventional fittings manufactured. We will first observe the effects of straight fittings on conductors and then on valves or any other elements which have ports to accept them. Assume that we have a nylon conductor going through a panel wall, requiring a bulkhead connector to maintain chamber air-pressure integrity within the enclosure. The conductor is split at the wall and its total length is 60 in, with an ID of 0.375 in. The connector fitting is of the internal-barb type with an ID of 0.250 in which mates the two conductor sections. The $C_v$ values of the tubing and fitting, respectively, are 2.38 [(33.22 × 0.375²)(0.375/0.0240 × 60)$^{0.5}$] and 1.44 (23 × 0.25²). Their combination equals 1.23. I used $33.22d^2$ in these calculations as it is the equivalent to $42.3a$ used in the earlier formula, since $a = 0.7854d^2$; then $42.3 × 0.7854 × d^2 = 33.22d^2$.

Now let us further assume that instead of using an internal-barb fitting, we replace it with an external-diameter gripping fitting to marry the two conductor sections to each other. This fitting has as its smallest ID a dimension somewhat greater than the ID of the tubing, and therefore the minimum dimension used to determine the $C_v$ of the fitting will be the ID of the tubing. Since the tubing terminates inside the fitting and is smaller than the smallest ID of the fitting, it therefore assumes the role of being the ID of the fitting. Accordingly, the fitting $C_v$ becomes 3.23, and the resultant combination with the tube $C_v$ of 2.38 is 1.92; this results in a healthy 56 percent increase, which is a significant improvement [(1.92 − 1.23)/1.23].

Now let us examine the effects of just straight fittings combining with valves or any other pneumatic appliances mating with them. An excellent example indicating the immense erosion of the combination $C_v$ of a valve body in conjunction with a port size can be seen in the tabulated values given in Fig. 6.1 (in Chap. 6). We used successively smaller ported ID apertures into the same size valve to arrive at the recorded results. The ultimate answer would be zero in each size of valve if it is used with a solid plug having no opening. Imagining the final consequence to be zero, perhaps one would be more apprehensive about applying any arbitrary fitting into a valve. We will discuss this aspect of valves in more detail in Chap. 6. We estimate that it is more appropriate to discuss this topic under the heading *valves* because of the major impact fittings have on valves. Several items worth mentioning about the straight fittings on the chart before passing on are as follows. First, a valve in combination with a fitting reaches a maximum $C_v$ somewhere during the increasing port size progression. For example, the Mk-55 valve seemingly reached a maximum of 5.73 when it combined with a 2-NPT straight fitting or ported with a 2-NPT pipe thread which has an ID of 2.067 in. Any larger port in combination with the internal components of the valve will not render any appreciably improved $C_v$ (calculated to two decimal places). Essentially the valve in combination with a very small resistance (large $C_v$ having a value of 59.6) reached the hypothetical maximum value of 5.73 as though it had an infinite port size. The reason is that the internal valve members have reached their ceiling and any outside contribution, as larger ports, is of negligible assistance. The $C_v$ reached a plateau, but theoretically it can never reach the ultimate objective of an independent valve having a value of 5.73. It is similar to taking interminable steps having lengths which always measure half the distance to the wall. Theoretically, no matter how many steps one takes, one continually gets closer but never reaches the wall. However, exhibiting the characteristic pragmatic trait of an engineer, for all intents and purposes, we do reach the wall as well as the value of 5.73. It just depends on how many decimal places one wishes to round the number to. The second item is that it is not always practical to fabricate valve bodies with as large a port as is required to reach maximum $C_v$. Obviously this designated point will take maximum advantage of the potential capability of the internal components of the device. Again being practical, one must always make the difficult judgment call of determining where the cutoff point is. By reviewing the chart (Fig. 6.1), it becomes evident that the smaller valves presented no perplexing problems and we took advantage of all opportunities. For the larger valves we have a cutoff point and are within 6 percent of the ideal. Therefore, we are within 94 percent of desired maximum, which again from a practical point of view is considered home. The other significant aspects which govern our decision are proportion, cost, size, and weight. The base may be totally out of proportion to the body, thus also making it cost-prohibitive. Since size and weight are always of concern, we are constantly deluged with requests to reduce the size and weight of the pneumatic appliance envelope to house the same or greater $C_v$ capability. The decision process requires compromises as always. They are in order, as are all these considerations, some of them at cross-purposes, and have to be factored into the equation to arrive at a suitable resolution. Again, this was obvious and declared before but bears repeating. The $C_{vs}$ of a right-angle fitting is the combination of its orifice $C_v$ along with its equivalent length because it is curved, and then is converted to a $C_v$.

It may be wise to refresh our memory by returning to the elbow problem in Chap. 2 and review how we handled it since we have now acquired a more thorough understanding and appreciation of the subject matter. The problem, including its explanation and solution, starts approximately in the middle of Chap. 2. One of the striking areas to investigate in any application is to determine what obstacles lie in the way of stringing the conductor in a straight path between the cylinder and the valve and proceeding with as few twists and turns as possible, dressing it up with gentle turns only where necessary so as to keep the actual length and equivalent length to a minimum.

Let us now appraise some different types of fittings besides right-angle and straights to assess their extensive effect on performance

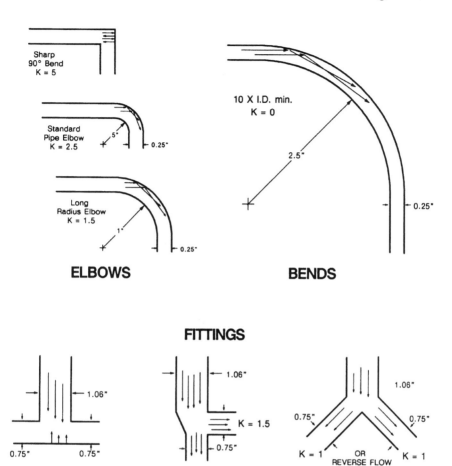

**ELBOWS**                    **BENDS**

**FITTINGS**

BRANCH TEE          RUN TEE          Y FITTING

**Figure 4.2**  Effects of bends on $K$ values.

time and other vital properties. Figure 4.2 shows some of the more common types encountered and their associated $K$ values (i.e., multiplying factor for a conductor) and expands on and goes into more detail than does Fig. 2.6.

One obvious conclusion, since bends are inevitable, especially in cramped or limited space conditions, is that it would be wise to make every effort to fashion the bend radii as large as possible. The advantages are indicated in Fig. 4.2 for various bend radii and their associated $K$ values. Whereas the bend shoes (tools for bending metal tubing) previously had only one bend radius for a specific OD tubing, they now have several to incorporate the gains wherever possible by offering an alternative to the knowledgeable pipefitter, technician, or millwright. An observation of mine concerning a fascinating trait of most humans is that they are inclined to think symmetrical when dealing with, desiring, designing, or constructing objects, articles, or items in general. Being creatures of habit, they tend to perpetuate this concept, which may be inconsequential in most instances, including pneumatic circuits; however, there is one area in fluid dynamics where this innate characteristic should be curbed or replaced with an asymmetrical outlook. I am alluding to the conventional branch tee shown in Fig. 4.2. Utilizing a branch tree to enter and disperse the air from the single vertical upright, called the *branch*; to the two opposing horizontal outlets, called the *runs*; through the conductors; and finally discharging into the actuators, the millwright would not deviate from this norm. Visualize the incoming air attempting to negotiate the sharp-right-angle turns necessary to eventually supply the two actuators. The vertical inrushing air would immediately bounce back, off the facing wall, interfering with the newly arriving air, creating chaos at the juncture, very similar to a heavily trafficked road intersection without the benefits of three-way stops or traffic lights having oncoming traffic incessantly pouring into the intersection regardless of the consequences. Obviously this is not a very viable installation, yet is considered to be the traditional method of assembly. A much more workable strategy would be to use a *run tee,* which is asymmetrical in shape when piped into the system. As can be seen from Fig. 4.2, one run leg distributes the air to the two locations without any hindrance in one direction and only a slight loss in the other. All flow is executed without the use of stop lights or signs and thus no confusion at the junction. The proposed rotation of the unit by 90° was the only difference between the two installations. There are a wide variety of run tee's available that even have the incoming air legs larger than the outgoing legs so that neither path will be starving for air.

There are currently fittings available which cater to the symmetrically oriented mind and are reasonably constructed so as to cause a minimum of upheaval at the intersection. Perhaps they will become more fashionable to use as time progresses since more individuals will have a greater appreciation of the consequences of the associated hardware employed.

The tactic or strategy to take for the individuals laying out and/or installing pneumatic circuits is to imagine oneself driving a car and think which would be the preferred type of intersection to be involved in when seeking to negotiate a turn.

It follows unmistakably that as the $K$ value increases, the equivalent length increases and the $C_v$ diminishes. As the $C_v$ is diminished, by whatever means, performance times will decline, thereby increasing costs. To compensate for this deficiency in $C_v$, it would be essential to increase pressures, thus necessitating more compressor horsepower with its attendant increased energy usage and costs, all due to misconceptions in the management of the use of fittings.

The extreme changes in pipe sizes is a topic which is somewhat related to tank sizing, which will be reviewed in a later chapter, but since the subject here falls primarily within the fitting category, it is ripe for discussion here. The reason that it falls into tank sizing is because one can consider a tank to be a very-large-diameter conductor having a very short length when it is conducting or flowing air during the dynamic portion of the cycle.

The equation for determining the loss coefficient $\underline{K}^1$ for a sudden enlargement is $[1 - (D_1/D_2)^2]^2$, whereas the loss coefficient $\underline{K}^1$ for a sudden contraction is $0.5[1 - (D_1/D_2)^2]$. From the equations it is quite apparent that there are losses when flowing into and out of two different-size conductors. Interestingly, the sudden enlargement is more detrimental to the flow of air than is the sudden contraction.

Where air is flowing into and out of a reservoir tank from a comparatively small supply and takeoff line, the ratio between $D_2$ and $D_1$ is essentially so large that the fraction of $(D_1/D_2)^2$ is so small that it can be considered zero for all practical purposes. This is evident by studying a sample 25-gal tank as viewed in Fig. 4.3 with its accompanying dimensions. The calculation reinforcing that conclusion follows: $D_1 = 0.052$ ft; and $D_2 = 1.25$ ft; thus $(D_1/D_2)^2 = 0.0017$ and $\underline{K} = 0.997$ for a sudden enlargement and $0.499$ for a sudden contraction, which can be considered $1.0$ and $0.5$ for all practical purposes. This simplifies the formulas rendering a $\underline{K}$ value of $1.0$ for the sudden-enlargement loss coefficient and $0.5$ for the sudden-contraction loss coefficient when the disparities between the two IDs are as great as those existing between the connecting conductors and the tank. Let us determine the equivalent length of additional conductor this imposes on the circuit:

$$L = \frac{KD}{f}$$

Assume we use a $\frac{1}{2}$-NPT pipe which has an $f$ value of $0.0285$, $D = 0.052$ ft, and $L = 1 \times 0.0285 = 1.82$ ft for sudden enlargement and $0.91$ ft for sudden contraction. As we can see, putting in a reservoir tank is not totally penalty-free, even though the penalty may be small.

---

[1]Henry Fleischer and Paul Tallant, *Practical Air Valve Sizing* (manual), Numatics, Inc., Dec. 1974

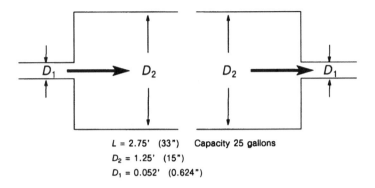

L = 2.75' (33")    Capacity 25 gallons
$D_2$ = 1.25' (15")
$D_1$ = 0.052' (0.624")

| Sudden enlargements | Sudden contractions |
|---|---|
| $K = \left[1 - (D_1{}^2/D_2{}^2)\right]^2$ | $K = 0.5\left[1 - (D_1{}^2/D_2{}^2)\right]$ |

**Figure 4.3**   Effects of sudden diameter changes on $K$ values.

The $K$ value we used earlier, called the *multiplying factor for a conductor*, is equal to $K/12f$ (where $K$ means fitting loss coefficient). Thus we can also solve for the equivalent length by using the equation $L = nKd$, which equals $nKd/12f = 1 \times 1 \times 0.622/12 \times 0.0285 = 1.82$ ft (sudden enlargement) and 0.91 ft (sudden reduction).

Let us go one step further and determine the $C_v$ of the tank, including its associated entry and exit losses and the impact they have on the tank $C_v$. The length is 2.75 ft plus the equivalent of 2.73 ft (1.82 ft + 0.91 ft) for a total of 5.48 ft. The $C_v$ is 46,000, excluding the exit and entry losses, and 33,000 with these losses included. Both are so large that their impact on any system would be minuscule, but on an absolute basis the impact of the sudden losses on the tank $C_v$ represents a 28 percent reduction. Specifically, $C_v = 33.2d^2(d/fl)^{0.5}$; with $f = 0.012$ (Chap. 5, Fig. 5.3), an $l$ of 68.76 in (5.73 ft $\times$ 12) and a $d$ of 15 in, we obtain 46,000 and 33,000, respectively, for the two conditions.

We can again conclude from all the above the same notion we've arrived at from our discussions in previous chapters; namely, one should strive to design the circuit with as few encumbrances as possible and that the most expensive item in the circuit should be the component having the smallest $C_v$.

*"Ah, but a man's reach should exceed his grasp, Or what's a heaven for?"*
ROBERT BROWNING, 1812–1889

```
NUMATICS NUMASIZING (R) SUMMARY SHEET                    Date:    04/10/95
NU301EED   Ver 3.01 (c) 1989 Numatics, Inc.             SURVEY # 4-1
========================================================================
Prepared for:                    Prepared by:    Michael Liberty
Company:                         Company:        Numatics Inc.
Address:                         Address:        1450 N. Milford Rd.
City,State,Zip:                  City,State,Zip: Highland, Mi. 48357
Telephone #                      Telephone #     (810) 887-4111
Fax #                            Fax #           (810) 887-9190
------------------------------------------------------------------------
                                    Avg/Tot/Oth     Extend      Retract
INITIAL CUSTOMER PARAMETERS:
Total weight of load (lbs)                          200.00       30.00
Angle of load from horizontal          90
Coefficient of Friction              0.00
Number of actuators                     1
Total load per actuator (lbs)                       228.45       46.32
Minimum line pressure (PSIG)          100
Design pressure used (PSIG)                          80.0         80.0
Shifts/day (1 shift=120,000 m/yr)     2.0
Cycles per year                  18000000

ACTUATOR:
Description:    Single Rod High Flow Numatics Actuator with 3/8 NPT ports
Bore/stroke/rod            2.50" bore x 3.00" stroke x 0.625" rod
Fitting                    3/8" - 3/8 NPT STR

CONDUCTOR & ASSOCIATED COMPONENTS:
Branch conductor /leg                  N/A
Branch manifold fitting /leg           N/A
Branch cond equiv ftg lg /leg (in)     N/A
Quick disconnect model /leg            N/A
In line flow control model /leg                     3FC2B        3FC2B
Main conductor             3/8" metal tube 72" long with 0.0 elbow(s)
Main manifold fitting                  N/A
Main cond equiv ftg lg (in)              0

VALVE ASSEMBLY & ASSOCIATED COMPONENTS:
Description     2 Pos Mk 8 on 1/4 NPT base with ext reg
Fitting                    3/8" - 1/4 NPT STR
Silencer model             N/A

SYSTEM PERFORMANCE TIMES:
Att'n stroke time (sec)                             0.37         0.21
Required stroke time (sec)                          0.37         0.21
Stroke time @ term vel (sec)                        0.17         0.16
Att'n cyclic rate (CPM)                74.25
Required cyclic rate (CPM)             75.00
Cyclic rate @ term vel (CPM)          109.92
System delay time (sec)                0.022
Dwell time after stroke (sec)                       0.15         0.07

SYSTEM INFORMATION:
Required system Cv                                  0.58         0.56
Attained system Cv                                  0.58         0.58
Att'n system air flow (SCFM)                        12.0         19.9
Att'n branch air vel (400 FPS max)     N/A                 N/A
Att'n main air vel (400 FPS max)                     64          122
Att'n % delta p (46% max)                             5           17
% Act. capacity used (75% max)                       58           13
Min pres necessary for 1d w/S.F. (PSIG)             62.1         13.4
Air per cycle (SCF)                    0.15
Att'n act leakage cost/yr @ $ 0.30 /KSCF   62       32           30
Att'n operating air cost/yr @ $ 0.30 /KSCF 778      398          380
Cost /1000 cyc @ att'n times @ $ 20.00 /hr 4.54
Att'n power input total (HP)           2.37

COMMENTS:
The conventional approach of a single pressure source and FC's. Discarding
the effect of 11 sharp right angle fittings located throughout the circuit.
```

```
NUMATICS NUMASIZING (R) SUMMARY SHEET              Date:    04/10/95
NU301EED  Ver 3.01 (c) 1989 Numatics, Inc.        SURVEY # 4-1
================================================================
Prepared for:                     Prepared by:    Michael Liberty
Company:                          Company:        Numatics Inc.
Address:                          Address:        1450 N. Milford Rd.
City,State,Zip:                   City,State,Zip: Highland, Mi. 48357
Telephone #                       Telephone #     (810) 887-4111
Fax #                             Fax #           (810) 887-9190
-----------------------------------------------------------------
                                                 Extend    Retract
Cv DATA PER ACTUATOR

Actuator Fitting Cv                               2.42      2.42
Flow Control Free Flow Cv from Chart              2.86      2.86
Flow Control Adjustable Cv from Chart             2.54      2.54
Flow Control Adjustable Cv Used                   1.65      1.51
Quick Disconnect Cv                               N/A       N/A
Branch Conductor Cv                               N/A       N/A
Additional Cv Due to Elbows in Branch Conductor   N/A       N/A
Branch Conductor Manifold Fitting Cv              N/A       N/A


Cv DATA - TOTAL SYSTEM

Actuator Fitting Cv                               2.42      2.42
Flow Control Free Flow Cv from Chart              2.86      2.86
Flow Control Adjustable Cv from Chart             2.54      2.54
Flow Control Adjustable Cv Used                   1.65      1.51
Quick Disconnect Cv                               N/A       N/A
Branch Conductor Cv                               N/A       N/A
Additional Cv Due to Elbows in Branch Conductor   N/A       N/A
Branch Conductor Manifold Fitting Cv              N/A       N/A
Main Conductor Cv                                 1.28      1.28
Additional Cv Due to Elbows in Main Conductor     N/A       N/A
Main Conductor Manifold Fitting Cv                N/A       N/A
Silencer Cv                                       N/A       N/A
Valve Fitting Cv                                  2.14      2.14
Valve Cv                                          0.83      0.83
Sandwich Regulator Cv                             N/A       N/A
Sandwich Speed Control Cv from Chart              N/A       N/A
Sandwich Speed Control Cv Used                    N/A       N/A
Sandwich Check Valve Cv (3 pos valve only)        N/A       N/A


Attained system Cv                                0.58      0.58

Required system Cv                                0.58      0.56

Flow Control Adjustable Cv Suggested              1.50      1.30
Valve Cv Suggested                                0.81      0.79
Sandwich Speed Control Cv Suggested               3.56      2.59
```

```
NUMATICS NUMASIZING (R) SUMMARY SHEET                    Date:   04/10/95
NU301EED  Ver 3.01 (c) 1989 Numatics, Inc.              SURVEY # 4-1a
==========================================================================
Prepared for:                     Prepared by:    Michael Liberty
Company:                          Company:        Numatics Inc.
Address:                          Address:        1450 N. Milford Rd.
City,State,Zip:                   City,State,Zip: Highland, Mi. 48357
Telephone #                       Telephone #     (810) 887-4111
Fax #                             Fax #           (810) 887-9190
-----------------------------------------------------------------------
                                     Avg/Tot/Oth    Extend     Retract
INITIAL CUSTOMER PARAMETERS:
Total weight of load (lbs)                         200.00      30.00
Angle of load from horizontal          90
Coefficient of Friction              0.00
Number of actuators                     1
Total load per actuator (lbs)                      228.45      46.32
Minimum line pressure (PSIG)          100
Design pressure used (PSIG)                         80.0        80.0
Shifts/day (1 shift=120,000 m/yr)     2.0
Cycles per year                  18000000

ACTUATOR:
Description:   Single Rod High Flow Numatics Actuator with 3/8 NPT ports
Bore/stroke/rod           2.50" bore x 3.00" stroke x 0.625" rod
Fitting                   3/8" - 3/8 NPT EL

CONDUCTOR & ASSOCIATED COMPONENTS:
Branch conductor /leg                    N/A
Branch manifold fitting /leg             N/A
Branch cond equiv ftg lg /leg (in)       N/A
Quick disconnect model /leg              N/A
In line flow control model /leg                     3FC2B       3FC2B
Main conductor           3/8" metal tube 72" long with 11.0 elbow(s)
Main manifold fitting                    N/A
Main cond equiv ftg lg (in)              141

VALVE ASSEMBLY & ASSOCIATED COMPONENTS:
Description    2 Pos Mk 8 on 1/4 NPT base with ext reg
Fitting                                  3/8" - 1/4 NPT EL
Silencer model                           N/A

SYSTEM PERFORMANCE TIMES:
Att'n stroke time (sec)                             0.43 ?     0.24 ?
Required stroke time (sec)                          0.37       0.21
Stroke time @ term vel (sec)                        0.19       0.18
Att'n cyclic rate (CPM)               67.18
Required cyclic rate (CPM)            75.00
Cyclic rate @ term vel (CPM)         101.04
System delay time (sec)                0.022
Dwell time after stroke (sec)                       0.15       0.07

SYSTEM INFORMATION:
Required system Cv                                  0.58       0.56
Attained system Cv                                 0.51       0.51
Att'n system air flow (SCFM)                       10.4       17.6
Att'n branch air vel (400 FPS max)       N/A               N/A
Att'n main air vel (400 FPS max)                    56        108
% Act. capacity used (75% max)                       5         17
Att'n % delta p (46% max)                           58         13
Min pres necessary for ld w/S.F. (PSIG)            62.1       13.4
Air per cycle (SCF)                    0.15
Att'n act leakage cost/yr @ $ 0.30 /KSCF   62       32         30
Att'n operating air cost/yr @ $ 0.30 /KSCF 704     360        344
Cost /1000 cyc @ att'n times @ $ 20.00 /hr 5.01
Att'n power input total (HP)           2.16

COMMENTS:
Identical to 4-1 except we've taken into account the 11 sharp right angle
fittings to observe the impact on cylinder performance results.
```

```
NUMATICS NUMASIZING (R) SUMMARY SHEET              Date:   04/10/95
NU301EED  Ver 3.01 (c) 1989 Numatics, Inc.        SURVEY # 4-1a
===================================================================
Prepared for:                  Prepared by:   Michael Liberty
Company:                       Company:       Numatics Inc.
Address:                       Address:       1450 N. Milford Rd.
City,State,Zip:                City,State,Zip: Highland, Mi. 48357
Telephone #                    Telephone #    (810) 887-4111
Fax #                          Fax #          (810) 887-9190
-------------------------------------------------------------------
                                                Extend    Retract
Cv DATA PER ACTUATOR

Actuator Fitting Cv                              1.89      1.89
Flow Control Free Flow Cv from Chart             2.86      2.86
Flow Control Adjustable Cv from Chart            2.54      2.54
Flow Control Adjustable Cv Used                  2.54      2.54
Quick Disconnect Cv                              N/A       N/A
Branch Conductor Cv                              N/A       N/A
Additional Cv Due to Elbows in Branch Conductor  N/A       N/A
Branch Conductor Manifold Fitting Cv             N/A       N/A

Cv DATA - TOTAL SYSTEM

Actuator Fitting Cv                              1.89      1.89
Flow Control Free Flow Cv from Chart             2.86      2.86
Flow Control Adjustable Cv from Chart            2.54      2.54
Flow Control Adjustable Cv Used                  2.54      2.54
Quick Disconnect Cv                              N/A       N/A
Branch Conductor Cv                              N/A       N/A
Additional Cv Due to Elbows in Branch Conductor  N/A       N/A
Branch Conductor Manifold Fitting Cv             N/A       N/A
Main Conductor Cv                                1.28      1.28
Additional Cv Due to Elbows in Main Conductor    1.01      1.01
Main Conductor Manifold Fitting Cv               N/A       N/A
Silencer Cv                                      N/A       N/A
Valve Fitting Cv                                 1.75      1.75
Valve Cv                                         0.83      0.83
Sandwich Regulator Cv                            N/A       N/A
Sandwich Speed Control Cv from Chart             N/A       N/A
Sandwich Speed Control Cv Used                   N/A       N/A
Sandwich Check Valve Cv (3 pos valve only)       N/A       N/A


Attained system Cv                               0.51      0.51

Required system Cv                               0.58      0.56

Flow Control Adjustable Cv Suggested             N/A       N/A
Valve Cv Suggested                               1.34      1.20
Sandwich Speed Control Cv Suggested              N/A       N/A
```

```
NUMATICS NUMASIZING (R) SUMMARY SHEET                          Date:    04/10/95
NU301EED  Ver 3.01 (c) 1989 Numatics, Inc.                    SURVEY # 4-1b
================================================================================
Prepared for:                    Prepared by:     Michael Liberty
Company:                         Company:         Numatics Inc.
Address:                         Address:         1450 N. Milford Rd.
City,State,Zip:                  City,State,Zip:  Highland, Mi. 48357
Telephone #                      Telephone #      (810) 887-4111
Fax #                            Fax #            (810) 887-9190
--------------------------------------------------------------------------------
                                        Avg/Tot/Oth      Extend      Retract
INITIAL CUSTOMER PARAMETERS:
Total weight of load (lbs)                                200.00       30.00
Angle of load from horizontal               90
Coefficient of friction                   0.00
Number of actuators                          1
Total load per actuator (lbs)                            228.45       46.32
Minimum line pressure (PSIG)               120
Design pressure used (PSIG)                               95.0         95.0
Shifts/day (1 shift=120,000 m/yr)          2.0
Cycles per year                       18000000

ACTUATOR:
Description:   Single Rod High Flow Numatics Actuator with 3/8 NPT ports
Bore/stroke/rod              2.50" bore x 3.00" stroke x 0.625" rod
Fitting                      3/8" - 3/8 NPT EL

CONDUCTOR & ASSOCIATED COMPONENTS:
Branch conductor /leg                  N/A
Branch manifold fitting /leg           N/A
Branch cond equiv ftg lg /leg (in)     N/A
Quick disconnect model /leg            N/A
In line flow control model /leg                          3FC2B        3FC2B
Main conductor               3/8" metal tube 72" long with 11.0 elbow(s)
Main manifold fitting                  N/A
Main cond equiv ftg lg (in)            141

VALVE ASSEMBLY & ASSOCIATED COMPONENTS:
Description     2 Pos Mk 8 on 1/4 NPT base with ext reg
Fitting                      3/8" - 1/4 NPT EL
Silencer model               N/A

SYSTEM PERFORMANCE TIMES:
Att'n stroke time (sec)                                  0.35 ?       0.23 ?
Required stroke time (sec)                               0.37         0.21
Stroke time @ term vel (sec)                            0.19         0.18
Att'n cyclic rate (CPM)                  74.98
Required cyclic rate (CPM)               75.00
Cyclic rate @ term vel (CPM)            101.04
System delay time (sec)                   0.022
Dwell time after stroke (sec)                            0.15         0.07

SYSTEM INFORMATION:
Required system Cv                                       0.46         0.54
Attained system Cv                                       0.51         0.51
Att'n system air flow (SCFM)                             14.9         21.2
Att'n branch air vel (400 FPS max)              N/A              N/A
Att'n main air vel (400 FPS max)                        72           115
Att'n % delta p (46% max)                                8            19
% Act. capacity used (75% max)                          49            11
Min pres necessary for ld w/S.F. (PSIG)                 62.1         13.4
Air per cycle (SCF)                       0.17
Att'n act leakage cost/yr @ $ 0.32 /KSCF    80          39            41
Att'n operating air cost/yr @ $ 0.32 /KSCF  971         497          474
Cost /1000 cyc @ att'n times @ $ 20.00 /hr  4.50
Att'n power input total (HP)              3.07

COMMENTS:
Identical to 4-1a except we've inc source pr to 120 PSIG to permit raising
the reg pr to 95 PSIG to achieve the 75 CPM.
```

```
NUMATICS NUMASIZING (R) SUMMARY SHEET                    Date:    04/10/95
NU301EED  Ver 3.01 (c) 1989 Numatics, Inc.              SURVEY # 4-1b
=========================================================================
Prepared for:                      Prepared by:     Michael Liberty
Company:                           Company:         Numatics Inc.
Address:                           Address:         1450 N. Milford Rd.
City,State,Zip:                    City,State,Zip:  Highland, Mi. 48357
Telephone #                        Telephone #      (810) 887-4111
Fax #                              Fax #            (810) 887-9190
-------------------------------------------------------------------------
                                                     Extend      Retract
   Cv DATA PER ACTUATOR

Actuator Fitting Cv                                   1.89        1.89
Flow Control Free Flow Cv from Chart                  2.86        2.86
Flow Control Adjustable Cv from Chart                 2.54        2.54
Flow Control Adjustable Cv Used                       2.54        2.54
Quick Disconnect Cv                                   N/A         N/A
Branch Conductor Cv                                   N/A         N/A
Additional Cv Due to Elbows in Branch Conductor       N/A         N/A
Branch Conductor Manifold Fitting Cv                  N/A         N/A

   Cv DATA - TOTAL SYSTEM

Actuator Fitting Cv                                   1.89        1.89
Flow Control Free Flow Cv from Chart                  2.86        2.86
Flow Control Adjustable Cv from Chart                 2.54        2.54
Flow Control Adjustable Cv Used                       2.54        2.54
Quick Disconnect Cv                                   N/A         N/A
Branch Conductor Cv                                   N/A         N/A
Additional Cv Due to Elbows in Branch Conductor       N/A         N/A
Branch Conductor Manifold Fitting Cv                  N/A         N/A
Main Conductor Cv                                     1.28        1.28
Additional Cv Due to Elbows in Main Conductor         1.01        1.01
Main Conductor Manifold Fitting Cv                    N/A         N/A
Silencer Cv                                           N/A         N/A
Valve Fitting Cv                                      1.75        1.75
Valve Cv                                              0.83        0.83
Sandwich Regulator Cv                                 N/A         N/A
Sandwich Speed Control Cv from Chart                  N/A         N/A
Sandwich Speed Control Cv Used                        N/A         N/A
Sandwich Check Valve Cv (3 pos valve only)            N/A         N/A


Attained system Cv                                    0.51        0.51

Required system Cv                                    0.46        0.54

Flow Control Adjustable Cv Suggested                  1.03        N/A
Valve Cv Suggested                                    0.67        1.02
Sandwich Speed Control Cv Suggested                   1.13        N/A
```

```
NUMATICS NUMASIZING (R) SUMMARY SHEET              Date:   04/10/95
NU301EED  Ver 3.01 (c) 1989 Numatics, Inc.        SURVEY # 4-1c
=================================================================
Prepared for:               Prepared by:    Michael Liberty
Company:                    Company:        Numatics Inc.
Address:                    Address:        1450 N. Milford Rd.
City,State,Zip:             City,State,Zip: Highland, Mi. 48357
Telephone #                 Telephone #     (810) 887-4111
Fax #                       Fax #           (810) 887-9190
-----------------------------------------------------------------
                               Avg/Tot/Oth    Extend    Retract
INITIAL CUSTOMER PARAMETERS:
Total weight of load (lbs)                    200.00     30.00
Angle of load from horizontal       90
Coefficient of Friction           0.00
Number of actuators                  1
Total load per actuator (lbs)                 228.45     46.32
Minimum line pressure (PSIG)       200
Design pressure used (PSIG)                   160.0 ?   160.0 ?
Shifts/day (1 shift=120,000 m/yr)  2.0
Cycles per year               18000000

ACTUATOR:
Description:   Single Rod High Flow Numatics Actuator with 3/8 NPT ports
Bore/stroke/rod             2.50" bore x 3.00" stroke x 0.625" rod
Fitting                     3/8" - 3/8 NPT EL

CONDUCTOR & ASSOCIATED COMPONENTS:
Branch conductor /leg               N/A
Branch manifold fitting /leg        N/A
Branch cond equiv ftg lg /leg (in)  N/A
Quick disconnect model /leg         N/A
In line flow control model /leg                3FC2B      3FC2B
Main conductor              3/8" metal tube 72" long with 11.0 elbow(s)
Main manifold fitting               N/A
Main cond equiv ftg lg (in)         141

VALVE ASSEMBLY & ASSOCIATED COMPONENTS:
Description     2 Pos Mk 8 on 1/4 NPT base with ext reg
Fitting                     3/8" - 1/4 NPT EL
Silencer model              N/A

SYSTEM PERFORMANCE TIMES:
Att'n stroke time (sec)                       0.37       0.21
Required stroke time (sec)                    0.37       0.21
Stroke time @ term vel (sec)                  0.30       0.18
Att'n cyclic rate (CPM)            74.73
Required cyclic rate (CPM)         75.00
Cyclic rate @ term vel (CPM)       85.73
System delay time (sec)            0.022
Dwell time after stroke (sec)                 0.15       0.07

SYSTEM INFORMATION:
Required system Cv                            0.32       0.49
Attained system Cv                            0.33       0.51
Att'n system air flow (SCFM)                  22.4       36.6
Att'n branch air vel (400 FPS max)  N/A                 N/A
Att'n main air vel (400 FPS max)               78        132
Att'n % delta p (46% max)                      20         24
% Act. capacity used (75% max)                 29          6
Min pres necessary for ld w/S.F. (PSIG)       62.1       13.4
Air per cycle (SCF)                0.27
Att'n act leakage cost/yr @ $ 0.39 /KSCF  162  83        79
Att'n operating air cost/yr @ $ 0.39 /KSCF 1879 961      917
Cost /1000 cyc @ att'n times @ $ 20.00 /hr 4.57
Att'n power input total (HP)       6.55

COMMENTS:
Identical to 4-1a except we've inc source pr to 200 PSIG to permit raising
the reg pr to 160 PSIG to achieve the individual cyl performance times.
```

```
NUMATICS NUMASIZING (R) SUMMARY SHEET              Date:    04/10/95
NU301EED  Ver 3.01 (c) 1989 Numatics, Inc.        SURVEY # 4-1c
=====================================================================
Prepared for:                   Prepared by:    Michael Liberty
Company:                        Company:        Numatics Inc.
Address:                        Address:        1450 N. Milford Rd.
City,State,Zip:                 City,State,Zip: Highland, Mi. 48357
Telephone #                     Telephone #     (810) 887-4111
Fax #                           Fax #           (810) 887-9190
---------------------------------------------------------------------
                                                 Extend    Retract
Cv DATA PER ACTUATOR

Actuator Fitting Cv                               1.89       1.89
Flow Control Free Flow Cv from Chart              2.86       2.86
Flow Control Adjustable Cv from Chart             2.54       2.54
Flow Control Adjustable Cv Used                   0.42       2.46
Quick Disconnect Cv                               N/A        N/A
Branch Conductor Cv                               N/A        N/A
Additional Cv Due to Elbows in Branch Conductor   N/A        N/A
Branch Conductor Manifold Fitting Cv              N/A        N/A

Cv DATA - TOTAL SYSTEM

Actuator Fitting Cv                               1.89       1.89
Flow Control Free Flow Cv from Chart              2.86       2.86
Flow Control Adjustable Cv from Chart             2.54       2.54
Flow Control Adjustable Cv Used                   0.42       2.46
Quick Disconnect Cv                               N/A        N/A
Branch Conductor Cv                               N/A        N/A
Additional Cv Due to Elbows in Branch Conductor   N/A        N/A
Branch Conductor Manifold Fitting Cv              N/A        N/A
Main Conductor Cv                                 1.28       1.28
Additional Cv Due to Elbows in Main Conductor     1.01       1.01
Main Conductor Manifold Fitting Cv                N/A        N/A
Silencer Cv                                       N/A        N/A
Valve Fitting Cv                                  1.75       1.75
Valve Cv                                          0.83       0.83
Sandwich Regulator Cv                             N/A        N/A
Sandwich Speed Control Cv from Chart              N/A        N/A
Sandwich Speed Control Cv Used                    N/A        N/A
Sandwich Check Valve Cv (3 pos valve only)        N/A        N/A


Attained system Cv                                0.33       0.51

Required system Cv                                0.32       0.49

Flow Control Adjustable Cv Suggested              0.40       1.75
Valve Cv Suggested                                0.70       0.79
Sandwich Speed Control Cv Suggested               1.31       2.49
```

```
NUMATICS NUMASIZING (R) SUMMARY SHEET                    Date:    04/10/95
NU301EED  Ver 3.01 (c) 1989 Numatics, Inc.              SURVEY # 4-1d
========================================================================
Prepared for:                    Prepared by:    Michael Liberty
Company:                         Company:        Numatics Inc.
Address:                         Address:        1450 N. Milford Rd.
City,State,Zip:                  City,State,Zip: Highland, Mi. 48357
Telephone #                      Telephone #     (810) 887-4111
Fax #                            Fax #           (810) 887-9190
------------------------------------------------------------------------
                                 Avg/Tot/Oth    Extend      Retract
INITIAL CUSTOMER PARAMETERS:
Total weight of load (lbs)                       200.00      30.00
Angle of load from horizontal          90
Coefficient of Friction              0.00
Number of actuators                     1
Total load per actuator (lbs)                    228.45      46.32
Minimum line pressure (PSIG)          100
Design pressure used (PSIG)                       80.0       80.0
Shifts/day (1 shift=120,000 m/yr)     2.0
Cycles per year                  18000000
```

ACTUATOR:
Description:   Single Rod High Flow Numatics Actuator with 3/8 NPT ports
Bore/stroke/rod              2.50" bore x 3.00" stroke x 0.625" rod
Fitting                              3/8" - 3/8 NPT EL

```
CONDUCTOR & ASSOCIATED COMPONENTS:
Branch conductor /leg                N/A
Branch manifold fitting /leg         N/A
Branch cond equiv ftg lg /leg (in)   N/A
Quick disconnect model /leg          N/A
In line flow control model /leg                  3FC2B       3FC2B
Main conductor        3/8" metal tube 72" long with 11.0 elbow(s)
Main manifold fitting                N/A
Main cond equiv ftg lg (in)           141
```

VALVE ASSEMBLY & ASSOCIATED COMPONENTS:
Description    2 Pos Mk 25 on 3/8 NPT base with ext reg
Fitting                              3/8" - 3/8 NPT EL
Silencer model                       N/A

```
SYSTEM PERFORMANCE TIMES:
Att'n stroke time (sec)                          0.37        0.21
Required stroke time (sec)                       0.37        0.21
Stroke time @ term vel (sec)                     0.17        0.16
Att'n cyclic rate (CPM)                74.30
Required cyclic rate (CPM)             75.00
Cyclic rate @ term vel (CPM)          109.98
System delay time (sec)                0.025
Dwell time after stroke (sec)                    0.15        0.07

SYSTEM INFORMATION:
Required system Cv                               0.58        0.56
Attained system Cv                               0.58        0.58
Att'n system air flow (SCFM)                     12.0        20.0
Att'n branch air vel (400 FPS max)      N/A                N/A
Att'n main air vel (400 FPS max)                  64         122
Att'n % delta p (46% max)                          5          17
% Act. capacity used (75% max)                    58          13
Min pres necessary for 1d w/S.F. (PSIG)          62.1        13.4
Air per cycle (SCF)                    0.15
Att'n act leakage cost/yr @ $ 0.30 /KSCF  62      32          30
Att'n operating air cost/yr @ $ 0.30 /KSCF 779   399         380
Cost /1000 cyc @ att'n times @ $ 20.00 /hr 4.53
Att'n power input total (HP)           2.37
```

COMMENTS:
Identical to 4-1a except to achieve the individual performance times we've
bumped the valve up two sizes and kept the original pr conditions.

```
NUMATICS NUMASIZING (R) SUMMARY SHEET                    Date:    04/10/95
NU301EED   Ver 3.01 (c) 1989 Numatics, Inc.             SURVEY # 4-1d
==========================================================================
Prepared for:                    Prepared by:    Michael Liberty
Company:                         Company:        Numatics Inc.
Address:                         Address:        1450 N. Milford Rd.
City,State,Zip:                  City,State,Zip: Highland, Mi. 48357
Telephone #                      Telephone #     (810) 887-4111
Fax #                            Fax #           (810) 887-9190
--------------------------------------------------------------------------
                                                  Extend     Retract
Cv DATA PER ACTUATOR

Actuator Fitting Cv                                1.89        1.89
Flow Control Free Flow Cv from Chart               2.86        2.86
Flow Control Adjustable Cv from Chart              2.54        2.54
Flow Control Adjustable Cv Used                    1.60        1.48
Quick Disconnect Cv                                N/A         N/A
Branch Conductor Cv                                N/A         N/A
Additional Cv Due to Elbows in Branch Conductor    N/A         N/A
Branch Conductor Manifold Fitting Cv               N/A         N/A

Cv DATA - TOTAL SYSTEM

Actuator Fitting Cv                                1.89        1.89
Flow Control Free Flow Cv from Chart               2.86        2.86
Flow Control Adjustable Cv from Chart              2.54        2.54
Flow Control Adjustable Cv Used                    1.60        1.48
Quick Disconnect Cv                                N/A         N/A
Branch Conductor Cv                                N/A         N/A
Additional Cv Due to Elbows in Branch Conductor    N/A         N/A
Branch Conductor Manifold Fitting Cv               N/A         N/A
Main Conductor Cv                                  1.28        1.28
Additional Cv Due to Elbows in Main Conductor      1.01        1.01
Main Conductor Manifold Fitting Cv                 N/A         N/A
Silencer Cv                                        N/A         N/A
Valve Fitting Cv                                   1.75        1.75
Valve Cv                                           2.05        2.05
Sandwich Regulator Cv                              N/A         N/A
Sandwich Speed Control Cv from Chart               N/A         N/A
Sandwich Speed Control Cv Used                     N/A         N/A
Sandwich Check Valve Cv (3 pos valve only)         N/A         N/A


Attained system Cv                                 0.58        0.58

Required system Cv                                 0.58        0.56

Flow Control Adjustable Cv Suggested               1.45        1.27
Valve Cv Suggested                                 1.76        1.59
Sandwich Speed Control Cv Suggested                3.45        2.53
```

```
NUMATICS NUMASIZING (R) SUMMARY SHEET                    Date:    04/10/95
NU301EED  Ver 3.01 (c) 1989 Numatics, Inc.              SURVEY # 4-1e
=========================================================================
Prepared for:                   Prepared by:    Michael Liberty
Company:                        Company:        Numatics Inc.
Address:                        Address:        1450 N. Milford Rd.
City,State,Zip:                 City,State,Zip: Highland, Mi. 48357
Telephone #                     Telephone #     (810) 887-4111
Fax #                           Fax #           (810) 887-9190
-------------------------------------------------------------------------
                                  Avg/Tot/Oth    Extend    Retract
INITIAL CUSTOMER PARAMETERS:
Total weight of load (lbs)                       200.00    30.00
Angle of load from horizontal        90
Coefficient of Friction            0.00
Number of actuators                   1
Total load per actuator (lbs)                    228.45    46.32
Minimum line pressure (PSIG)        100
Design pressure used (PSIG)                       80.0     80.0
Shifts/day (1 shift=120,000 m/yr)   2.0
Cycles per year                18000000

ACTUATOR:
Description:  Single Rod High Flow Numatics Actuator with 3/8 NPT ports
Bore/stroke/rod             2.50" bore x 3.00" stroke x 0.625" rod
Fitting                     3/8" - 3/8 NPT STR

CONDUCTOR & ASSOCIATED COMPONENTS:
Branch conductor /leg                 N/A
Branch manifold fitting /leg          N/A
Branch cond equiv ftg lg /leg (in)    N/A
Quick disconnect model /leg           N/A
In line flow control model /leg                  3FC2B     3FC2B
Main conductor              3/8" metal tube 72" long with 0.0 elbow(s)
Main manifold fitting                 N/A
Main cond equiv ftg lg (in)             0

VALVE ASSEMBLY & ASSOCIATED COMPONENTS:
Description    2 Pos Mk 8 on 1/4 NPT base with ext reg
Fitting                     3/8" - 1/4 NPT STR
Silencer model              N/A

SYSTEM PERFORMANCE TIMES:
Att'n stroke time (sec)                           0.37      0.21
Required stroke time (sec)                        0.37      0.21
Stroke time @ term vel (sec)                      0.17      0.16
Att'n cyclic rate (CPM)              74.25
Required cyclic rate (CPM)           75.00
Cyclic rate @ term vel (CPM)        109.92
System delay time (sec)              0.022
Dwell time after stroke (sec)                     0.15      0.07

SYSTEM INFORMATION:
Required system Cv                                0.58      0.56
Attained system Cv                                0.58      0.58
Att'n system air flow (SCFM)                      12.0      19.9
Att'n branch air vel (400 FPS max)      N/A              N/A
Att'n main air vel (400 FPS max)                   64       122
Att'n % delta p (46% max)                           5        17
% Act. capacity used (75% max)                     58        13
Min pres necessary for ld w/S.F. (PSIG)          62.1      13.4
Air per cycle (SCF)                  0.15
Att'n act leakage cost/yr @ $ 0.30 /KSCF   .62     32        30
Att'n operating air cost/yr @ $ 0.30 /KSCF 778    398       380
Cost /1000 cyc @ att'n times @ $ 20.00 /hr 4.54
Att'n power input total (HP)         2.37

COMMENTS:
Identical to 4-1 except used generous bends to negotiate the 11  90 degree
bends eliminating need to consider them and thus obtain identical results.
```

```
NUMATICS NUMASIZING (R) SUMMARY SHEET                 Date:    04/10/95
NU301EED  Ver 3.01 (c) 1989 Numatics, Inc.           SURVEY # 4-1e
=====================================================================
Prepared for:              Prepared by:     Michael Liberty
Company:                   Company:         Numatics Inc.
Address:                   Address:         1450 N. Milford Rd.
City,State,Zip:            City,State,Zip:  Highland, Mi. 48357
Telephone #                Telephone #      (810) 887-4111
Fax #                      Fax #            (810) 887-9190
---------------------------------------------------------------------
                                               Extend      Retract
Cv DATA PER ACTUATOR

Actuator Fitting Cv                             2.42        2.42
Flow Control Free Flow Cv from Chart            2.86        2.86
Flow Control Adjustable Cv from Chart           2.54        2.54
Flow Control Adjustable Cv Used                 1.65        1.51
Quick Disconnect Cv                             N/A         N/A
Branch Conductor Cv                             N/A         N/A
Additional Cv Due to Elbows in Branch Conductor N/A         N/A
Branch Conductor Manifold Fitting Cv            N/A         N/A

Cv DATA - TOTAL SYSTEM

Actuator Fitting Cv                             2.42        2.42
Flow Control Free Flow Cv from Chart            2.86        2.86
Flow Control Adjustable Cv from Chart           2.54        2.54
Flow Control Adjustable Cv Used                 1.65        1.51
Quick Disconnect Cv                             N/A         N/A
Branch Conductor Cv                             N/A         N/A
Additional Cv Due to Elbows in Branch Conductor N/A         N/A
Branch Conductor Manifold Fitting Cv            N/A         N/A
Main Conductor Cv                               1.28        1.28
Additional Cv Due to Elbows in Main Conductor   N/A         N/A
Main Conductor Manifold Fitting Cv              N/A         N/A
Silencer Cv                                     N/A         N/A
Valve Fitting Cv                                2.14        2.14
Valve Cv                                        0.83        0.83
Sandwich Regulator Cv                           N/A         N/A
Sandwich Speed Control Cv from Chart            N/A         N/A
Sandwich Speed Control Cv Used                  N/A         N/A
Sandwich Check Valve Cv (3 pos valve only)      N/A         N/A


Attained system Cv                              0.58        0.58

Required system Cv                              0.58        0.56

Flow Control Adjustable Cv Suggested            1.50        1.30
Valve Cv Suggested                              0.81        0.79
Sandwich Speed Control Cv Suggested             3.56        2.59
```

```
NUMATICS NUMASIZING (R) SUMMARY SHEET              Date:    04/10/95
NU301EED   Ver 3.01 (c) 1989 Numatics, Inc.        SURVEY # 4-1f
========================================================================
Prepared for:                   Prepared by:    Michael Liberty
Company:                        Company:        Numatics Inc.
Address:                        Address:        1450 N. Milford Rd.
City,State,Zip:                 City,State,Zip: Highland, Mi. 48357
Telephone #                     Telephone #     (810) 887-4111
Fax #                           Fax #           (810) 887-9190
------------------------------------------------------------------------
                                    Avg/Tot/Oth    Extend      Retract
INITIAL CUSTOMER PARAMETERS:
Total weight of load (lbs)                         200.00       30.00
Angle of load from horizontal          90
Coefficient of Friction              0.00
Number of actuators                     1
Total load per actuator (lbs)                      228.45       46.32
Minimum line pressure (PSIG)          100
Design pressure used (PSIG)                         74.5        67.9
Shifts/day (1 shift=120,000 m/yr)     2.0
Cycles per year                  18000000

ACTUATOR:
Description:   Single Rod High Flow Numatics Actuator with 3/8 NPT ports
Bore/stroke/rod            2.50" bore x 3.00" stroke x 0.625" rod
Fitting                          3/8" - 3/8 NPT STR

CONDUCTOR & ASSOCIATED COMPONENTS:
Branch conductor /leg                  N/A
Branch manifold fitting /leg           N/A
Branch cond equiv ftg lg /leg (in)     N/A
Quick disconnect model /leg            N/A
In line flow control model /leg                    NONE        NONE
Main conductor         3/8" metal tube 72" long with 0.0 elbow(s)
Main manifold fitting                  N/A
Main cond equiv ftg lg (in)             0

VALVE ASSEMBLY & ASSOCIATED COMPONENTS:
Description    2 Pos Mk 8 on 1/4 NPT base with ext reg
Fitting                          3/8" - 1/4 NPT STR
Silencer model                   N/A

SYSTEM PERFORMANCE TIMES:
Att'n stroke time (sec)                            0.37         0.21
Required stroke time (sec)                         0.37         0.21
Stroke time @ term vel (sec)                       0.15         0.14
Att'n cyclic rate (CPM)             74.97
Required cyclic rate (CPM)          75.00
Cyclic rate @ term vel (CPM)       116.34
System delay time (sec)             0.022
Dwell time after stroke (sec)                      0.15         0.07

SYSTEM INFORMATION:
Required system Cv                                 0.62         0.61
Attained system Cv                                 0.64         0.64
Att'n system air flow (SCFM)                       11.4         17.7
Att'n branch air vel (400 FPS max)     N/A                N/A
Att'n main air vel (400 FPS max)                   64          120
Att'n % delta p (46% max)                           4           14
% Act. capacity used (75% max)                     62           15
Min pres necessary for 1d w/S.F. (PSIG)            62.1         13.4
Air per cycle (SCF)                  0.13
Att'n act leakage cost/yr @ $ 0.30 /KSCF    55     30           26
Att'n operating air cost/yr @ $ 0.30 /KSCF 713    379          334
Cost /1000 cyc @ att'n times @ $ 20.00 /hr 4.49
Att'n power input total (HP)         2.17

COMMENTS:
Identical to 4-1e except eliminated the use of FC's and used the dual pr
approach instead to achieve the same cylinder performance times.
```

```
NUMATICS NUMASIZING (R) SUMMARY SHEET                    Date:    04/10/95
NU301EED  Ver 3.01 (c) 1989 Numatics, Inc.              SURVEY # 4-1f
==========================================================================
Prepared for:                   Prepared by:    Michael Liberty
Company:                        Company:        Numatics Inc.
Address:                        Address:        1450 N. Milford Rd.
City,State,Zip:                 City,State,Zip: Highland, Mi. 48357
Telephone #                     Telephone #     (810) 887-4111
Fax #                           Fax #           (810) 887-9190
--------------------------------------------------------------------------
                                                     Extend     Retract
Cv DATA PER ACTUATOR

Actuator Fitting Cv                                   2.42       2.42
Flow Control Free Flow Cv from Chart                  N/A        N/A
Flow Control Adjustable Cv from Chart                 N/A        N/A
Flow Control Adjustable Cv Used                       N/A        N/A
Quick Disconnect Cv                                   N/A        N/A
Branch Conductor Cv                                   N/A        N/A
Additional Cv Due to Elbows in Branch Conductor       N/A        N/A
Branch Conductor Manifold Fitting Cv                  N/A        N/A

Cv DATA - TOTAL SYSTEM

Actuator Fitting Cv                                   2.42       2.42
Flow Control Free Flow Cv from Chart                  N/A        N/A
Flow Control Adjustable Cv from Chart                 N/A        N/A
Flow Control Adjustable Cv Used                       N/A        N/A
Quick Disconnect Cv                                   N/A        N/A
Branch Conductor Cv                                   N/A        N/A
Additional Cv Due to Elbows in Branch Conductor       N/A        N/A
Branch Conductor Manifold Fitting Cv                  N/A        N/A
Main Conductor Cv                                     1.28       1.28
Additional Cv Due to Elbows in Main Conductor         N/A        N/A
Main Conductor Manifold Fitting Cv                    N/A        N/A
Silencer Cv                                           N/A        N/A
Valve Fitting Cv                                      2.14       2.14
Valve Cv                                              0.83       0.83
Sandwich Regulator Cv                                 N/A        N/A
Sandwich Speed Control Cv from Chart                  N/A        N/A
Sandwich Speed Control Cv Used                        N/A        N/A
Sandwich Check Valve Cv (3 pos valve only)            N/A        N/A


Attained system Cv                                    0.64       0.64

Required system Cv                                    0.62       0.61

Flow Control Adjustable Cv Suggested                  N/A        N/A
Valve Cv Suggested                                    0.80       0.77
Sandwich Speed Control Cv Suggested                   2.85       2.15
```

# 5

# Conductors

Methods for solving incompressible-fluid problems dealing with cylinders, conductors, fittings, and valves have been available and formalized for some time, going back to the nineteenth century. There is a good deal of documentation and texts to draw on and data that is readily accessible. More recently, approximately at the termination of World War II, in an effort to accomplish standardization, the hydraulics industry, drawing on these informational resources, assigned specific port sizes to cylinder bore diameters. Obviously, since the stroke plays a major role in the selection of a port size (to achieve peak flow vis-à-vis the bore diameter), it was a compromise. Nevertheless, from a practical point of view, this was a giant step forward. The port sizes were established to render optimum flow over a range of stroke lengths, and thus they in turn dictated the conductor size. The pneumatic-cylinder manufacturers did not have this access to compressed-air technology that was available to the hydraulic-cylinder manufacturers for establishing and correlating optimum port sizes to bore diameters and ultimately to conductors. This reverts back to the basic nature of the compressibility problem, which is the bane of the compressed-air industry and a subject that they must continually wrestle with. Thus, what emerged from the pneumatics industry in an effort to emulate the hydraulics industry, in order to gain the corresponding advantages of standardization, was to embrace the authenticated and validated hydraulic specifications for themselves. As related previously, in the overwhelming number of cases, the results are not applicable to pneumatics, rendering erroneous sizes and pressures. Today in pneumatics, this practice of sizing a conductor to fit the hydraulic cylinder port size, which in turn dictates the valve port size and thus the physical valve size, is still the conventional approach. Today's marketplace needs indicate that it should be considered an outdated method because it generates inefficient circuits and unnecessary expenses. To quickly review, not only is the port size in many cases inappropriate for the cylinder bore diameter, but the conductor may be incorrectly sized because it was influenced by the port size. Taking this situation further, by virtue of the conductor size being prescribed, it now directs the valve port size and often the valve $C_v$ as well. This process should not occupy a position in today's pneumatic sizing procedure as there is a logical and analytical approach readily accessible.

[*Note:* A *pneumatic conductor* is any device such as a pipe, tube, or hose, permitting the passage of gas or vapor, which is expressed in scfm; this is very similar to an electrical conductor permitting the passage of electricity, which is expressed in amperes. A hydraulic conductor serves a similar purpose for the hydraulics industry, namely, to accommodate the passage of liquids, which is expressed in gallons per minute (gpm) or cubic feet per minute (cfm).]

There are three major shortcomings with this old technique of using port sizes designed for hydraulic cylinders to be applied to pneumatic cylinders:

1. Even if one has the proper port outlet, it does not guarantee an adequate-size conductor or valve. The possibility of combining an insufficient valve or conductor size with a large port exists. Therefore, it is essential to have a valve and conductor capability tied to a port size. One would not consider the selection for a main subdivision branch line to be a 1-NPT Schedule 40 pipe emanating from a 20-in water main; nor a 1-hp pump supplying the 20-in main. By the same token, it would be unthinkable to have a 200-hp pump supplying an individual subscriber via a required 1½-NPT pipe. I've used extremes to accentuate the comparisons, but the incorrectness is just as applicable for closer matings. The point is that a thorough investigation is required to ascertain the proper match. The shortcomings of these disparities hold equally true in pneumatics and are just as crucial. [*Note:* A valve must always have a specified $C_v$ accompanying an explicit port size (discussed in detail in Chap. 6).]

2. Pneumatic layouts, designs, component sizing, and pressure selection require that pneumatic systems or features be extended the same courtesies as mechanical handling systems, electrical distribution systems, hydraulic-line circuit layouts and designs, etc. The main reason why this does not exist in pneumatics is not because the discipline does not warrant the attention but rather there was no interest in developing a system to handle a compressible medium, as there was a presumed analogous hydraulics technology which was thought to be apropos. Thus an entirely groundless procedure emerged along with quick supposed justifiable rules of thumb. These practices must

give way to an obtainable scientific means which examines energy, capital costs, and productivity. These are substantial considerations which are vital today if one is to compete successfully in a world market which has no room for wastefulness.

3. The parallel idea of having an optimum actuator bore applies as well to pinpointing the optimum conductor ID. We have found that there is only one optimum conductor ID for every specified length. Up to the optimal point, as the diameter grows, its $C_v$ increases or improves at a faster pace than its volume, thus enhancing the performance. Beyond the optimal point, similar to a cylinder's loss of performance, the $C_v$ increases at a slower pace than the volume, thereby reducing its performance and thus adversely affecting cylinder speed. Mathematically, here, too, the resultant performance time is a function of both volume and $C_v$. As the diameter of the conductor grows, its $C_v$ increases, improving the performance time, but by the same token its volume increases as well, which worsens the performance time. So, once again we are involved in this assessment of seeking the one conductor which will render the optimum result.

Let us examine the effects of various valve-cylinder-conductor circuits that are identical in all respects except for different size conductors. The summary of the results is shown in Fig. 5.1.

The same valve having a $C_v$ of 3.5, the same Schedule 40 NPT pipe conductor material having a length of 120 in, and the same extend and retract pressures of 80 psig were used for all Surveys 5-1 to 5-1d, and the optimum fittings were used to mate standard available valve and cylinder ports with the conductors for all these surveys. The only difference between the summaries (Surveys 5-2 to 5-2d) in Fig. 5.2 are the replacement of Schedule 40 pipe ID sizes with approximate equivalent standard rubber hose ID sizes.

As we've stated above, one can readily discern the steady improvement in speed as we approach the apex and then continually worsening beyond this point in both the pipe and hose circuits. In reviewing

| Survey No. | Valve Port | Conductor Size | Conductor I.D. | $f$ | Cylinder Port | $T_e/T_r$ Sec. | $T_t$ Sec. | HP Required | Operating Cost $ |
|---|---|---|---|---|---|---|---|---|---|
| 5–1 | 3/8 NPT | 3/8 NPT | 0.493" | 0.0305 | 1/2 NPT | 0.41/0.34 | 0.75 | 3.54 | 1,254 |
| 5–1a | 1/2 NPT | 1/2 NPT | 0.622" | 0.0285 | 1/2 NPT | 0.36/0.28 | 0.64 | 4.05 | 1,436 |
| 5–1b | 3/4 NPT | 3/4 NPT | 0.824" | 0.0265 | 3/4 NPT | 0.36/0.28 | 0.64 | 4.85 | 1,721 |
| 5–1c | 3/4 NPT | 1 NPT | 1.049" | 0.0248 | 3/4 NPT | 0.41/0.33 | 0.74 | 5.83 | 2,068 |
| 5–1d | 3/4 NPT | 1¼ NPT | 1.380" | 0.0232 | 3/4 NPT | 0.51/0.44 | 0.95 | 7.48 | 2,652 |

Figure 5.1    Effect of NPT conductors on cylinder performance.

| Survey No. | Valve Port | Conductor Size | Conductor I.D. | $f$ | Cylinder Port | $T_e/T_r$ Sec. | $T_t$ Sec. | HP Required | Operating Cost $ |
|---|---|---|---|---|---|---|---|---|---|
| 5-2 | 3/8 NPT | 3/8" | 0.375" | 0.0240 | 1/2 NPT | 0.60/0.56 | 1.16 | 2.94 | 1,043 |
| 5-2a | 1/2 NPT | 1/2" | 0.500" | 0.0228 | 1/2 NPT | 0.43/0.37 | 0.80 | 3.52 | 1,247 |
| 5-2b | 3/4 NPT | 3/4" | 0.750" | 0.0213 | 3/4 NPT | 0.36/0.28 | 0.64 | 4.53 | 1,608 |
| 5-2c | 3/4 NPT | 1" | 1.000" | 0.0203 | 3/4 NPT | 0.40/0.32 | 0.72 | 5.58 | 1,978 |
| 5-2d | 3/4 NPT | 1 1/4" | 1.250" | 0.0198 | 3/4 NPT | 0.47/0.39 | 0.86 | 6.81 | 2,415 |

**Figure 5.2**  Effect of rubber-hose conductors on cylinder performance.

both Figs. 5.1 and 5.2 one also observes a dramatic increase in operating costs as the diameter increases despite the longer stroke times, representing less cycles per year (cost is based on the number of completed cycles performed per year).

Another interesting observation is the difference in total time ($T_t = T_e + T_r$) between pipe and hose of equivalent diameters. The reason for this apparent discrepancy is that the friction factor $f$ is greater for the pipe than it is for the hose as the interior surface is rougher. The rougher the surface, the larger the $f$ value and the slower the air speed.

Let us therefore explore and analyze the particulars of the friction factor $f$ of the internal surface communicating with the flowing air molecules in order to assess the meaning, function, and significance of it, since this was another vital feature necessary to complete our jigsaw puzzle. We will derive $f$ by using an approximation and a traditional method. We felt that the traditional approach is the more appropriate method to use for our purposes since it renders more conservative results. First, let me start with some important terms and their definitions:

$\varepsilon$ = absolute roughness factor of the internal diameter of the conductor; it depends on the type and age of the material and is expressed in feet—it is essentially a variation in height describing the roughness of the surface

$d$ = conductor diameter, expressed in inches

$D$ = conductor diameter, expressed in feet

$\varepsilon/D$ = relative roughness which relates the internal surface conditions $\varepsilon$ to the diameter $D$

Assume a $\frac{1}{2}$-NPT Schedule 40 pipe having an ID ($d$) of 0.622 in or a $D$ of 0.052 ft. The roughness factor $\varepsilon$ for relatively new Schedule 40 pipe is 0.00015 ft, as taken from the L. F. Moody chart dealing with relative roughness factors for new clean pipe as shown in Fig. 5.3.

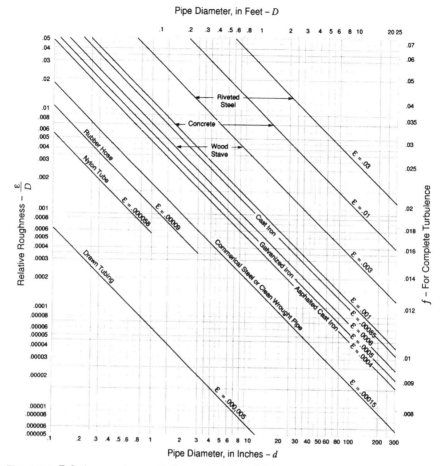

**Figure 5.3**  Relative roughness of pipe materials and friction factors for complete turbulence. (*Source: L. F. Moody, "Friction Factors for Pipe Flow," ASME Transactions,* **66,** *671–677, Nov. 1944.*)

(*Note:* The term *pipe* in this context is intended to include various materials and is not restricted to wrought-iron pipe. Using the term *pipe* to express both the specific and the general classification was rather confusing, and therefore we currently use the term *conductor* for the general grouping and retained the commonly used term *pipe* for the specific category.)

We augmented the chart in Fig. 5.3 with the introduction of two new conductors to the existing categories which were not in common use in pneumatic circuits by American Industry, if at all, in 1944 when the graphs were drawn. Rubber hose and plastic tubing (nylon, polyethylene, polyurethane, etc.) are widely used in industry today and therefore should be accorded their rightful place among conductors. We gathered some empirical data on these materials by comparing their results to commercial steel (wrought pipe) and drawn tubing and found that both are nearer to the roughness figures for commercial steel, with the rubber hose being the closer neighbor. We also expanded the chart to include conductors down to a $d$ of 0.062 in, as the overwhelming quantity of pneumatic appliances operating today require <1-in conductors. Today conductors having internal diameters of $\geq 1$ in are intended primarily, but not exclusively, for subdistribution trunk lines supplying the <1-in conductors. The relative roughness $\varepsilon/D$ for our example of $\frac{1}{2}$ NPT was 0.00015/0.052 = 0.00289. Using this same L. F. Moody chart (Fig. 5.3) will render an $f$ value of 0.026 for an $\varepsilon/D$ of 0.00289 and a $d$ of 0.622 in. Essentially a similar result of 0.027 is extracted by using Fig. 5.4 for a relative roughness factor of 0.00289.

Figure 5.4 is an approximation for it takes into account only a limited number of factors, keeping many variable properties constant. To include these other elements into the calculations, one must introduce into the discussion the Reynolds number (Re), which is a dimensionless entity established to correlate the following four factors:

1. Conductor ID given in feet, as used above = $D$

2. Velocity of flow, expressed in ft/s = $v$

3. Fluid density ($\rho$) given in pounds force (lbf)•$s^2$/ft$^4$ or slugs/ft$^3$ (a *slug* is stated in lbf•$s^2$/ft)

4. Fluid viscosity, expressed as absolute or dynamic viscosity ($\mu$) and kinematic viscosity ($\nu$)

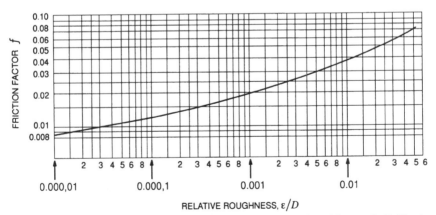

**Figure 5.4**   Friction factors for fully developed turbulent pipe flow. (*Source: L. F. Moody, "Friction Factors for Pipe Flow," ASME Transactions, 66, 671–677, Nov. 1944.*)

The *kinematic viscosity* is defined as the dynamic viscosity divided by density or $v = \mu/\rho$. The *dynamic viscosity* is expressed in lbf•s/ft$^2$ or slugs/ft•s. The kinematic viscosity is therefore expressed in square feet per second when substituting the proper terms. Combining the four constituents of the Reynolds number renders the following equation:

$$\text{Re} = \frac{Dv\rho}{\mu} \quad \text{or} \quad \frac{Dv}{v}$$

We saw earlier that the specific weight of one standard cubic foot of air, at 68°F and sea-level pressure and humidity conditions, is 0.076 lbf/ft$^3$ ($w$). To obtain the density $\rho$, this number must be divided by the acceleration due to gravity $g$, namely, 32.2 ft/s$^2$ for a result of 0.00236 lbf•s$^2$/ft$^4$ or slugs/ft$^3$.

The graph in Fig. 5.5 indicates an absolute viscosity of $0.375 \times 10^{-6}$ for air functioning under standard conditions. For those preferring to use kinematic viscosity, Fig. 5.6 indicates it to be approximately $1.4 \times 10^{-4}$ when applying a logarithmic scale to read the graph. To prove the result, we will solve for $v$ by using the formula $v = \mu/\rho$ and compare the result to $1.4 \times 10^{-4}$:

$$\frac{\mu}{\rho} = 0.375 \times 10^{-6}/0.00233 = 160 \times 10^{-6} = 1.6 \times 10^{-4}$$

The correlation is not very good because it is rather difficult to read the graph since it is based on a logarithmic scale. Interestingly, if we would read the graph linearly, we would be much closer to the $1.6 \times 10^{-6}$. There is no need for concern, for the difference will barely affect the ultimate goal of determining an $f$ factor, as we soon shall see. We use the viscosity figure to determine an Re and then enter it along with the relative roughness factor into the Moody diagram to extract the $f$ factor. You will shortly observe that the results are very flat, and thus the supposed large variation has essentially very little influence on the $f$ value eventually arrived at.

From all our experience and collected data, in order to simplify the calculations, we use an average $f$ for each conductor diameter within a material classification based on a velocity ranging from 100 to 400 ft/s. This is the range of velocities that can be encountered for the relatively small conductors with which the industry is confronted downstream of the valve (as stated earlier, to be in the <1-in size grouping). I have heard a recommendation often repeated by various compressed-air specialists, namely, that if one encounters velocities over 400 ft/s, it is wise to go to the next-larger-size conductor in order to reduce the compressed-air speed. It is felt that any velocity over the 400-ft/s ceiling can create undue stresses and disturbances in the lines. We have never seen any substantiation for this criterion nor encountered any

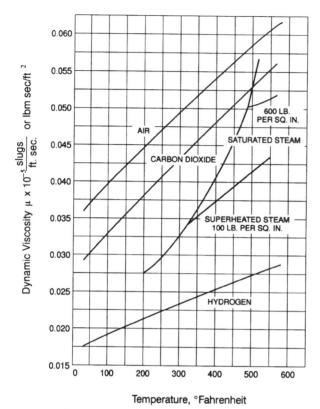

Temperature, °Fahrenheit

**Figure 5.5**  Dynamic (absolute) viscosities or internal friction of gases (English units). [*Sources: Data for steam from G. A. Hawkins, H. L. Solberg, and A. A. Potter, "The Viscosity of Superheated Steam," ASME Transactions, 26(8), 677, 1940. Other data adapted from M. Jakob and S. Erk, Der Chemic-Ingenieur, Akademische Verlagsgesellschaft and M. B. H., Leipzig, 1933, vol. 1, part 1, p. 73.*]

problems nor conducted any investigations, and thus, for lack of any other standard, we use these same velocity yardsticks throughout the pneumatic circuits for all sizes of conductors that we recommend. Upstream of the valve these velocities are seldom reached, and thus this rule renders very conservative trunk lines (rarely venturing beyond the 2½-NPT size) which supply the valve distribution network. The mains supplying the trunks are planned, as are the trunks, to accommodate the demand, length of runs, pressure drops, and velocity specifications, and therefore here, too, the designs render very conservative results. The mains can range up to approximately 12-NPT pipe; however, the bulk of the industrial compressed-air involvement is confined to conductors having an internal diameter of 2.5 in or less.

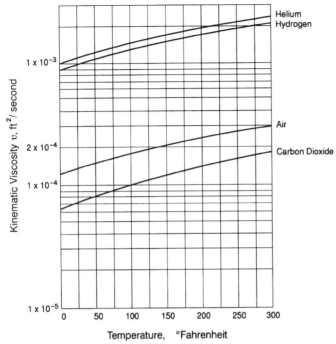

**Figure 5.6**  Kinematic viscosities of several gases, English units (atmospheric pressure).

The range of $f$ values for the 100- to 400-ft/s bandwidth for any specific conductor size and material we normally use was extremely narrow for the smaller conductors (<1 in). For the larger conductors (1 to $2\frac{1}{2}$ in) the variation was insignificant even when taken to three decimal places. The tabular data that we developed is taken to four decimal places. The method used to generate the $f$ factors for these tables was to calculate the Reynolds numbers for velocities from 0 to 600 ft/s for every size of the five material categories investigated in increments of 10 ft/s. Once we determined the Re we consulted the Moody chart to determine the $f$ factor. The $f$ factor leveled at slightly over 300 ft/s for the small diameters, and as the diameters increased, the plateau height continually decreased. In order to obtain the most conservative figures, we averaged the $f$ factors from 100 to 400 ft/s.

Let us run an example to indicate the method employed to create the database for the tables we use. We continue with our example of a $\frac{1}{2}$-NPT pipe having a $D$ of 0.052 ft. The average $f$ from the data that we use is 0.0285, and it corresponds to a velocity $v$ of 140 ft/s. The density $\rho$ is 0.00233 slugs/ft³, and $\mu$ equals $0.375 \times 10^{-6}$ ft/s. By using this information, we should return to an $f$ value of 0.0285:

$$\text{Re} = \frac{0.052 \times 140 \times 0.00233}{0.375 \times 10^{-6}} = 45{,}200$$

Since gas viscosities are frequently stated in centipoise $\mu_c$ (cP) and conductor diameters in inches $d$, the following equation for Re may be more useful:

$$\text{Re} = \frac{123.9 dvw}{\mu_c}$$

where $\mu_c = 0.018$ centipoise (Fig. 5.7) for air at 68°F. Substituting 0.622 in for $d$, 140 ft/s for $v$, 0.076 lbf/ft³ for $w$, and 0.018 for $\mu_c$, we obtain the following for Re:

$$\frac{123.9 \times 0.622 \times 140 \times 0.076}{0.018} = 45{,}500$$

which is essentially the same number of 45,200 as above, and rightly so.

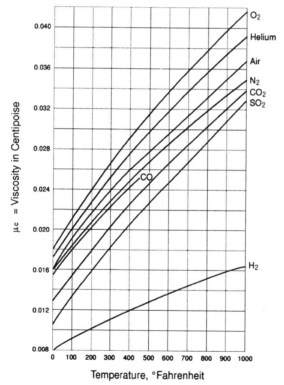

**Figure 5.7**  Viscosity of various gases. (*Source: Crane Co. Technical Paper no. 410, 1982.*)

The precision with which one can read the $f$ factor on the Moody chart (Fig. 5.8) does not allow for accurate readings beyond the third decimal place. In fact, even a 10 percent variation in the Reynolds number will not affect the reading of the $f$ factor when taken to three decimal places.

*Item:* An additional conversion that is useful is the constant for converting dynamic viscosity expressed in $lbf/ft^2$ (slugs/ft•s) to centipoise. There are $2.088 \times 10^{-5}$ lbf•s/ft$^2$ or slugs/ft•s to one centipoise. Applying the conversion to our case transforms 0.018 cP to $0.376 \times 10^{-6}$ slugs/ft•s. We used $0.375 \times 10^{-6}$ slugs/ft•s, which, as explained previously, is quite good for the reading of these charts.

We will now enter Fig. 5.8 and see how well we compare to the $f$ of 0.027 that we had from our simple chart readings of either Fig. 5.3 or 5.4 (determined previously, which did not consider all aspects) as well as how close we come to the 0.0285 we utilize.

The 0.0285 number that this method (Fig. 5.8) produces is the one that is entered and employed in our tables. Again this is based on the compressed-air speed through the conductor to be 140 ft/s. The number is slightly larger than the $f = 0.027$ and therefore renders slower cylinder speeds than can be expected, thus generating more conservative results for a greater safety factor. This is precisely why we use this approach, and the sample table in Fig. 5.9 illustrates this very well, where the $f$ factor for the ½-NPT pipe is 0.0285.

Using the suggested maximum allowable of 400 ft/s and going through the same ritual an Re of 128,000 will result in an $f$ of 0.027. Again, since we use 0.0285, we will benefit by erring on the conservative side as we use 0.0285 across the board. The reason for this will be evident when we recap the formulas for the $C_v$ of a conductor using an $l$ of 1200 in for an $f$ of both 0.027 and 0.0285 and tie that in with their respective velocities, $Q$ (flow in scfm) and $\Delta p$ values. Let us not forget that a $C_v$, whether used independently or in concert with other $C_v$ values, the smaller the $C_v/C_{vs}$ we calculate the device or devices to be, the less air it or they can transport to the actuator and therefore the slower the actuator speed will be. Generally conductor air speeds under 140 ft/s generate relatively slow actuator speeds and thus have very little significance in that area. We therefore arrived at an $f$ which would be useful without penalizing our selection too greatly.

Let us also review some of these formulas which we have thus far derived and utilized to note their interrelationships and how we make use of them.

$$Q = 0.489 C_v p_{1a}$$

($Q$ in scfm; maximum flow without any obstructions or resistance and emptying into a container without any backpressure—flowing at criti-

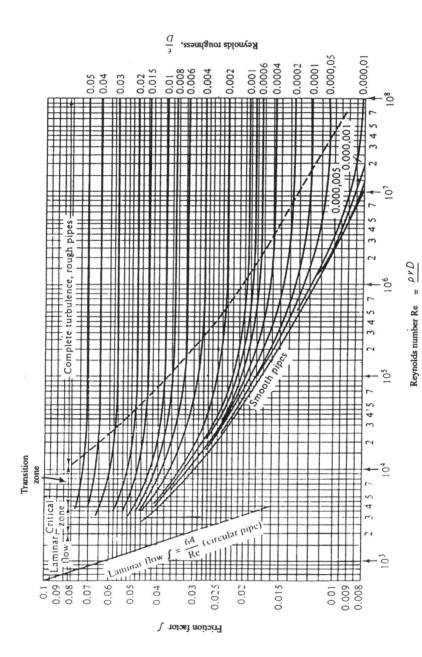

**Figure 5.8** Friction factors for pipe flow. (*Adapted from L. F. Moody, "Friction Factors for Pipe Flow," Transactions ASME, **68**, 672, 1944.*)

168

| Conductor Size | Material | ID | $f$ | K Value |
|---|---|---|---|---|
| 1/8 NPT | Pipe | 0.269 | 0.0365 | 2.5 |
| 1/4 NPT | Pipe | 0.364 | 0.0333 | 2.5 |
| 3/8 NPT | Pipe | 0.493 | 0.0305 | 2.5 |
| 1/2 NPT | Pipe | 0.622 | 0.0285 | 2.5 |
| 3/4 NPT | Pipe | 0.824 | 0.0265 | 2.5 |
| 1 NPT | Pipe | 1.049 | 0.0248 | 2.5 |
| 1-1/4 NPT | Pipe | 1.380 | 0.0232 | 2.5 |
| 1-1/2 NPT | Pipe | 1.610 | 0.0223 | 2.5 |
| 2 NPT | Pipe | 2.067 | 0.0211 | 2.5 |
| 2-1/2 NPT | Pipe | 2.469 | 0.0202 | 2.5 |
| 1/8" | Metal Tube | 0.069 | 0.0359 | 3.5 |
| 3/16" | Metal Tube | 0.131 | 0.0301 | 3.5 |
| 1/4" | Metal Tube | 0.180 | 0.0278 | 3.5 |
| 5/16" | Metal Tube | 0.249 | 0.0257 | 3.5 |
| 3/8" | Metal Tube | 0.305 | 0.0245 | 3.5 |
| 7/16" | Metal Tube | 0.368 | 0.0234 | 3.5 |
| 1/2" | Metal Tube | 0.430 | 0.0226 | 3.5 |
| 5/8" | Metal Tube | 0.555 | 0.0213 | 3.5 |
| 3/4" | Metal Tube | 0.652 | 0.0206 | 3.5 |
| 7/8" | Metal Tube | 0.777 | 0.0199 | 3.5 |
| 1" | Metal Tube | 0.902 | 0.0193 | 3.5 |
| 1-1/4" | Metal Tube | 1.152 | 0.0183 | 3.5 |
| 1-1/2" | Metal Tube | 1.370 | 0.0177 | 3.5 |
| 2" | Metal Tube | 1.870 | 0.0166 | 3.5 |
| 1/8" | Nylon Tube | 0.080 | 0.0360 | 3.0 |
| 5/32" | Nylon Tube | 0.106 | 0.0331 | 3.0 |
| 3/16" | Nylon Tube | 0.125 | 0.0317 | 3.0 |
| 1/4" | Nylon Tube | 0.180 | 0.0288 | 3.0 |
| 5/16" | Nylon Tube | 0.232 | 0.0270 | 3.0 |
| 3/8" | Nylon Tube | 0.275 | 0.0258 | 3.0 |
| 1/2" | Nylon Tube | 0.375 | 0.0240 | 3.0 |
| 1/8" | Polyethylene Tube | 0.085 | 0.0342 | 3.5 |
| 5/32" | Polyethylene Tube | 0.106 | 0.0322 | 3.5 |
| 3/16" | Polyethylene Tube | 0.127 | 0.0305 | 3.5 |
| 1/4" | Polyethylene Tube | 0.170 | 0.0290 | 3.5 |
| 5/16" | Polyethylene Tube | 0.188 | 0.0282 | 3.5 |
| 3/8" | Polyethylene Tube | 0.250 | 0.0260 | 3.5 |
| 1/2" | Polyethylene Tube | 0.375 | 0.0243 | 3.5 |
| 1/8" | Urethane Tube | 0.063 | 0.0361 | 3.5 |
| 1/4" | Urethane Tube | 0.125 | 0.0305 | 3.5 |
| 5/16" | Urethane Tube | 0.188 | 0.0260 | 3.5 |

**Figure 5.9** Friction factors for various materials and diameters. (*Source: Numasizing Manual, Numatics, Inc., 1993.*)

cal flow). One obvious possibility is if the container is the atmosphere, which is not the case when air is coursing down a conductor supplying a pneumatic appliance. It should be borne in mind, however, that there can exist a combination of valve, conductor, and a gravity-assisted unloaded cylinder, traveling unusually fast or having an extensive stroke, that can experience over the entire circuit a zero-backpressure condition, causing critical flow. The cylinder in the course of its travel, under these conditions, is moving faster than the inrushing air, thereby experiencing a lower pressure than the initial starting pressure, generating in extreme cases the equivalent of air expelling to atmosphere. This was briefly described in Chap. 3. However, in the overwhelming majority of cases for a conductor supplying even an unloaded cylinder, within even a smoothly drawn conductor, there still is a modicum of resistance or backpressure preventing the attainment of critical flow. We must therefore use the more general form of the equation which follows. [Note: The general condensed basic expression for noncritical vs. critical flow as covered in Chap. 2 was given as $Q = 0.978 \times C_{vs}(\Delta pp_{2a})^{0.5}$ ($Q$ in scfm) at standard sea-level conditions of temperature, humidity, and atmospheric pressure. For the derivation of the complete equation containing all the variables, see Chap. 2.]

By rearranging the terms and solving for the eligible answer to the quadratic equation formed from the general flow formula, we have

$$\frac{Q^2}{0.9565(C_{vs})^2} = \Delta pp_{2a}$$

($Q$ here and in the following equations and text is expressed in scfm unless indicated otherwise). Since $p_{2a} = p_{1a} - \Delta p$ (see Chap. 2), the equation will now read

$$\Delta p(p_{1a} - \Delta p) = \frac{Q^2}{0.9565(C_{vs})^2}$$

Grouping the terms and arranging them into the quadratic form yields the following:

$$\Delta p^2 - p_{1a}\Delta p + \frac{Q^2}{0.9565(C_{vs})^2} = 0$$

The quadratic form reads $aX^2 + bX + c = 0$, and we will substitute in our equation $\Delta p$ for $X$ and therefore $a = 1$, $b = -p_{1a}$, and $c = Q^2/0.9565(C_{vs})^2$.

Solving the quadratic equation provides two solutions, of which only the negative term is applicable. The other argument or positive term does not apply as a real or true answer is not rendered by its use:

$$\Delta p = \frac{p_{1a} \pm [(p_{1a})^2 - 4.18(Q/C_{vs})^2]^{0.5}}{2}$$

and finally

$$\Delta p = \frac{p_{1a} - [(p_{1a})^2 - 4.18(Q/C_{vs})^2]^{0.5}}{2}$$

We will now introduce the standard equation $Q = Av$ (where $Q$ is in ft³/min and $v$ is in ft/min) for relating these three variables so as to be able to investigate the velocity of air. This is a convenient equation for it furnishes us with a means for determining whether we are within the permissible limits.

In the equation $Q = Av$, $A$ is the cross-sectional area expressed in square feet, $Q$ is the flow expressed in cfm (ft³/min), and $v$ is the velocity expressed in ft/min. Since our objective is to have $v$ expressed in ft/s and $Q$ expressed in scfm, the constant 60 is required, and we must also insert the number of atmospheres as $Q$ must be stated in scfm, rendering the final form of the equation to be:

$$Q = Av60p_{1a}/14.7 = 4.08Avp_{1a}$$

($Q$ in scfm; $v$ in ft/s). This now represents all the variables in the terms we have traditionally been using.

Let us continue with the use of the ½-NPT Schedule 40 pipe and observe the pressure drops $\Delta p$ under various conditions. Assume the pressure $p_{1a}$ to be 114.7 psia (100 psig) and again the length to be 1200 in (100 ft). As above, $C_{vs} = 33.2d^2(d/fl)^{0.5}$, and in this case since we are dealing only with the conductor, the $C_{vs}$ is equal to the conductor $C_v$:

$$C_v = 33.2(0.622)^2(0.622/0.0285 \times 1200)^{0.5} = 1.73$$

resulting in an $f$ of 0.0285 and 1.78 for an $f$ of 0.027.

$$A = \frac{0.7854(0.622)^2}{144} = 0.0021 \text{ ft}^2$$

Having all the ingredients, let us explore two velocities, namely, 140 ft/s, which is an average for tubing of this diameter, and 400 ft/s, which is extraordinarily high in addition to being the maximum allowable. We will observe the effect on the pressure drops by folding in the two $C_v$ values generated by the $f$ factors of 0.027 and 0.0285. We can then clearly determine how much of an added built-in safety factor we have due to this $f$ aspect alone: $Q = 4.08Av114.7$ or 137.6 scfm for 140 ft/s and 393.3 scfm for 400 ft/s.

It is wise at this time to apply the formula for critical flow, even though it is quite remote, to determine whether these velocities are feasible.

The maximum $Q$ (in scfm) = $0.488C_v p_{1a}$; $Q$ = $0.488 \times 1.73 \times 114.7$ = 97.1 scfm, which translates into a maximum velocity through this 100-ft length of conductor of 98.3 ft/s. With a $C_v$ of 1.78, the $Q$ becomes 99.8 scfm and the maximum velocity becomes 101.0 ft/s. On the basis of these figures it would not be possible to achieve 140 ft/s, much less 400 ft/s, and therefore to traverse 100 ft it would take, for the smaller $C_v$ of 1.73, 1.02 s (100/98.3); and for the larger $C_v$ of 1.78, it would take 0.99 s (100/101.0). Let us close the loop by tying in other variables to verify that we demonstrate similar results.

The volume for the 100-ft length is equal to the area multiplied by the length or 0.0021 ft$^2$ × 100 ft or 0.211 ft$^3$. The compressed volume expanded to scf is 0.211 multiplied by 114.7/14.7 (7.8 atm) or 1.65 scf. Thus, the flow rate $Q$ for the 0.99-s travel time would be (1.65 × 60)/0.99 or 100 scfm, which compares favorably with the 99.8 scfm farrived at earlier. Variations are all due to rounding. The flow rate for the other velocity or travel time when applying the same reasoning becomes (1.65 × 60)/1.02 = 97.0 scfm, which, again due to rounding, is still very close to the above derived figure of 97.1 scfm.

Now let us evaluate the pressure drops and how they are impacted by the other properties to determine whether this flow is possible:

$$\Delta p = \frac{p_{1a} - [(p_{1a})^2 - 4.18(Q/C_v)^2]^{0.5}}{2}$$

Substituting the $Q$ terms (97.1 and 99.8 scfm) for each of the two velocities (98.3 and 101.0 ft/s) and the $C_v$ terms (1.73 and 1.78) for their respective $f$ factors (0.0285 and 0.027) renders the following $\Delta p$ values. When using the conservative $f$ of 0.0285 with either of the flow rates, we obtain a negative number which indicates that it is impossible to reach the flow under these conditions and thus a larger diameter must be used. When using the smaller $f$ of 0.027, we obtain positive answers of 44- and 55-psi $\Delta p$ values, respectively, for the two flows and therefore can be construed as a valid conductor to use. In reviewing the 55 psi $\Delta p$ result we find it to be 48%, and since the maximum is 46.7% it can be no more than 53.6 psi. As a result, our flow can only reach 99.6, and not the stated 99.8 scfm. This represents a minor variation but nonetheless a present one. In any event for any $Q$ (scfm) we should obviously experience a greater pressure drop with an $f$ of 0.0285 than we do for an $f$ of 0.027.

It seems quite apparent that the flows and velocities we have chosen to investigate for this diameter and conductor are borderline choices depending on one's conservatism. Let us therefore select some velocities and attendant flows that are readily attainable to see the impact of the two different $f$ factors.

Assume at the end of the same conductor we now require a flow of only 50 scfm, which is somewhat more feasible. Knowing $Q$ and $A$, we can solve for $v$:

$$v = \frac{Q \times 14.7}{114.7 \times 60 \times A} = \frac{50 \times 14.7}{114.7 \times 60 \times 0.0021} = 50.6 \text{ ft/s}$$

The $\Delta p$ from this equation becomes 8.2 psi for a $C_v$ of 1.73 ($f$ of 0.0285) and 7.7 psi for a $C_v$ of 1.78 ($f$ of 0.027). The variation is approximately 6 percent. If we had a specified maximum of 8.00 psi for a required flow of 50 scfm, we would have been undersized with the $\frac{1}{2}$-NPT pipe by using the smaller $f$ factor. It bears repeating that we do not necessarily limit the $\Delta p$ in any of the lines downstream of the valve. The only ceiling we impose is on the air velocity, which should not exceed 400 ft/s. I said "not necessarily" because velocity is a direct function of a pressure drop, and since we monitor the velocity, we indirectly monitor the $\Delta p$. In other words, a critical flow $\Delta p$ may be reached without the velocity attaining 400 ft/s. Obviously the limiting factor was not the 400-ft/s velocity. However, if the reverse condition exists where the 400-ft/s velocity is reached and we are below critical flow, even if the $\Delta p$ is as high as 40 psi with a $p_{1a}$ of 100 psig for a percentage of 35 [40/(100 + 14.7)], it is still perfectly permissible. The critical flow is reached when $\Delta p$ is approximately 47 percent, as we've discussed in an earlier chapter. The third possibility is where both limits are reached, and obviously that is acceptable, also. The point again is that the only limitation is the velocity, and if the velocity allows one to reach critical flow, then that is quite acceptable. However, when we deal with supply lines (trunks and mains) to valves and machines, we must apply different bench marks so that the 8-psi $\Delta p$ may very well be a proper limiting specification (we will discuss supply lines shortly) in addition to having to invoke the maximum velocity limit. In many cases when dealing with supply lines upstream of the valve, the maximum specified $\Delta p$ is reached well before the maximum velocity limitation is reached, which is generally just the opposite for the conductor downstream of the valve which bridges the valve to the actuator. To return to our original point of assessing $\Delta p$ values, the same reasoning and equivalent conclusions obviously apply for any flow.

The mathematicians can obviously see that it is not necessary to involve all the figures to arrive at the final results. The only relationships to be considered are the squares of the $C_v$ values to arrive at the percent variation, for they are the only variables: $(1.73)^2/(1.78)^2 = 94$ percent, or the two results vary by approximately 6 percent and thus obtain the same result.

Let us now travel upstream of the valve to its mated conductor, called either a *drop* or a *trunk,* and investigate the criteria for its selection. This conductor bridges the span between the valve and the main supply line or header. Since both of these conductors are upstream of the valve, we use the same yardstick for their selection. Unlike the conductor between the valve and the actuator, the line supplying the valve never has to be emptied and filled every cycle of the actuator; therefore, it could be as large as possible and ideally have a negligible $\Delta p$. From a realistic point of view that is not practical, and therefore specific pragmatic limits are imposed. We suggest a maximum of 2 psi for a $\Delta p$ in supply lines, but economics dictate otherwise, for in some cases companies will permit 5 psi and in some rare circumstances even 10 psi. Let us reevaluate the same conductor except this time consider its location to be upstream of the valve rather than downstream, where it can be viewed as a supply reservoir for the circuit. Let us invoke the 2-psi criterion for this conductor reservoir and determine the $Q$ (in scfm) and $v$ (in ft/s) using the two different $f$ factors:

$$C_v = \begin{cases} 1.73 & (f = 0.0285) \\ 1.78 & (f = 0.027) \end{cases}$$

Since $\Delta p$ is 2 psi, then $p_{2a}$ equals 112.7 psia (114.7 − 2).

The flow equation reads $Q = 0.978C_v(\Delta p p_{2a})^{0.5}$, where $Q = 25.4$ scfm for the larger, rougher $f$ and 26.1 scfm for the smaller, smoother $f$ factor. Again by utilizing the larger $f$, we arrive at a more conservative figure for what we can expect and use for determining velocities. The area $a$ is traditionally expressed in in² and not in ft² ($A$) as we've been using, and therefore the equation for velocity should be altered to reflect that change and would read as follows:

$$v = \frac{Q \times 144}{4.08(ap_{1a})} \times 144 = \frac{35.3Q}{ap_{1a}}$$

($v$ in ft/s). We make one additional alteration to this equation to more closely simulate actual flow and that is to use $p_{2a}$ rather than $p_{1a}$. In this way it more accurately reflects the flow at the end of the conductor after the pressure has experienced its drop of $\Delta p$, thereby rendering a slightly larger velocity and requiring the selection of a larger conductor (reflective of our suggested conservative approach to sizing). Up to this point we've been performing the calculations with the higher pressure $p_{1a}$, but from here on we will alter our approach and use the lower pressure $p_{2a}$ as this is indicative of what we normally suggest:

$$v = 35.3Q/ap_{2a} = 26.2 \text{ ft/s}$$

for the 0.0385 $f$ as opposed to 25.7 if we used the higher pressure of
114.7 psia. The results for the smaller 0.027 $f$ factor render a $v$ of 26.9
ft/s for the 0.027 $f$ as opposed to 26.4 ft/s if we used the higher pressure of 114.7 psia. The differences are not dramatic, but the approach
is consistent with our philosophy.

The Reynolds number also serves to determine whether the flow is
laminar or turbulent or some critical or transition zone in between.
As is seen in Fig. 5.7, laminar flow is present up to a Reynolds number of 2000, where the friction factor $f$ is a function of only Re. The
formula is 64/Re. Between Re 2000 and 4000 lies a critical zone where
flow losses are difficult to predict. If one assumes flow to be turbulent
in this region, the resultant $f$ will render the greatest pressure losses,
thereby supplying conservative results, which we suggest and use.
Within an Re range of 4000 to 10,000 at start (see dotted line in Fig.
5.8), depending on the relative roughness ratio, lies a transition zone
where we apply the same line of reasoning as we do to the critical
zone to again render the conservative results we desire. This zone lies
partially in the turbulent zone but is not completely turbulent. Beyond an Re of 10,000 at start (see dotted line in Fig. 5.8) lies again a
region where the $f$ factor is predictable and is called the *complete turbulent zone*. The use of compressed air in the size of conductors and
pressures that industry uses will invariably render a Reynolds number that will fall in the turbulent region. A Reynolds number of 10,000
or less is the area that the mechanical air-handling designers are
more apt to encounter as the velocities are justifiably lower. Some distinctions are appropriate here:

*Laminar flow* is characterized by streamline concentric cylindrical
layers of fluid (in this case, a gas) flowing past one another in an
orderly fashion without any overlapping to cause any disturbances.
The velocity is greatest at the center of the conductor and decreases
sharply to zero at the wall or boundary layer. Laminar flow is also
known as *viscous, steady,* or *streamline flow.*

*Turbulent flow* is an irregular random movement of fluid particles
across the main stream without an observable frequency or pattern.
The velocity distribution over the cross section is more uniform, but
if the wall is smooth, there is always a boundary layer moving in
laminar flow.

The *critical zone* where flow losses cannot be predicted does not
have exact limits and can be defined only. These limits depend
somewhat on conductor roughness and the existence of bends and
fittings. Again in pressure piping practice, which is the area we are
predominantly dealing with, turbulent flow is the normal condition.

Additional background and an excellent treatment of this subject, along with superb photos and analogies, can be gleaned from consulting three excellent references on fluid mechanics.[1-3]

It is abundantly obvious by this time that long line lengths and small diameters are damaging when selecting trunks of mains. The long line lengths may be unavoidable, but the small diameters are not. The guiding principle is that any conductor upstream of the valve should be considered as an accumulator for it does not have to be filled and exhausted each and every cycle. Rules for conductors downstream of the valve follow different paths because they are charged and emptied each and every cycle. In the majority of instances the discharging of the air controls the performance time of the actuator. Thus, as we've also learned, small diameters are not necessarily harmful for valve-to-actuator conductors. The key here is to seek out the optimum diameter which may be smaller than the traditional choice for satisfying one's objective. However, long conductors should be avoided for in this instance they become restrictive.

Let us use a 50-scfm requirement at 100 psig for a 100-ft drop line. We determined earlier that for a $\frac{1}{2}$-NPT Schedule 40 pipe, the consequent pressure drop would be 7.8 psi. This pressure drop would be inappropriate if we had a 2.0-psi suggested requirement for drop lines. We would be confronted with two choices, namely, to reduce the length if we insisted on using $\frac{1}{2}$ NPT, or if we were unable to reduce the length, we would have to increase the conductor size. In this case we can use only Schedule 40 pipe. Let us solve for both possibilities and weigh the solutions with respect to flow, $\Delta p$, velocity, minimum length, diameter, and other parameters.

Let us first determine the minimum diameter to use for a 1200-in (100-ft) length of Schedule 40 pipe conductor which would satisfy the 2-psi $\Delta p$ specification. The next standard size following a $\frac{1}{2}$-NPT conductor is $\frac{3}{4}$ NPT, which has an ID of 0.824 in and an assigned $f$ of 0.0265:

$$p_{1a} = p_1 + 14.7 = 100 + 14.7 = 114.7 \text{ psia}$$

$$p_{2a} = p_{1a} - \Delta p = 114.7 - 2.0 = 112.7 \text{ psia}$$

$$Q = 0.978 C_v (\Delta p p_{2a})^{0.5}; \quad 50 = 0.978 C_v (2 \times 112.47); \quad \text{required } C_v = 3.41$$

[1]B. R. Munson, D. F. Young, and T. H. Okiishi, *Fundamentals of Fluid Mechanics,* John Wiley & Sons, Inc., New York, 1990.

[2]James E. A. John and William L. Haberman, *Introduction to Fluid Mechanics,* Prentice-Hall, Englewood Cliffs, N.J., 1988.

[3]R. C. Binder, *Fluid Mechanics,* Prentice-Hall, New York, 1943.

($Q$ in scfm). We can also solve for $C_v$ using the $\Delta p$ equation (derived from a formula seen earlier in this chapter) for a value of 2 psi, namely

$$\Delta p = \frac{p_{1a} - [(p_{1a})^2 - 4.18(Q/C_v)^2]^{0.5}}{2}; C_v = 3.40$$

(variance from 3.41 above due to rounding; $Q$ in scfm). Then the $C_v$ of the

$$\text{Attained} = \tfrac{3}{4}\text{-NPT} = 33.2d^2\left(\frac{d}{fl}\right)^{0.5};$$

$$C_v = 33.2(0.824)^2\left(\frac{0.824}{0.0265 \times 1200}\right)^{0.5}$$

$$\text{Attained } \tfrac{3}{4}\text{-NPT pipe } C_v = 3.62$$

$$a = 0.533 \text{ in}^2 \text{ for a } \tfrac{3}{4}\text{-NPT Schedule 40 pipe}$$

Our resultant $C_v$ is somewhat larger than required; therefore, the $\Delta p$ will be somewhat less, or

$$\Delta p = \frac{p_{1a} - [(p_{1a})^2 - 4.18(Q/C_v)^2]^{0.5}}{2}$$

$$= \frac{114.7 - [(114.7)^2 - 4.18(50/3.62)^2]^{0.5}}{2} = 1.77 \text{ psi}$$

$$p_{2a} = 114.7 - 1.77 = 112.93$$

($Q$ in scfm). Our velocity $v$ would be $35.3Q/ap_{2a} = (35.3 \times 50)/(0.533 \times 112.93) = 29.3$ ft/s, which is well within the acceptable range.

This essentially is our choice, for it is the next standard available pipe size. If this would not have rendered a solution within the specified window, we would have continued to the next available standard size until we would be successful.

Now let us solve for the longest length possible utilizing the $\frac{1}{2}$-NPT pipe size and maintaining the 2-psi $\Delta p$. We found out earlier that in order to achieve a $\Delta p$ of 2 psi flowing 50 scfm at a $p_{1a}$ of 114.7 psig, a $C_v$ of 3.41 is required. Let us determine now what is the length of $\frac{1}{2}$-NPT pipe that will fulfill those specifications:

$d = 0.622$ in
$f = 0.0285$
$C_v = 33.2d^2(d/fl)^{0.5}; 3.41 = 33.2(0.622)^2(0.622/0.02851)^{0.5}$
$l = 310''$ or $L = 5.8'$

Let us also check on the velocity of the air under these conditions:

$Q = 50$ scfm
$a = 0.303$ in$^2$
$p_{2a} = 112.7$ psia
$v = 35.3Q/ap_{2a} = 35.3 \times 50/0.303 \times 112.7 = 51.7$ ft/s

While we are on the subject of velocity, this is as good a location as any to derive the performance time of a cylinder at terminal velocity. *Terminal velocity,* as we define it, is the fastest possible extend $(T_{ne})$ or retract $(T_{nr})$ performance time that the cylinder can achieve with the specific chosen components regardless of how high a pressure or how small a load is used. In fact, this time assumes that there is absolutely no load, totally frictionless, not even an exhaust-pressure load opposing piston movement. Thus neither the load nor the pressure is a factor in the equation. It is in essence the time necessary to fill a vessel, where all moving parts are excluded. Its purpose is pure and simple. We determine it to establish a benchmark for comparing the customer's requested time to ascertain its feasibility, and if it is beyond, we suggest other options. The resultant performance times in these calculations will thus favor the retract stroke. In the real world the performance times under no outside load conditions will favor the extend stroke because of friction, exhaust-pressure loads, and cross-sectional areas; however, both times will be slower than the ideal calculated performance times. In certain vertical applications where there are gravity-assist outside loads, it is feasible to approach the ideal terminal-velocity stroke times. The time at terminal velocity is therefore strictly a function of total volumetric content (conductor and actuator) and the system's $C_v$. Terminal velocity occurs at critical flow:

$$\text{Critical flow } Q = 0.488 C_{vs} p_{1a} \quad \text{scfm} \quad \text{or} \quad \frac{0.488 C_{vs} p_{1a}}{60} \quad \text{scfs}$$

The performance time at terminal velocity $T_{ne}$ or $T_{nr}$, whichever is the subject of the investigation, is expressed in seconds and equals a constant multiplied by the volume at standard conditions expressed in standard cubic inches (sci) divided by critical flow expressed in standard cubic inches per second (scfs). Or, if it is more convenient, we can express them in standard cubic feet (scf) and standard cubic feet per second (scfs), which will render the same result:

$$T_{n(e \text{ or } r)} = \frac{V_{ft^3} p_{1a}/14.7}{0.488 C_{vs} p_{1a}/60} = \frac{8.36 V_{ft^3}}{C_{vs}} \text{ s} \quad \text{or} \quad T_{ne} = \frac{0.0048 V_{in^3}}{C_{vs}} \text{ s}$$

where $V_{ft^3}$ = volume in cubic feet
$V_{in^3}$ = volume in cubic inches
$V_{in^3} = V_{ft_3}/1728$ in$^2$

In this particular instance it doesn't make any difference whether we consider $p_{1a}$ or $p_{2a}$ as they cancel out. Let us quickly run through an example to verify its worth when confronted with an exceptionally fast stroke time. We will use Survey 4-1 as an example. Assume that the customer requests a valve no larger than a Mk 8 and an extend stroke time of 0.15 s instead of 0.37 s. We would determine that the minimum with a Mk 8 is 0.17 s as indicated in the survey results and review alternatives.

Proof is as follows:

$$\text{Volume of extend stroke} = \left(\frac{\pi d^2}{4}\right)s = \left(\frac{\pi 2.5^2}{4}\right)3 = 14.73 \text{ in}^3$$

$$\text{ID of } \tfrac{3}{8}\text{-in metal tubing} = 0.305 \text{ in}$$

$$\text{Volume of conductor} = \left(\frac{\pi d^2}{4}\right)l = \frac{\pi(0.305^2)}{4} = 5.26 \text{ in}^3$$

$$\text{Total volume} = 19.99 \text{ in}^3$$

$$\text{System } C_v = 0.58$$

$$T_{ne} = \frac{0.00484 V_{in^3}}{C_{vs}} = \frac{0.00484 \times 19.99}{0.58} = 0.17$$

When surveying a facility to determine the size of the header which supplies the various drops stemming from it, one should accumulate the required flows for all the drops and use that as the figure for calculating purposes. If there is a possibility that all drops will not demand air simultaneously, as that is more likely, the experienced pneumatic designer should have supporting data as to the potential usage necessary for each drop and take a percentage of the number of drops for the figure to be used. The plant industrial engineer is an excellent source for acquiring this information.

I've continually referred to the interesting similarities between compressed air and electricity as a source of power, with reference to their properties and behavior. We are obviously all very much aware of their striking differences. What has impressed me was that in a few special instances they are very much alike, and I've attempted to shed light on that restricted area. Perhaps some proponents will in the future embellish on the subject even further. However, at this time I would like to point out two major distinctions between the two as they relate to conductors. Air has mass, and electricity has none. From a practical aspect that means we cannot continue to increase conductor sizes between valves and cylinders ad infinitum for improved performance, whereas in electricity one can with no adverse consequences except cost. The other distinction is the need to be continually cognizant of the effect of bends and sharp elbows in pneumatic circuits because of the dramatic repercussions they can have on the cylinder performance times. Once again, because of the no-mass aspect of electricity, one can have many sharp bends in an electrical circuit with no ill effects. Obviously we try to avoid them, but for reasons other than flow. Electricity has no equivalent concerns in these areas.

In summary, needless conductor lengths, inappropriate diameters, and unessential tight bends (further contributing superfluous equivalent length) can be devastating to the performance time of actuators. Consequently, these presumed minor accessories must be taken into consideration. They contribute to the delay function of the extend/retract time, preventing the actuator piston from initiating its stroke. We have had situations where they accounted for two thirds of the total stroke time. The circuit experiences a dual burden of having increased actual and equivalent length, due to the need to bridge the elbows, and increased volume due to the increased actual length. The increased length reduces the $C_{vs}$, thus impairing stroke time, and the increased volume compounds the felony. The elbows further hinder the stroke time because they represent an additional equivalent (volume not affected) length to contend with. The conductor path should be as straight and as short as possible. Cosmetically, a machine may look better if the conductor follows the contours of the machine (that is questionably, as well), but such arrangements are compressed-air wasters and thus energy wasters depriving the end user of valuable productivity. As stated in previous chapters, since bends are an essential element of every installation, they must be taken into account; however, they should be made as generous as possible so as to have negligible impact on productivity (minimum of 10 × conductor ID).

*"Once a man's mind is stretched by a new
idea it will never return to its old dimension."*
OLIVER WENDELL HOLMES

```
NUMATICS NUMASIZING (R) SUMMARY SHEET                    Date:    04/10/95
NU301EED   Ver 3.01 (c) 1989 Numatics, Inc.             SURVEY # 5-1
========================================================================
Prepared for:                    Prepared by:      Michael Liberty
Company:                         Company:          Numatics Inc.
Address:                         Address:          1450 N. Milford Rd.
City,State,Zip:                  City,State,Zip:   Highland, Mi. 48357
Telephone #                      Telephone #       (313) 887-4111
Fax #                            Fax #             (313)-887-9190
------------------------------------------------------------------------
                                    Avg/Tot/Oth    Extend     Retract
INITIAL CUSTOMER PARAMETERS:
Total weight of load (lbs)                         315.00      45.00
Angle of load from horizontal            9
Coefficient of Friction               0.21
Number of actuators                      1
Total load per actuator (lbs)                      236.24      47.52
Minimum line pressure (PSIG)           100
Design pressure used (PSIG)                         80.0       80.0
Shifts/day (1 shift=120,000 m/yr)      2.0
Cycles per year                    4419980

ACTUATOR:
Description:   Single Rod High Flow Numatics Actuator with 1/2 NPT ports
Bore/stroke/rod            3.25" bore x 12.00" stroke x 1.000" rod
Fitting                    3/8 NPT - 1/2 NPT EL

CONDUCTOR & ASSOCIATED COMPONENTS:
Branch conductor /leg                  N/A
Branch manifold fitting /leg           N/A
Branch cond equiv ftg lg /leg (in)     N/A
Quick disconnect model /leg            N/A
In line flow control model /leg                     NONE        NONE
Main conductor             3/8 NPT pipe 120" long with 2.0 elbow(s)
Main manifold fitting                  N/A
Main cond equiv ftg lg (in)             30

VALVE ASSEMBLY & ASSOCIATED COMPONENTS:
Description      2 Pos Mk 40 on 3/8 NPT base with ext reg
Fitting                    3/8 NPT - 3/8 NPT EL
Silencer model             N/A

SYSTEM PERFORMANCE TIMES:
Att'n stroke time (sec)                             0.41        0.34
Required stroke time (sec)                          0.41        0.34
Stroke time @ term vel (sec)                        0.31        0.29
Att'n cyclic rate (CPM)               18.41
Required cyclic rate (CPM)            18.42
Cyclic rate @ term vel (CPM)          19.35
System delay time (sec)               0.022
Dwell time after stroke (sec)                       1.40        1.10

SYSTEM INFORMATION:
Required system Cv                                  1.98        2.00
Attained system Cv                                  1.89        1.89
Att'n system air flow (SCFM)                        66.1        73.4
Att'n branch air vel (400 FPS max)     N/A                 N/A
Att'n main air vel (400 FPS max)                    156         185
Att'n % delta p (46% max)                            17          23
% Act. capacity used (75% max)                       36           8
Min pres necessary for ld w/S.F. (PSIG)             38.0         8.4
Air per cycle (SCF)                   0.88
Att'n act leakage cost/yr @ $ 0.30 /KSCF             36          54
Att'n operating air cost/yr @ $ 0.30 /KSCF  1164    605         559
Cost /1000 cyc @ att'n times @ $ 20.00 /hr  18.39
Att'n power input total (HP)          3.54

COMMENTS:
```

```
NUMATICS NUMASIZING (R) SUMMARY SHEET                    Date:   04/10/95
NU301EED  Ver 3.01 (c) 1989 Numatics, Inc.              SURVEY # 5-1a
========================================================================
Prepared for:                      Prepared by:     Michael Liberty
Company:                           Company:         Numatics Inc.
Address:                           Address:         1450 N. Milford Rd.
City,State,Zip:                    City,State,Zip:  Highland, Mi. 48357
Telephone #                        Telephone #      (313) 887-4111
Fax #                              Fax #            (313)-887-9190
------------------------------------------------------------------------
                                       Avg/Tot/Oth    Extend    Retract
INITIAL CUSTOMER PARAMETERS:
Total weight of load (lbs)                           315.00      45.00
Angle of load from horizontal              9
Coefficient of Friction                 0.21
Number of actuators                        1
Total load per actuator (lbs)                        271.02      59.53
Minimum line pressure (PSIG)             100
Design pressure used (PSIG)                           80.0       80.0
Shifts/day (1 shift=120,000 m/yr)        2.0
Cycles per year                      4582202

ACTUATOR:
Description:   Single Rod High Flow Numatics Actuator with 1/2 NPT ports
Bore/stroke/rod           3.25" bore x 12.00" stroke x 1.000" rod
Fitting                   1/2 NPT - 1/2 NPT EL

CONDUCTOR & ASSOCIATED COMPONENTS:
Branch conductor /leg                      N/A
Branch manifold fitting /leg               N/A
Branch cond equiv ftg lg /leg (in)         N/A
Quick disconnect model /leg                N/A
In line flow control model /leg                       NONE       NONE
Main conductor            1/2 NPT pipe 120" long with 2.0 elbow(s)
Main manifold fitting                      N/A
Main cond equiv ftg lg (in)                 37

VALVE ASSEMBLY & ASSOCIATED COMPONENTS:
Description    2 Pos Mk 40 on 1/2 NPT base with ext reg
Fitting                                    1/2 NPT - 1/2 NPT EL
Silencer model                             N/A

SYSTEM PERFORMANCE TIMES:
Att'n stroke time (sec)                               0.36       0.28
Required stroke time (sec)                            0.36       0.28
Stroke time @ term vel (sec)                          0.25       0.23
Att'n cyclic rate (CPM)                   19.09
Required cyclic rate (CPM)                19.09
Cyclic rate @ term vel (CPM)              20.10
System delay time (sec)                   0.022
Dwell time after stroke (sec)                         1.40       1.10

SYSTEM INFORMATION:
Required system Cv                                    2.75       2.79
Attained system Cv                                   2.62       2.62
Att'n system air flow (SCFM)                         83.8      101.2
Att'n branch air vel (400 FPS max)         N/A              N/A
Att'n main air vel (400 FPS max)                     119        160
Att'n % delta p (46% max)                             14         22
% Act. capacity used (75% max)                        41         10
Min pres necessary for 1d w/S.F. (PSIG)              43.6       10.6
Air per cycle (SCF)                       0.98
Att'n act leakage cost/yr @ $ 0.30 /KSCF    90        36         54
Att'n operating air cost/yr @ $ 0.30 /KSCF 1346      697        649
Cost /1000 cyc @ att'n times @ $ 20.00 /hr 17.77
Att'n power input total (HP)               4.05

COMMENTS:
```

```
NUMATICS NUMASIZING (R) SUMMARY SHEET                    Date:   04/10/95
NU301EED  Ver 3.01 (c) 1989 Numatics, Inc.              SURVEY # 5-1b
=========================================================================
Prepared for:                      Prepared by:    Michael Liberty
Company:                           Company:        Numatics Inc.
Address:                           Address:        1450 N. Milford Rd.
City,State,Zip:                    City,State,Zip: Highland, Mi. 48357
Telephone #                        Telephone #     (313) 887-4111
Fax #                              Fax #           (313)-887-9190
-------------------------------------------------------------------------
                                    Avg/Tot/Oth     Extend      Retract
INITIAL CUSTOMER PARAMETERS:
  Total weight of load (lbs)                        315.00      45.00
  Angle of load from horizontal         9
  Coefficient of Friction            0.21
  Number of actuators                   1
  Total load per actuator (lbs)                     271.93      60.55
  Minimum line pressure (PSIG)        100
  Design pressure used (PSIG)                        80.0       80.0
  Shifts/day (1 shift=120,000 m/yr)   2.0
  Cycles per year                 4589537

ACTUATOR:
  Description:   Single Rod High Flow Numatics Actuator with 3/4 NPT ports
  Bore/stroke/rod           3.25" bore x 12.00" stroke x 1.000" rod
  Fitting                   3/4 NPT - 3/4 NPT EL

CONDUCTOR & ASSOCIATED COMPONENTS:
  Branch conductor /leg              N/A
  Branch manifold fitting /leg       N/A
  Branch cond equiv ftg lg /leg (in) N/A
  Quick disconnect model /leg        N/A
  In line flow control model /leg                    NONE        NONE
  Main conductor            3/4 NPT pipe 120" long with 2.0 elbow(s)
  Main manifold fitting              N/A
  Main cond equiv ftg lg (in)         49

VALVE ASSEMBLY & ASSOCIATED COMPONENTS:
  Description    2 Pos Mk 40 on 3/4 NPT base with ext reg
  Fitting                   3/4 NPT - 3/4 NPT EL
  Silencer model                     N/A

SYSTEM PERFORMANCE TIMES:
  Att'n stroke time (sec)                            0.36        0.28
  Required stroke time (sec)                         0.36        0.28
  Stroke time @ term vel (sec)                       0.25        0.23
  Att'n cyclic rate (CPM)           19.12
  Required cyclic rate (CPM)        19.12
  Cyclic rate @ term vel (CPM)      20.14
  System delay time (sec)           0.022
  Dwell time after stroke (sec)                      1.40        1.10

SYSTEM INFORMATION:
  Required system Cv                                 3.37        3.40
  Attained system Cv                                 3.20        3.20
  Att'n system air flow (SCFM)                      101.0       125.2
  Att'n branch air vel (400 FPS max)      N/A              N/A
  Att'n main air vel (400 FPS max)                    81         114
  Att'n % delta p (46% max)                           13          23
  % Act. capacity used (75% max)                      41          10
  Min pres necessary for 1d w/S.F. (PSIG)            43.7        10.7
  Air per cycle (SCF)                1.18
  Att'n air leakage cost/yr @ $ 0.30 /KSCF    90      36          54
  Att'n operating air cost/yr @ $ 0.30 /KSCF 1631    839         791
  Cost /1000 cyc @ att'n times @ $ 20.00 /hr 17.81
  Att'n power input total (HP)       4.85

COMMENTS:
```

```
NUMATICS NUMASIZING (R) SUMMARY SHEET                     Date:   04/10/95
NU301EED   Ver 3.01 (c) 1989 Numatics, Inc.             SURVEY # 5-1c
=========================================================================
Prepared for:                    Prepared by:     Michael Liberty
Company:                         Company:         Numatics Inc.
Address:                         Address:         1450 N. Milford Rd.
City,State,Zip:                  City,State,Zip:  Highland, Mi. 48357
Telephone #                      Telephone #      (810) 887-4111
Fax #                            Fax #            (810) 887-9190
-------------------------------------------------------------------------
                                     Avg/Tot/Oth    Extend      Retract
INITIAL CUSTOMER PARAMETERS:
Total weight of load (lbs)                          315.00       45.00
Angle of load from horizontal           9
Coefficient of Friction              0.21
Number of actuators                     1
Total load per actuator (lbs)                       238.57       49.53
Minimum line pressure (PSIG)          100
Design pressure used (PSIG)                          80.0        80.0
Shifts/day (1 shift=120,000 m/yr)     2.0
Cycles per year                   4444444

ACTUATOR:
Description:   Single Rod High Flow Numatics Actuator with 3/4 NPT ports
Bore/stroke/rod             3.25" bore x 12.00" stroke x 1.000" rod
Fitting                     1 NPT - 3/4 NPT EL

CONDUCTOR & ASSOCIATED COMPONENTS:
Branch conductor /leg                   N/A
Branch manifold fitting /leg            N/A
Branch cond equiv ftg lg /leg (in)      N/A
Quick disconnect model /leg             N/A
In line flow control model /leg                     NONE        NONE
Main conductor              1 NPT pipe 120" long with 2.0 elbow(s)
Main manifold fitting                   N/A
Main cond equiv ftg lg (in)             63

VALVE ASSEMBLY & ASSOCIATED COMPONENTS:
Description      2 Pos Mk 40 on 3/4 NPT base with ext reg
Fitting                                 1 NPT - 3/4 NPT EL
Silencer model                          N/A

SYSTEM PERFORMANCE TIMES:
Att'n stroke time (sec)                              0.41        0.33
Required stroke time (sec)                           0.41        0.33
Stroke time @ term vel (sec)                         0.29        0.28
Att'n cyclic rate (CPM)               18.57
Required cyclic rate (CPM)            18.52
Cyclic rate @ term vel (CPM)          19.50
System delay time (sec)               0.022
Dwell time after stroke (sec)                        1.40        1.10

SYSTEM INFORMATION:
Required system Cv                                   3.45        3.47
Attained system Cv                                   3.34        3.34
Att'n system air flow (SCFM)                        112.0       133.2
Att'n branch air vel (400 FPS max)        N/A                N/A
Att'n main air vel (400 FPS max)                      57          76
Att'n % delta p (46% max)                             16          25
% Act. capacity used (75% max)                        36           8
Min pres necessary for 1d w/S.F. (PSIG)              38.3         8.8
Air per cycle (SCF)                   1.48
Att'n act leakage cost/yr @ $ 0.30 /KSCF      90      36          54
Att'n operating air cost/yr @ $ 0.30 /KSCF  1978    1013         966
Cost /1000 cyc @ att'n times @ $ 20.00 /hr 18.41
Att'n power input total (HP)          5.83
```

```
NUMATICS NUMASIZING (R) SUMMARY SHEET              Date:    04/10/95
NU301EED  Ver 3.01 (c) 1989 Numatics, Inc.        SURVEY # 5-1d
=====================================================================
Prepared for:                   Prepared by:    Michael Liberty
Company:                        Company:        Numatics Inc.
Address:                        Address:        1450 N. Milford Rd.
City,State,Zip:                 City,State,Zip: Highland, Mi. 48357
Telephone #                     Telephone #     (810) 887-4111
Fax #                           Fax #           (810) 887-9190
---------------------------------------------------------------------
                                     Avg/Tot/Oth   Extend     Retract
INITIAL CUSTOMER PARAMETERS:
Total weight of load (lbs)                        315.00      45.00
Angle of load from horizontal           9
Coefficient of Friction              0.21
Number of actuators                     1
Total load per actuator (lbs)                    197.37      38.30
Minimum line pressure (PSIG)          100
Design pressure used (PSIG)                       80.0       80.0
Shifts/day (1 shift=120,000 m/yr)     2.0
Cycles per year                   4173913

ACTUATOR:
Description:  Single Rod High Flow Numatics Actuator with 3/4 NPT ports
Bore/stroke/rod          3.25" bore x 12.00" stroke x 1.000" rod
Fitting                  1-1/4 NPT - 3/4 NPT EL

CONDUCTOR & ASSOCIATED COMPONENTS:
Branch conductor /leg              N/A
Branch manifold fitting /leg       N/A
Branch cond equiv ftg lg /leg (in) N/A
Quick disconnect model /leg        N/A
In line flow control model /leg                   NONE       NONE
Main conductor            1-1/4 NPT pipe 120" long with 2.0 elbow(s)
Main manifold fitting              N/A
Main cond equiv ftg lg (in)         83

VALVE ASSEMBLY & ASSOCIATED COMPONENTS:
Description    2 Pos Mk 40 on 3/4 NPT base with ext reg
Fitting                  1-1/4 NPT - 3/4 NPT EL
Silencer model           N/A

SYSTEM PERFORMANCE TIMES:
Att'n stroke time (sec)                           0.51       0.44
Required stroke time (sec)                        0.51       0.44
Stroke time @ term vel (sec)                      0.40       0.39
Att'n cyclic rate (CPM)             17.39
Required cyclic rate (CPM)          17.39
Cyclic rate @ term vel (CPM)        18.26
System delay time (sec)             0.022
Dwell time after stroke (sec)                     1.40       1.10

SYSTEM INFORMATION:
Required system Cv                                3.51       3.50
Attained system Cv                                3.38       3.38
Att'n system air flow (SCFM)                     122.0      137.8
Att'n branch air vel (400 FPS max)   N/A                      N/A
Att'n main air vel (400 FPS max)                   37         47
Att'n % delta p (46% max)                          19         26
% Act. capacity used (75% max)                     30          6
Min pres necessary for ld w/S.F. (PSIG)          31.7        6.8
Air per cycle (SCF)                  2.05
Att'n act leakage cost/yr @ $ 0.30 /KSCF           36         55
Att'n operating air cost/yr @ $ 0.30 /KSCF       1303       1259
Cost /1000 cyc @ att'n times @ $ 20.00 /hr  19.80
Att'n power input total (HP)         7.48

COMMENTS:
```

```
NUMATICS NUMASIZING (R) SUMMARY SHEET                    Date:   04/10/95
NU301EED  Ver 3.01 (c) 1989 Numatics, Inc.              SURVEY # 5-2
=========================================================================
Prepared for:                     Prepared by:      Michael Liberty
Company:                          Company:          Numatics Inc.
Address:                          Address:          1450 N. Milford Rd.
City,State,Zip:                   City,State,Zip:   Highland, Mi. 48357
Telephone #                       Telephone #       (810) 887-4111
Fax #                             Fax #             (810) 887-9190
-------------------------------------------------------------------------
                                        Avg/Tot/Oth   Extend    Retract
INITIAL CUSTOMER PARAMETERS:
Total weight of load (lbs)                            315.00     45.00
Angle of load from horizontal              9
Coefficient of Friction                 0.21
Number of actuators                        1
Total load per actuator (lbs)                        176.84     32.82
Minimum line pressure (PSIG)             100
Design pressure used (PSIG)                           80.0       80.0
Shifts/day (1 shift=120,000 m/yr)        2.0
Cycles per year                      3938216

ACTUATOR:
Description:   Single Rod High Flow Numatics Actuator with 1/2 NPT ports
Bore/stroke/rod         3.25" bore x 12.00" stroke x 1.000" rod
Fitting                             3/8" - 1/2 NPT EL

CONDUCTOR & ASSOCIATED COMPONENTS:
Branch conductor /leg               N/A
Branch manifold fitting /leg        N/A
Branch cond equiv ftg lg /leg (in)  N/A
Quick disconnect model /leg         N/A
In line flow control model /leg                       NONE       NONE
Main conductor          3/8" rubber hose 120" long with 2.0 elbow(s)
Main manifold fitting               N/A
Main cond equiv ftg lg (in)          32

VALVE ASSEMBLY & ASSOCIATED COMPONENTS:
Description     2 Pos Mk 40 on 3/8 NPT base with ext req
Fitting                             3/8" - 3/8 NPT EL
Silencer model                      N/A

SYSTEM PERFORMANCE TIMES:
Att'n stroke time (sec)                               0.60       0.56
Required stroke time (sec)                            0.60       0.56
Stroke time @ term vel (sec)                          0.51       0.47
Att'n cyclic rate (CPM)                 16.41
Required cyclic rate (CPM)              16.41
Cyclic rate @ term vel (CPM)            17.25
System delay time (sec)                 0.022
Dwell time after stroke (sec)                         1.40       1.10

SYSTEM INFORMATION:
Required system Cv                                    1.10       1.10
Attained system Cv                                    1.07       1.07
Att'n system air flow (SCFM)            42.3                     41.4
Att'n branch air vel (400 FPS max)                 N/A        N/A
Att'n main air vel (400 FPS max)                      187        180
Att'n % delta p (46% max)                             24         23
% Act. capacity used (75% max)                        27          5
Min pres necessary for 1d w/S.F. (PSIG)              28.4        5.8
Air per cycle (SCF)                     0.81
Att'n act leakage cost/yr @ $ 0.30 /KSCF  91         35         56
Att'n operating air cost/yr @ $ 0.30 /KSCF 952       497        455
Cost /1000 cyc @ att'n times @ $ 20.00 /hr 20.58
Att'n power input total (HP)            2.94

COMMENTS:
```

```
NUMATICS NUMASIZING (R) SUMMARY SHEET                Date:    04/10/95
NU301EED  Ver 3.01 (c) 1989 Numatics, Inc.          SURVEY # 5-2a
=====================================================================
Prepared for:                   Prepared by:    Michael Liberty
Company:                        Company:        Numatics Inc.
Address:                        Address:        1450 N. Milford Rd.
City,State,Zip:                 City,State,Zip: Highland, Mi. 48357
Telephone #                     Telephone #     (810) 887-4111
Fax #                           Fax #           (810) 887-9190
---------------------------------------------------------------------
                                Avg/Tot/Oth     Extend      Retract
INITIAL CUSTOMER PARAMETERS:
 Total weight of load (lbs)                      315.00      45.00
 Angle of load from horizontal         9
 Coefficient of Friction            0.21
 Number of actuators                   1
 Total load per actuator (lbs)                   227.15      44.74
 Minimum line pressure (PSIG)        100
 Design pressure used (PSIG)                      80.0        80.0
 Shifts/day (1 shift=120,000 m/yr)   2.0
 Cycles per year                 4366764

ACTUATOR:
 Description:   Single Rod High Flow Numatics Actuator with 1/2 NPT ports
 Bore/stroke/rod          3.25" bore x 12.00" stroke x 1.000" rod
 Fitting                           1/2" - 1/2 NPT EL

CONDUCTOR & ASSOCIATED COMPONENTS:
 Branch conductor /leg              N/A
 Branch manifold fitting /leg       N/A
 Branch cond equiv ftg lg /leg (in) N/A
 Quick disconnect model /leg        N/A
 In line flow control model /leg                   NONE        NONE
 Main conductor            1/2" rubber hose 120" long with 2.0 elbow(s)
 Main manifold fitting              N/A
 Main cond equiv ftg lg (in)         42

VALVE ASSEMBLY & ASSOCIATED COMPONENTS:
 Description    2 Pos Mk 40 on 1/2 NPT base with ext reg
 Fitting                            1/2" - 1/2 NPT EL
 Silencer model                     N/A

SYSTEM PERFORMANCE TIMES:
 Att'n stroke time (sec)                          0.43        0.37
 Required stroke time (sec)                       0.43        0.37
 Stroke time @ term vel (sec)                     0.33        0.31
 Att'n cyclic rate (CPM)            18.20
 Required cyclic rate (CPM)         18.19
 Cyclic rate @ term vel (CPM)       19.12
 System delay time (sec)            0.022
 Dwell time after stroke (sec)                    1.40        1.10

SYSTEM INFORMATION:
 Required system Cv                               1.87        1.88
 Attained system Cv                               1.79        1.79
 Att'n system air flow (SCFM)                     63.8        69.6
 Att'n branch air vel (400 FPS max)      N/A               N/A
 Att'n main air vel (400 FPS max)                 148         171
 Att'n % delta p (46% max)                        18          23
 % Act. capacity used (75% max)                   34          7
 Min pres necessary for 1d w/S.F. (PSIG)          36.5        7.9
 Air per cycle (SCF)                0.88
 Att'n act leakage cost/yr @ $ 0.30 /KSCF         36          55
 Att'n operating air cost/yr @ $ 0.30 /KSCF       1157        601         555
 Cost /1000 cyc @ att'n times @ $ 20.00 /hr       18.60
 Att'n power input total (HP)       3.52

COMMENTS:
```

```
NUMATICS NUMASIZING (R) SUMMARY SHEET                        Date:   04/10/95
NU301EED   Ver 3.01 (c) 1989 Numatics, Inc.                 SURVEY # 5-2b
==============================================================================
Prepared for:                      Prepared by:      Michael Liberty
Company:                           Company:          Numatics Inc.
Address:                           Address:          1450 N. Milford Rd.
City,State,Zip:                    City,State,Zip:   Highland, Mi. 48357
Telephone #                        Telephone #       (810) 887-4111
Fax #                              Fax #             (810) 887-9190
------------------------------------------------------------------------------
                                        Avg/Tot/Oth      Extend      Retract
INITIAL CUSTOMER PARAMETERS:
Total weight of load (lbs)                              315.00       45.00
Angle of load from horizontal              9
Coefficient of Friction                 0.21
Number of actuators                        1
Total load per actuator (lbs)                          271.73       60.67
Minimum line pressure (PSIG)             100
Design pressure used (PSIG)                             80.0        80.0
Shifts/day (1 shift=120,000 m/yr)        2.0
Cycles per year                      4589840

ACTUATOR:
Description:   Single Rod High Flow Numatics Actuator with 3/4 NPT ports
Bore/stroke/rod             3.25" bore x 12.00" stroke x 1.000" rod
Fitting                              3/4" - 3/4 NPT EL

CONDUCTOR & ASSOCIATED COMPONENTS:
Branch conductor /leg                    N/A
Branch manifold fitting /leg             N/A
Branch cond equiv ftg lg /leg (in)       N/A
Quick disconnect model /leg              N/A
In line flow control model /leg                        NONE         NONE
Main conductor              3/4" rubber hose 120" long with 2.0 elbow(s)
Main manifold fitting                    N/A
Main cond equiv ftg lg (in)               63

VALVE ASSEMBLY & ASSOCIATED COMPONENTS:
Description     2 Pos Mk 40 on 3/4 NPT base with ext req
Fitting                                  3/4" - 3/4 NPT EL
Silencer model                           N/A

SYSTEM PERFORMANCE TIMES:
Att'n stroke time (sec)                                 0.36        0.28
Required stroke time (sec)                              0.36        0.28
Stroke time @ term vel (sec)                           0.25        0.23
Att'n cyclic rate (CPM)                19.12
Required cyclic rate (CPM)             19.12
Cyclic rate @ term vel (CPM)           20.13
System delay time (sec)                0.022
Dwell time after stroke (sec)                          1.40        1.10

SYSTEM INFORMATION:
Required system Cv                                      3.13        3.18
Attained system Cv                                     2.98        2.98
Att'n system air flow (SCFM)                           94.4       116.0
Att'n branch air vel (400 FPS max)           N/A              N/A
Att'n main air vel (400 FPS max)                        92         127
Att'n % delta p (46% max)                               14          23
% Act. capacity used (75% max)                          41          10
Min pres necessary for 1d w/S.F. (PSIG)                43.7        10.8
Air per cycle (SCF)                      1.10
Att'n act leakage cost/yr @ $ 0.30 /KSCF    90          36          54
Att'n operating air cost/yr @ $ 0.30 /KSCF 1518        783         735
Cost /1000 cyc @ att'n times @ $ 20.00 /hr 17.78
Att'n power input total (HP)             4.53
COMMENTS:
```

```
NUMATICS NUMASIZING (R) SUMMARY SHEET              Date:   04/10/95
NU301EED  Ver 3.01 (c) 1989 Numatics, Inc.         SURVEY # 5-2c
==================================================================
Prepared for:                 Prepared by:   Michael Liberty
Company:                      Company:       Numatics Inc.
Address:                      Address:       1450 N. Milford Rd.
City,State,Zip:               City,State,Zip: Highland, Mi. 48357
Telephone #                   Telephone #    (810) 887-4111
Fax #                         Fax #          (810) 887-9190
------------------------------------------------------------------
                              Avg/Tot/Oth    Extend      Retract
INITIAL CUSTOMER PARAMETERS:
 Total weight of load (lbs)                   315.00       45.00
 Angle of load from horizontal       9
 Coefficient of Friction          0.21
 Number of actuators                 1
 Total load per actuator (lbs)                242.11       50.85
 Minimum line pressure (PSIG)      100
 Design pressure used (PSIG)                    80.0        80.0
 Shifts/day (1 shift=120,000 m/yr)   2.0
 Cycles per year               4464036

ACTUATOR:
 Description:   Single Rod High Flow Numatics Actuator with 3/4 NPT ports
 Bore/stroke/rod         3.25" bore x 12.00" stroke x 1.000" rod
 Fitting                 1 " - 3/4 NPT EL

CONDUCTOR & ASSOCIATED COMPONENTS:
 Branch conductor /leg            N/A
 Branch manifold fitting /leg     N/A
 Branch cond equiv ftg lg /leg (in)  N/A
 Quick disconnect model /leg      N/A
 In line flow control model /leg              NONE        NONE
 Main conductor        1" rubber hose 120" long with 2.0 elbow(s)
 Main manifold fitting            N/A
 Main cond equiv ftg lg (in)       84

VALVE ASSEMBLY & ASSOCIATED COMPONENTS:
 Description    2 Pos Mk 40 on 3/4 NPT base with ext req
 Fitting                          1" - 3/4 NPT EL
 Silencer model                   N/A

SYSTEM PERFORMANCE TIMES:
 Att'n stroke time (sec)                        0.40        0.32
 Required stroke time (sec)                     0.40        0.32
 Stroke time @ term vel (sec)                   0.29        0.28
 Att'n cyclic rate (CPM)         18.60
 Required cyclic rate (CPM)      18.60
 Cyclic rate @ term vel (CPM)    19.55
 System delay time (sec)         0.022
 Dwell time after stroke (sec)                  1.40        1.10

SYSTEM INFORMATION:
 Required system Cv                             3.35        3.40
 Attained system Cv                             3.21        3.21
 Att'n system air flow (SCFM)                  107.4       127.8
 Att'n branch air vel (400 FPS max)   N/A            N/A
 Att'n main air vel (400 FPS max)                60          80
 Att'n % delta p (46% max)                       15          24
 % Act. capacity used (75% max)                  36           8
 Min pres necessary for ld w/S.F. (PSIG)       38.9         9.0
 Air per cycle (SCF)              1.41
 Att'n act leakage cost/yr @ $ 0.30 /KSCF   90   36          54
 Att'n operating air cost/yr @ $ 0.30 /KSCF 1888 967        920
 Cost /1000 cyc @ att'n times @ $ 20.00 /hr 18.37
 Att'n power input total (HP)     5.58

COMMENTS:
```

```
NUMATICS NUMASIZING (R) SUMMARY SHEET                    Date:   04/10/95
NU301EED  Ver 3.01 (c) 1989 Numatics, Inc.              SURVEY # 5-2d
=============================================================================
Prepared for:                      Prepared by:    Michael Liberty
Company:                           Company:        Numatics Inc.
Address:                           Address:        1450 N. Milford Rd.
City,State,Zip:                    City,State,Zip: Highland, Mi. 48357
Telephone #                        Telephone #     (810) 887-4111
Fax #                              Fax #           (810) 887-9190
-----------------------------------------------------------------------------
                                     Avg/Tot/Oth    Extend      Retract
INITIAL CUSTOMER PARAMETERS:
  Total weight of load (lbs)                        315.00       45.00
  Angle of load from horizontal          9
  Coefficient of Friction             0.21
  Number of actuators                    1
  Total load per actuator (lbs)                     212.60       42.33
  Minimum line pressure (PSIG)         100
  Design pressure used (PSIG)                        80.0        80.0
  Shifts/day (1 shift=120,000 m/yr)    2.0
  Cycles per year                  4293176

ACTUATOR:
  Description:   Single Rod High Flow Numatics Actuator with 3/4 NPT ports
  Bore/stroke/rod           3.25" bore x 12.00" stroke x 1.000" rod
  Fitting                            1-1/4" - 3/4 NPT EL

CONDUCTOR & ASSOCIATED COMPONENTS:
  Branch conductor /leg                  N/A
  Branch manifold fitting /leg           N/A
  Branch cond equiv ftg lg /leg (in)     N/A
  Quick disconnect model /leg            N/A
  In line flow control model /leg                   NONE         NONE
  Main conductor          1-1/4" rubber hose 120" long with 2.0 elbow(s)
  Main manifold fitting                  N/A
  Main cond equiv ftg lg (in)            105

VALVE ASSEMBLY & ASSOCIATED COMPONENTS:
  Description     2 Pos Mk 40 on 3/4 NPT base with ext reg
  Fitting                            1-1/4" - 3/4 NPT EL
  Silencer model                     N/A

SYSTEM PERFORMANCE TIMES:
  Att'n stroke time (sec)                            0.47         0.39
  Required stroke time (sec)                         0.47         0.39
  Stroke time @ term vel (sec)                       0.35         0.34
  Att'n cyclic rate (CPM)            17.89
  Required cyclic rate (CPM)         17.89
  Cyclic rate @ term vel (CPM)       18.78
  System delay time (sec)            0.022
  Dwell time after stroke (sec)                      1.40         1.10

SYSTEM INFORMATION:
  Required system Cv                                 3.50         3.53
  Attained system Cv                                 3.37         3.37
  Att'n system air flow (SCFM)                      118.6       136.5
  Att'n branch air vel (400 FPS max)      N/A                N/A
  Att'n main air vel (400 FPS max)                   44          56
  Att'n % delta p (46% max)                          17          26
  % Act. capacity used (75% max)                     32           7
  Min pres necessary for ld w/S.F. (PSIG)            34.2         7.5
  Air per cycle (SCF)                 1.81
  Att'n act leakage cost/yr @ $ 0.30 /KSCF    90     36          54
  Att'n operating air cost/yr @ $ 0.30 /KSCF 2325  1185        1140
  Cost /1000 cyc @ att'n times @ $ 20.00 /hr 19.20
  Att'n power input total (HP)        6.81

COMMENTS:
```

# 6

# Valves

The traditional practice of picking air valves and piping, as discussed earlier, is to select a valve and conductor size equal to the port size of the chosen cylinder. In most instances this practice results in oversizing the valve and conductor, and, as we've discovered, contrary to popular belief, increasing the conductor size for any given system containing a cylinder will not always reduce the stroke time. We have shown that there is an optimum conductor diameter that if surpassed can be as detrimental to the cylinder's performance times as if it were undersized. Obviously this historical selection method is not only outdated but wrong. If we apply what we have learned thus far by having established the dominant objective, having determined the $C_{vs}$ by assuming a cylinder bore (to be refined during the study), decided on a preliminary conductor diameter with associated applicable fittings (to be optimized in the course of the investigation), and knowing the available pressure and loads, we can readily solve for a valve $C_v$. By computing the $C_{vs}$ and subsequently removing all the known $C_v$ values from the $C_{vs}$, we are left with a recommended valve $C_v$. This is precisely what is done in the $C_{vs}$ approach to selecting a valve, as will be illustrated later in the chapter.

In reflecting on the function and application of a pneumatic valve we find that it is comparable to an electrical switch. The valve will allow air molecules to pass or not to pass, similar to its electrical counterpart which serves the same function for electrons. The $C_v$ rating is a measure of this ability to transmit air under pressure differentials. The larger the $C_v$ of the valve, the greater is the amount of air that can pass through it under the same pressure conditions. This can be directly equated to the conductance of an electrical device. $C_v$ can be viewed as the conductance of an electrical device, as stated earlier, and thus under the same voltage (pressure) conditions the greater the conductance of the device, the more current (airflow) is able to pass.

The relationship I am describing is Ohm's law [$E = IR$ (where $R$ is resistance)] as reviewed and compared to the airflow equation [$Q$ (in scfm) at critical pressure = $0.489C_v p_{1a}$], its pneumatic equivalent, in Chap. 2.

The value of the $C_v$ of a valve is indicated by the smallest ID in its entry or exit port, very similar to the major ingredient which controls the $C_v$ of the cylinder. The dependence of the valve's $C_v$ on the minimum ID in its port is clearly evident in Fig. 6.1.

To simplify the chart in Fig. 6.1 we combined the independent valve $C_v$ and $C_v$ of the ID of the associated port size only, i.e., the smallest diameter of the two without involving the conductor. This value is therefore representative of what is offered to the customer in catalogs. Obviously when selecting a conductor, its ID is then compared to the already smallest ID determined for the valve port combination to establish the final $C_v$ of the valve. In Fig. 6.1 the largest achievable $C_v$ is indicated by a single asterisk (*). Any port size above this crucial point will not appreciably improve the $C_v$ of the valve as the limitation now becomes the internal flow paths and parts. This should serve as a caveat to the designer or buyer, for a very small $C_v$ valve can be affiliated with a very large port implying a large $C_v$ but in reality is dictated by the modest value of the valve $C_v$. The valve is in fact a combination of individual internal valve components, each with their own $C_v$ value making up the entire valve $C_v$. If any one of these entities—and in many cases it is not the port or its drill size—is restrictive, the valve $C_v$ is impacted.

The importance of linking the $C_v$ of a valve with a port size will be demonstrated shortly. There is no point in having a large port size with a minuscule valve $C_v$. Returning now to Fig. 6.1 and our original

| Valve | Plug | 10–32 UNF | 1/8 NPT | 1/4 NPT | 3/8 NPT | 1/2 NPT | 3/4 NPT | 1 NPT | 1–1/4 NPT | 1–1/2 NPT | 2 NPT | 2–1/2 NPT |
|---|---|---|---|---|---|---|---|---|---|---|---|---|
| M1 | 0 | 0.12 | 0.13*,** | 0.13 | --- | --- | --- | --- | --- | --- | --- | --- |
| MK3 | 0 | 0.18 | 0.25*,** | 0.25 | --- | --- | --- | --- | --- | --- | --- | --- |
| MK7 | 0 | 0.23 | 0.40 | 0.41*,** | 0.41 | --- | --- | --- | --- | --- | --- | --- |
| MK8 | 0 | 0.26 | 0.74 | 0.80** | 0.82 | 0.83* | 0.83 | --- | --- | --- | --- | --- |
| MK15 | 0 | 0.27 | 1.14 | 1.39 | 1.50** | 1.54 | 1.55 | 1.56* | 1.56 | --- | --- | --- |
| MK25 | 0 | 0.27 | 1.29 | 1.70 | 1.92 | 2.00** | 2.03 | 2.04 | 2.05* | 2.05 | --- | --- |
| MK40 | 0 | 0.27 | 1.50 | 2.31 | 3.00 | 3.30 | 3.46** | 3.52 | 3.54 | 3.55* | 3.55 | --- |
| MK55 | 0 | 0.27 | 1.59 | 2.69 | 4.00 | 4.82 | 5.38** | 5.59 | 5.68 | 5.70 | 5.73* | 5.73 |
| MK140 | 0 | 0.27 | 1.65 | 3.00 | 5.31 | 7.87 | 11.46 | 14.05 | 15.77** | 16.26 | 16.66 | 16.78 |

**Figure 6.1** Valve $C_v$ with associated port sizes. [*Key:* single asterisk (*) indicates the largest achievable $C_v$; double asterisk (**) indicates the largest practical port available in that series of valves due to machining, design, and die-casting considerations.]

examination of the influence on the valve $C_v$ by port sizes, this time let us evaluate the effect assuming that we are below the pivotal point. The $C_v$ is adversely affected and continues to drop with successive port sizes down to the ultimate, zero, i.e., when using a plug. This is very similar to the exhaust system of an automobile, where if the exhaust path is restricted, the engine horsepower would be reduced commensurately. The maximum effect would be if the system were totally plugged, preventing any evacuation thus having no hp available at all.

Again, the smallest ID can be either the conductor, the fitting, or the internal port of the valve. Typically, the valve's internal configuration, referred to as the *port size,* is made as large as is practical so that it is not the restricting constituent but rather what is mated into it. In order to take advantage of the valve's maximum $C_v$, it is therefore wise to use a fitting that is as large as the maximum port size available to take full advantage of the largest internal ID or limitation of the valve. There is seldom any complication to this point in proceeding with this approach, as no volume is involved. Reduced ports prevent the full potential of the internal members' capability to be realized. The conductor is somewhat more complex, for its $C_v$ is not only dependent on its ID, which is folded into the determination of the valve $C_v$ as it terminates inside the appliance port, but also on its length, and therefore volume is involved. We've learned about this volume aspect in Chap. 5, that it may not always be wise to select the same internal diameter as the fitting or port size for the conductor. It is clearly evident from reviewing Fig. 6.1 that the optimum size is not necessarily the same ID as the fitting and many times may be smaller.

An interesting deduction drawn from examining Fig. 6.1 is the dramatic disparity in $C_v$ between a Mk 8 with a $\frac{1}{4}$-NPT fitting and a Mk 55 with a $\frac{10}{32}$-UNF fitting. This highlights the importance of having proper conductor and fittings mated with valves. It is not possible to just consider the isolated capability of a valve. The valve is only one link in the chain. Since the $C_v$ values of all links are of equal importance, it is vital that we do not have an abnormally small or weak link in the system. A Mk 8 has less than one sixth of the capability of a Mk 55 when both are compared on an absolute basis. Yet, when the Mk 8 is joined with an appropriate $\frac{1}{4}$-NPT fitting, it can achieve a $C_{vs}$ of 0.8 as compared to only 0.27 when the Mk 55 is united, unknowingly and unwittingly, with an inappropriate $\frac{10}{32}$-UNF fitting. The $C_{vs}$ yield is 3:1 in favor of the Mk 8 after mating, whereas prior to mating it was 6.9:1 in favor of the Mk 55. When you factor into the equation the expense of a Mk 8 being approximately half that of a Mk 55, the ratio that follows for $C_{vs}$ per dollar expended becomes a dramatic 6:1

in favor of the Mk 8. Another way of viewing this disparity is that the Mk-8 union can provide more air to an actuator than the Mk-55 combination so that its cyclic rate can be up to three times greater than the Mk-55 alliance. Obviously this is an unusual and extreme case to use as an example, but the striking contrast does send the proper message.

In further reviewing Fig. 6.1, a noteworthy point which bears repeating is to make certain when selecting or specifying a valve that it is accompanied with a $C_v$ corresponding to a specific port size. Not only are we confronted with valves of different $C_v$ values having the same size port, but the same-size valve is customarily tapped in several port sizes where each port size has a companion $C_v$. Purchasing a valve by simply requesting it by a port size alone is similar to purchasing an automobile without concern for the size of the engine under the hood. The same automobile can be purchased with several sizes of engine, and automobiles of different weights are available with the same-horsepower engine. Somehow we are all well acquainted with these taken-for-granted automotive factors and arrive at logical decisions without any difficulty. Yet, when it comes to pneumatics, which offers considerably less complicated choices, we are at a loss to come to rational and intelligent conclusions.

To help reduce some of the selection process confusion, we will provide you with some indication of the extraordinary $C_v$ divergence by comparing a Mk 15, a Mk 25, a Mk 40, a Mk 55, and a Mk 140, having identical $\frac{3}{8}$-NPT ports. This is atypical of (but not unusual as to) how valves are applied on the plant floor. We will not venture into the various reasons for some of these misapplications, although some are quite legitimate. Nevertheless, let us refer to Fig. 6.1 again for the comparison of the values. [*Note:* We provided those valves that did not have $\frac{3}{8}$-NPT ports with reducing bushings to render equivalent combinations. The Mk 15 is not detectably harmed as its port is not throttling the ability of the internal components. Independently it has a $C_v$ of 1.56, and with a $\frac{3}{8}$-NPT port it reads 1.50. The Mk 140 is considerably throttled, but nevertheless with a $\frac{3}{8}$-NPT port it renders a $C_v$ of 5.31. As an unrestricted autonomous valve, the value is 16.9. The first observation confirms that calling out a valve by its port size alone is dangerous. A variation in the $C_v$, for the same port size in the five valves, ranging from 5.31 down to 1.5, for a ratio in excess of 3:1, is substantial. To carry this argument to the extreme, one could conceivably manufacture an M 1 valve (max $C_v$ of 0.13 due to internal limitations) having a $\frac{3}{8}$-NPT port and wind up with a $C_v$ no larger than 0.13. To repeat an earlier observation, since all these valves have the same port size yet vary within this wide spectrum of $C_v$ values, we must exercise careful specifying precautions. The second observation is that it is extremely extravagant to specify a valve having a large $C_v$

value and then wasting it by mating it with a choking fitting, as proved in the earlier examples of the Mk 55 with $^{10}\!/_{32}$-UNF fittings having a variation of 21:1 (5.73 to 0.27) and now for the Mk 140 using $^{3}\!/_{8}$-NPT fittings having a variation of 3:1 (16.26 to 5.31). If we would employ the same basis of comparison for the Mk 140 as we did for the Mk 55, the ratio would be an astonishing 60:1 (16.26 to 0.27).]

We will now direct our attention to those understanding the need for having port sizes linked to the $C_v$ of a valve but failing to follow through with optimizing conductors. This lack of conductor appreciation has a negative impact on the size of the valve required even though the valve has the smallest $C_v$. At this juncture we must point out that we have a flaw in the chain-to-$C_v$ analogy and must depart from it on a very specific point. If the next-weakest link in the chain is replaced with a stronger link, the strength of the chain remains unaltered because the weakest link has not been changed and thus still prevails. On the other hand, unlike the chain, if the second-weakest component is supplanted with a larger $C_v$, the system's $C_v$ will improve (which is clearly evident from the formula for combining $C_v$ values). How close this second $C_v$ was to the smallest or weakest device will determine the extent of the improvement. Thus, to gain more than incremental advances (as you will soon see), all that is necessary is to increase the conductor size (obviously up to a point) without changing the valve. This is relatively inexpensive. Needless to say, if one does not have a respectable appreciation for this concept, the valve will be removed and replaced with a larger valve needlessly. This entails by far the greater expense and should be avoided. This clearly indicates the dangers of standardizing on a single hose size for the majority of applications in a facility. This happens to be a very prevalent practice in industry today with many defenders but really without a defense. Again the fascinating aspect is that in these encountered cases, the conductor has the dubious distinction of being the second in line. Therefore, if the conductor is not improved, by increasing its size, the valve is negatively and unnecessarily impacted. Needless to say, this approach is applicable to pneumatic devices other than conductors and applies to the third- and fourth-weakest links as well but to a lesser and lesser degree. The need to review the summary $C_v$ list is paramount to obtain an economical and energy-efficient circuit. Even though the valve, being the smallest and most expensive component, prevails as the major determination in the $C_{vs}$, the $C_{vs}$ can still be improved by replacing lesser, and inexpensive, components with larger $C_v$ values (obviously up to a point). The means is within our hands.

To digress for a moment in order to qualify my statement, I would like to share the findings of my many trips to plant maintenance departments both abroad and in the United States. Usually I find a host of electrical conductors strung out or against a wall, ranging in size from perhaps 00-gauge (heavy-duty, about 0.365 in in diameter—for large motors or distribution loads) to 24-gauge (light-duty, about 0.02 in in diameter—for electronic circuits). There may be perhaps two dozen or more different sizes between the two extremes. Looking intently around for the number of sizes of pneumatic conductors required to properly run a plant, I am struck to find only two or perhaps three different sizes. When questioned, I am immediately told that they have standardized on these pneumatic sizes and do not require anymore. Frankly, there is as much need, if not more, to optimize a pneumatic conductor as there is an electrical conductor. In electricity, if a conductor is oversized, it doesn't impair the cyclic rate of an electrical device, although it may be rather expensive. In pneumatics, as we are well aware by now, an oversized conductor can be as damaging to the speed of a pneumatic device as an undersized conductor. This is because you are coping with mass when moving air. There is no property comparable to this in electricity. Unfortunately, this misguided mentality is not restricted to a few isolated cases but is the norm rather than the exception.

Let us now compare the performance times of a Mk 15, a Mk 25, and a Mk 40 having appropriate fittings first joined to 48-in lengths of $\frac{3}{4}$-in rubber hose and then to optimized conductors of the same length. The remaining pneumatic elements as well as loads and pressures are identical in all respects for all the networks. Figure 6.2 contains the resulting performance times for each of these valves. We will also compare, alongside these results, the consequent findings assuming that the lengths were extended to 96 in.

| Survey # | Valve | $C_v$ | Port Size | Total Stroke Time* | Hose Diameter x Length | $C_{vs}$ |
|---|---|---|---|---|---|---|
| 6–1 | MK15 | 1.56 | 3/8 NPT | 0.70 sec | 3/4" x 48" | 1.46 |
| 6–2 | MK25 | 2.05 | 1/2 NPT | 0.60 sec | 3/4" x 48" | 1.87 |
| 6–3 | MK40 | 3.55 | 3/4 NPT | 0.47 sec | 3/4" x 48" | 2.90 |
| 6–4 | MK15 | 1.56 | 3/8 NPT | 0.67 sec | 1/2" x 48" | 1.33 |
| 6–5 | MK25 | 2.05 | 1/2 NPT | 0.58 sec | 5/8" x 48" | 1.79 |
| 6–6 | MK40 | 3.55 | 3/4 NPT | 0.47 sec | 3/4" x 48" | 2.90 |
| 6–7 | MK15 | 1.56 | 3/8 NPT | 0.85 sec | 3/4" x 96" | 1.45 |
| 6–8 | MK25 | 2.05 | 1/2 NPT | 0.70 sec | 3/4" x 96" | 1.86 |
| 6–9 | MK40 | 3.55 | 3/4 NPT | 0.53 sec | 3/4" x 96" | 2.86 |
| 6–10 | MK15 | 1.56 | 3/8 NPT | 0.75 sec | 1/2" x 96" | 1.29 |
| 6–11 | MK25 | 2.05 | 1/2 NPT | 0.66 sec | 5/8" x 96" | 1.76 |
| 6–12 | MK40 | 3.55 | 3/4 NPT | 0.53 sec | 3/4" x 96" | 2.86 |

* Excludes dwell times

Figure 6.2  Effect of conductor diameter and length on total stroke time.

First, Fig. 6.2 confirms the fact that the universal use of one diameter is wrong. Second, even as short a length as 48 in can have an appreciable effect on the performance time of an actuator. The relationship between the conductor volume and the actuator volume plays a major role in the potential effect of the conductor on performance times. In our case the ratio is approximately 36 percent, and the conductor represents 26 percent of the total volume. When the length is 96 in (not unusually long, especially in welding robots), the relationship is even more dramatic: 72 percent, and now the conductor represents 42 percent of the total system volume. Obviously, as the length increases, the effect becomes more significant and thus the need to consider diameter more acute and not on an absolute basis, for it affects $C_v$ profoundly. The supporting documentation for Fig. 6.2 is presented in Surveys 6-1 to 6-12.

This (Fig. 6.2) provides another opportunity to view the dramatic effects of volume on the elapsed stroke time of an actuator. Or examining how damaging it is, from the conventional perspective, where the length of the conductor is considered to be of little or no import. Figure 6.3, when compared to Fig. 6.2, will dispel that myth. I would like to emphasize the point that the results in Fig. 6.3 are what one could expect for actuator performance times without taking into account conductor lengths. It thus leaves us with a two-pronged message, namely, one should not only always include conductor length into the equation for arriving at the performance time but also optimize its diameter.

The supporting documentation for Fig. 6.3 can be found in Surveys 6-13 to 6-15. The only difference between Figs. 6.2 and 6.3 is that the valve is located 48 and 96 in from the actuator in Fig. 6.2 and in close proximity to the actuator in Fig. 6.3. The distance of 48 in is considered quite close, and still the effect is enormous. Obviously, as the distance increases, its volume represents a greater portion of the total volume and thus its consequence on performance time is greater.

The comparison of the total stroke times for the Mk 15 (Survey 6-1 vs. Survey 6-13) shows a 23 percent difference for the 48-in length (0.70 vs. 0.57) and a 49 percent difference (0.85 − 0.57) for the 96-in

| Survey # | Valve | $C_v$ | Port Size | Total Stroke Time* | $C_{vs}$ |
|----------|-------|-------|-----------|--------------------|----------|
| 6–13 | MK15 | 1.56 | 3/8 NPT | 0.57 sec | 1.46 |
| 6–14 | MK25 | 2.05 | 1/2 NPT | 0.49 sec | 1.88 |
| 6–15 | MK40 | 3.55 | 3/4 NPT | 0.41 sec | 2.95 |

* Excludes dwell times

**Figure 6.3**   Effect on total stroke time with minimal conductor length.

length (Survey 6-7 vs. Survey 6-13). To examine it assuming that a circuit had a 48- or 96-in conductor, as we have, and the designer failed to account for it in the calculations, the stroke would be 23 or 49 percent slower than what would be expected and indicated by appropriate computations. If one approaches this problem assuming that conductors are of no import, one would attempt to continue to increase the valve size until the desired speed is achieved. Let us briefly review several scenarios as to the consequences of this line of reasoning. Our first assumption will be that the conductor is the weak link, and perhaps even without a valve, the $C_{vs}$ of the remaining circuit would be inadequate to support the speed demanded of the actuator. In that event no valve would fulfill that requirement. The next scenario is that the conductor is not the weakest component but quite close to the valve which is the weakest, and thus in order to achieve the speed, both the valve and the conductor may require improvement. Improving the valve by itself would be an exercise in futility. Now we begin to understand the repercussions of every component on the capability of the valve. We must be continually on our toes in our selection process to make absolutely certain that we select the optimum components and thus do not waste energy or money.

There are several other interesting comparisons, namely, those of the $C_{vs}$ values and those of the total times and their decreasing variations as the valve sizes increase. The results of Surveys 6-3 and 6-6 are identical, as are those of Surveys 6-9 and 6-12 since the initial hose size selected happened to coincide with the optimum size for that valve to actuator combination.

The first of several additional points worth touching on at this juncture is the frequently asked question of recommending the best valve for a pneumatic-circuit application. As though the valve were the only component, feature, or physical property controlling the cylinder's performance time. This presents a dilemma, for by now we should all be aware that the request must be accompanied with a specific objective. Clearly there can be no single valve which could satisfy every conceivable objective (see Chap. 1 for a full evaluation of many of the objectives). The solution to the problem at the end of Chap. 1 serves as an excellent example displaying the marked contrast between the three different sizes of valves recommended for the identical circuit and equipment and specifications, because there were three distinct objectives (OEM, end user, and facilities engineer). A valve with an independent $C_v$ of 1.06, which in conjunction with its $\frac{3}{8}$-in hose to $\frac{1}{4}$-NPT port fitting, attains a $C_v$ of 1.00, was selected for one of the objectives which used FCs (flow controls) to arrive at the required actuator performance times. The other two valves had $C_v$ values of 1.75 and 1.63 and 5.73 and 4.29, and in order to satisfy the initial low-speed specifications, the conventional FCs were employed here as well. All three circuits intended for the same machine but having three different targets demanded three distinct valves to fulfill their respective operating specifications.

The second point is the response time of a valve. In most instances it is essentially the response time of the solenoid, for the overwhelming number of valves are operated by solenoids. Some valves are air-operated and obtain a signal from a remote valve, which in turn is operated by a solenoid. In this instance the response time is now increased to include the travel time of the air through the conductor telegraphing the signal from the pilot to the power valve, etc. Certain other valves are operated manually. However, as stated earlier, the response time is reserved primarily for delineating the response of the solenoid operating the valve, which is usually astride (direct) or on top (pilot) of the valve housing. These responses could vary in time from approximately 8 milliseconds (ms) to as much as 20 ms. This amounts to a savings of 12 ms in the operation of the valve. A good deal of emphasis is placed on this savings, which obviously is important. Notwithstanding, if one is stressing savings in time, there is a considerably greater amount available to the designer via the dual-pressure approach than settling for the solenoid savings at the expense of everything else. If one is truly interested in improving productivity, the avenue to take should include every aspect of the circuit. Once this is done, the speed of the valve is found to be only an infinitesimal portion of the total elapsed time of the entire cycle of the system, in the majority of applications. Some valves having slower response times have the advantage of being able to be dual-pressured, thus more than offsetting the time lost in the valve response. Here again, what we are suggesting is for the designer to place the central reason for selection not on valve response time, but rather on total stroke time. This requires an investigative method which takes into consideration the breakout and running friction of a cylinder, the exhaust-pressure loads, the loads themselves, the conductor diameter, and the length with their associated fittings, and so on. Collectively, these factors play a much more significant role in the performance time of the network than does the response of a solenoid. From many of the examples thus cited, there is at least one order-of-magnitude improvement over the 12 ms of solenoid savings possible by utilizing this new approach. Don't discount an approach which requires a specific type of valve to implement it which may be a little slower in one aspect of the cycle. Consider the entire cycle time before making a judgment call, for it may be faster. We must be ever-alert for new ideas, for as astute designers, it is our obligation to explore them for their worthiness.

The third important issue is to understand when dealing with what has come to be termed "sandwich" modules, that by their very nature they are restrictive. These devices are interspersed into the valve assembly and are thus governed by the valve's dimensions. When incorporating a sandwich component between the valve and the base, one is limited by the configuration and flow paths of the valve, thereby restricting its $C_v$ and rendering a reduced $C_{vs}$. It is possible to introduce sandwich regulators, check valves, speed-control valves, etc., which makes for a very compact, clean, and labor-free installation but at the expense of the flow capability. At times because of confined valve dimensions, the $C_v$ of the sandwich unit is less than that of the valve. The combination $C_{vs}$ will obviously be less than the smallest device. It is therefore incumbent on the designer to fully investigate the combined $C_{vs}$ of the module to determine whether it is time-deficient. If it is, it would be wise to utilize similar-functioning external devices having greater $C_v$ values. One is less hampered by space limitations working outside the confines of sandwich components. The weakest link in the new chain will then be the valve. If space permits, the sandwich concept can save countless hours of labor as well as enhance the cosmetics of the installation and should therefore always be a viable consideration. The design method we propose has the capability of supplying this valuable information as it weighs the various combinations, enabling the selection of the optimum components per the major objective.

The fourth feature that requires understanding and attention is the availability to the designer today of what is termed *valve manifolding*. The advent on the scene of valve manifolding with and without its integral sandwich units is capturing a greater percentage of the market yearly and still increasing. *Manifolding* is essentially the unlimited grouping or clustering of valves via special base stations that bolt together to form one assembly for easy installation and central adjustment. It is convenient and makes for very rapid setups and a very clean and professional-looking piece of equipment which saves much design time, labor, and space. Commendable, except for the fact that this may require a layout that calls for excessive lengths (to the furthest location), which may hamper production for the duration of this adjusted setup period. Therefore, one must not go exclusively with single-location manifolds and conclude with extensive conductor runs (restricting production) simply to satisfy the designer or setup person's needs and convenience. Here again the method will allow the designer to evaluate single manifolding, splitting the manifold in half or thirds, and locating them strategically throughout the equipment. Or, one may elect to isolate one valve from the main group to improve productivity even for a few percentage points. It depends again on the major objective. Sometimes a single manifold may require one valve of the group to be larger (to fulfill production requirements) in order to supply a distant actuator necessitating a long conductor run. If the objective is one grouping, the larger valve is in order. If, however, the objective is to limit the installation to using only one size valve, it would behoove the designer to investigate the possibility of isolating it from the manifold and moving it close to the actuator. The hope is that shortening the conductor length would allow for valve size reduction. The specific reason for this objective may be less inventory to carry for maintenance, the less record keeping for purchasing and all its associated advantages. I've been told by the finance people of the large automotive companies that the need to carry an added item in inventory may impose as much as a 20 percent tariff added to the cost of the product. In essence the cost of the larger valve will thus be more than its initial price, which must be included into the entire evaluation process when determining the savings of single, split, or multiple manifolding. This is the type of feasibility study that should be performed as we now possess the vehicle for comparing valve to length investigations to provide the results that lead to intelligent decisions.

This is a very suitable location to briefly review the original manual graphical method used to determine the size of a valve and compare the results to the present computerized method for correlation. Bear in mind that the information used in both methods originates from the same data. A little history is always useful to shed some additional light as well as indicate the logic for a fuller understanding of the subject.

We will use the specific family of graphs in Fig. 6.4 to solve our problem. They were plotted from the test data of a 4-in bore $(d)$ (actuator circumferential friction value $f$ of 2.5) by 6-in stroke(s) actuator using three different valves with associated conductors and fittings in conjunction with an extend pressure of 60 psig and retract pressures of 60, 40, and 20 psig. We charted the entire range of loads that could possibly be propelled at these pressures, from zero to almost stalling conditions in 50-lb increments (for a 4-in bore). This process was repeated with other pressure combinations for an entire spectrum of performance capabilities of a 4-in-bore actuator. This complete process was repeated in total for actuators of other sizes until we built a complete reservoir of information for almost all available-size actuators under almost every conceivable pressure and load condition.

[*Note:* We chose a 4-in bore for this set of load conditions because the most stringent load necessary to be moved (solved in the succeeding paragraphs, with reference to Fig. 6.4) fell within the acceptable range of 33 to 66 percent of its actuator capacity. In Chap. 3 we do state that our recommended maximum is 75 percent. The 4-in bore is a good starting point for this investigation, and cylinder optimization can be reviewed with a customer depending on the objectives and

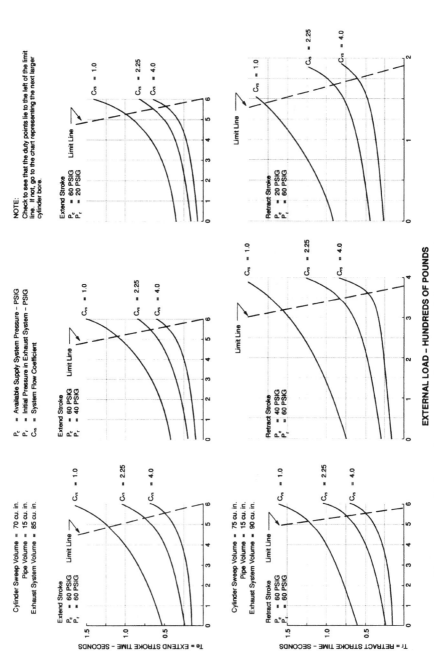

**Figure 6.4** Double-acting air cylinder performance, 4-in bore × 6-in stroke (noncushioned).

preferences during the course of a survey. For such an exercise, please refer to Chap. 3, on actuators.]

Refer to Fig. 6.4. The two external loads that we will use on the actuator problem, with the rod facing up, are based on moving a 215-lb block on a 215-lb carriage (total external extend weight $W_e$ = 430 lb) up a 5° incline (coefficient of friction between two surfaces $u$ = 0.85) and returning the empty carriage (total external retract weight $W_r$ = 215 lb) down the incline. The intent is to perform the extend time $T_e$ and retract time $T_r$ in 0.5 s each, using the smallest-size valve possible without exceeding the maximum design pressure limit of 60 psig. These stroke times are the minimum acceptable. We will also be solving for the fastest attainable stroke times, as that usually accompanies the customer's requests. We will review the hardware in both cases necessary to achieve the desired results.

Let us determine the loads using the unified condensed formulas as derived in Chap. 3, and then enter the applicable segments of the 4-in-bore graphs. Let us not forget that the total load the actuator must overcome includes its internal actuator frictional load $fd$ as well:

$$L_e = \frac{0.00518W_e s}{T_e^2} + uW_e\cos\theta + W_e\sin\theta + fd$$

$$= \frac{0.00518 \times 430 \times 6}{0.25} + 0.85 \times 430 \times 0.9962 + 430 \times 0.0872 + 2.5 \times 4$$

$$= 53.46 + 364.11 + 37.50 + 10 = 465 \text{ lb}$$

(where $L_e$ = extend load). The blind-end capacity of a double-acting 4-in-bore single-rod actuator at 60 psig is 754 lb. Therefore, the 465-lb moving load represents 62 percent of its capacity.

$$L_r = \frac{0.00518W_r s}{T_r^2} + uW_r\cos\theta - W_r\sin\theta + fd$$

$$= 26.73 + 182.06 - 18.75 + 10 = 200 \text{ lb}$$

(where $L_r$ = retract load). The rod-end capacity of a double-acting 4-in-bore single-rod actuator at 60 psig is 708 lb. Therefore, the 200-lb moving load represents 28 percent of its capacity.

All the load, pressure, time, and bore tests, whose composite results are depicted by the graphs in Fig. 6.4, were conducted with a multiplicity of static loads applied to the actuator ends [the $x$ axis (abscissa) represents these static loads, and the $y$ axis (ordinate) represents time]. Therefore one must enter the graph with the entire static load, which in this case would be 411 lb (465 − 54) for the extend portion and 173 lb (200 − 27) for the retract portion. One cannot include the accelerating share of the load, as it is time-dependent and varies. This is why the $C_{vs}$ lines on the graph are not linearly spaced, for even though the static load remains constant the dynamic load continues to increase as the time decreases. Let us focus on the 60/60-psig extend-stroke portion of Fig. 6.4 (upper leftmost segment) to determine the various $C_{vs}$ values at the same static load but at various time requirements. (*Note:* Keep in mind that the dynamic load is varying depending on the timeframe.)

Thus, a 411-lb load that has to travel 6 in in 1.00 s needs a $C_{vs}$ of 1.0, whereas moving the same static load in 0.30 s requires a $C_{vs}$ of 4.0. If it were a function of time only and linear, the $C_{vs}$ would be smaller, specifically, 3.3 (1.00/0.30); however, as we surmise, it is more complex. The extra $C_{vs}$, regardless of what the relationship may be, is needed to move the additional dynamic load, which in turn is obviously caused by the faster stroke time.

The plotting of the curves in Fig. 6.4 presented somewhat of a dilemma. We chose the simplest approach and plotted only the static loads, which remained constant, thereby allowing the $C_{vs}$ curves to assume their proper locations on the time versus load grid for the various pressure combinations. In time we conducted tests with smaller incremental pressure changes and also dropped the propelling pressures to the point of stalling and below. We also conducted tests with elevated propelling pressures (>100 psig) to enhance our database and to confirm our earlier hypothesis (for those tests that demanded >100 psig to reach the critical pressure) that beyond a certain point the stroke time plateaus off.

We wish to determine from the graphs (in Fig. 6.4) the $C_{vs}$ necessary to achieve a specific time and from that ascertain the necessary valve $C_v$ by extracting all the other $C_v$ values. A further constraint is to realize these prerequisites by using the lowest possible pressures. We will perform this exercise for both the extend stroke and the retract stroke. To accomplish this using the graphical approach, our first attempt again will be to consult Fig. 6.4 and specifically the extend-stroke portion of the 60/60-psig family of curves for the 4 × 6-in actuator to locate the point of intersection of the 411-lb vertical line with the 0.5-s horizontal line. The point of intersection falls on the 2.25 $C_{vs}$ curve. (*Note:* The spacings between the $C_{vs}$ curves are not linear in this family of curves; this discrepancy is explained in the text above.)

We will state the $C_v$ of each component and go through the mathematics to arrive at our valve $C_v$. The $C_v$ values of all components in the circuit are 5.85 for the actuator fitting, 10.00 for the conductor, 9.56 for the elbows, 4.19 for the valve fitting, and 8.00 for the sandwich regulator. The combined $C_{vs}$ is 2.85. By removing all other component $C_v$ values (2.85) from the $C_{vs}$ of 2.25, we are left with the required valve $C_v$ ($C_{vv}$) of 3.7. Thus, this valve $C_v$ of 3.7 at 60/60 psig is able to extend the total load of 465 lb in 0.5 s. This graphical analysis was a rather primitive method to use but was the prevailing technique in 1972/1973, when we conducted the bulk of our testing program. We still used slide rules, and the hp-35 costing $395 had not as yet appeared on the scene. If it had, we undoubtedly still would have been skeptical. Generating good graphs was an art, and reading them was a skill. Nevertheless, this method was appropriate for the time and was used successfully. Clearly, generating equations from data and deciphering them via germane computer programs are considerably more accurate, precise, simpler, and substantially faster than using french curves to plot the graphs and then attempting to extract exact readings from them. Incidentally, we are no longer skeptical; in fact, we are beholden to our computers, programs, etc. The equation and solution for these observations would be as follows:

$$\frac{1}{C_{vv}^2} = \frac{1}{2.25^2} - \left( \frac{1}{5.85^2} + \frac{1}{10.00^2} + 9.56^2 + 4.19^2 + \frac{1}{8.00^2} \right)$$

$$C_{vv} = 3.67 \quad \text{or rounded to 3.7}$$

By the same process we would enter the lower retract-stroke graph, which indicates a $C_{vs}$ of approximately 1.5 to move the 173-lb load in 0.5 s under the same 60/60-psig conditions. Also note the following:

1. It was always very difficult to interpolate because of the nonlinear spacing of the curves, and thus the end results were very rough. The valve $C_v$ that would be necessary for the retract stroke would be 1.76 or rounded to 1.8. Since valves are generally symmetrical in their flow passages, the most stringent requirement must be met, and therefore the valve having a $C_v$ of 3.7 would be chosen. With a valve of 3.7 and an ensuing $C_{vs}$ of 2.25, we can reenter the lower graph (in Fig. 6.4) to find that it would move the load in approximately 0.33 seconds.

2. The acceleration component of the total load on the retract-stroke end of the actuator, as a result of the faster stroke time, from 0.5 to 0.33 s, has been increased from 26.73 to 61.36 lb (35-lb increase). The entire load has, therefore, been increased from 200 to 235 lb (this will be discussed in more detail shortly).

This obviously is too fast, and some means would have to be provided to slow it down to 0.5 s. As we've stated so often, the conventional approach under these circumstances would be to interface a flow-control valve and crank it down (restricting the flow, not the pressure) until the 0.5 s is reached. This, however, is based on maintaining 60 psig on the rod end of the actuator. We know better now, and thus we will utilize the dual-pressure concept for our solution. We observe that we are too fast in one direction and satisfy the time constraint in the other. By virtue of our new-found knowledge, we know that reducing the pressure on the fast-retract stroke-end will slow it down without the need for any outside device and simultaneously reduce the exhaust pressure load for the extend side. This reduction in exhaust load with the same extend pressure will result in decreasing the 0.5 s with the same $2.25C_{vs}$. In essence, by reducing the pressure on the faster end of the cylinder, we are equalizing the required $C_{vs}$ values. As the pressure drops, the $C_{vs}$ required must increase in order to generate the same 0.5-s performance time (applies to extract end). The corollary is that, as this exhaust-pressure load decreases, the same $C_{vs}$ will render a better performance time (applies to the extend end). The object is to find the two pressures that render the identical and thus the smallest possible $C_{vs}$ to produce the targeted times.

Applying this logic, we will now enter the 60/40-psig portion of the extend stroke under the same conditions and requirements. We find the point of intersection of the 411-lb and 0.5-s lines to fall above the $2.25C_{vs}$ curve (approximately 2.0). We perform the identical exercise for the retract stroke; namely, the 173-lb and 0.5-s lines intersect also above the $2.25C_{vs}$ curve (approximately 2.0). Removing all the components as we did before leaves us with a valve requirement now of only 2.8. This also reveals to us that the previous valve of 3.7 will require neither 60 psig for the extend stroke nor 40 psig for the retract stroke to execute their stroke times in 0.5 s but somewhat less in each case. In this situation, since we do not have a valve to accurately match this $C_v$ of 2.8, we will have to use the largest valve closest to it and adjust both pressures downward accordingly. If we left the $C_{vs}$ of 2.25 as is by leaving the valve $C_v$ as is at 3.7, the extend time at the 411-lb load and 60/40 psig would be 0.45 s and the retract time at the 173-lb load and 40/60 psig would be 0.47 s. We will compare these results shortly with those of the computer program for correlation.

Now let us perform the first aspect, the 60/60-psig portion, of this problem via the computer. We will enter into the computer program the identical information used earlier and use a standard Mk-40 valve. One of our current standard industrial valves, having a $C_v$ of 3.55, which is very close to the 3.7 (3.67), is determined graphically to compare the results. (Survey 6-16 shows these results.) The graphical solution had the $C_{vs}$ requirements as 2.25 for both strokes. The computer result suggests 2.23 in each case. Graphically the times were 0.5 and 0.33 as compared to 0.49 and 0.33 for the computer. Thus far the correlation is rather good with the use of a slightly smaller valve $C_v$ [within 97 percent (3.55/3.67) of each other].

Now let us review the computer-program results using the pressures of 60 and 40 psig, respectively, for the extend and retract strokes. Again we are using the valve having a $C_v$ of 3.55. (See the printout of the performance results for this in Survey 6-17.) In reviewing the results, we find the performance figures to be essentially the same, namely, 0.45 for the extend direction and 0.46 for the retract direction as opposed to the graphical solution of 0.45 and 0.47 s in their respective directions. Obviously computing the results renders more accurate findings than does reading the graphs. Another interesting observation is the required $C_{vs}$ to be 2.23 as compared to 2.25 graphically (which are basically identical).

We will run another printout (Survey 6-18), using the same valve size, except this time zeroing in precisely on the pressures required to render the specific times of 0.5 s in each direction. Again, it is quite evident that the computer allows us to more closely hone in on the recommended pressures of 55.5 and 36.3 psig than simply stating via the graphical method that the pressures are somewhat less than 60/40 psig to achieve our appointed performance times.

It should be noted that all our test observations and readings were done to two decimal places, and therefore we carry out our computer-program calculations to only two decimal places as well. In the Survey 6-18 printout the attained cyclic rate reads 23.98 cpm, and not 24.00 cpm, even though the performance times seemed to have been satisfied at 0.50 s in each direction. If the times were exactly 0.5 s in each direction, and since the dwell times are constant and unalterable at a total of 1.50 s for a grand-total cycle time of 2.5 s, the cyclic rate would be exactly 24.00. Since we have a 23.98-cpm figure, the only variation that can exist would be in the performance times, and they would have to be slightly greater than 0.50 s but still be capable of rounding out to 0.50 s. This would not be evident if we extended the performance times to three decimal places and kept the cyclic rate rounded out to the existing two places.

There is another bit of information that is quite useful and available to use both graphically and via the computer program that is worth comparing. It is the $C_{vs}$ and consequent $C_{vv}$ required to move a weight at a specific pressure (e.g., 60/60 psig in our current case) to render a specific time (e.g., 0.5/0.5). Survey 6-19 (4-in-bore $\times$ 6-in-stroke actuator—performance and $C_v$ printouts) states that a valve $C_v$ of 3.37 ($C_{vs}$ of 2.18) is necessary to move a 411-lb static load in 0.5 s with the blind end of the actuator using 60 psig and exhausting 60 psig from the rod end. In addition, a valve $C_v$ of 1.53 ($C_{vs}$ of 1.35) is all that is necessary to move a 173-lb static load in 0.5 s with the rod end of the actuator using 60 psig and exhausting 60 psig from the blind end. Let us compare these results to the ones extracted from the graphs to see how well they compare. We did this earlier for the graphical solution, if you recall, and found the $C_{vv}/C_{vs}$ for the extend to be 3.67/2.25 and for the retract to be 1.76/1.50. The extend $C_{vv}/C_{vs}$ has a correlation of 92 percent (3.37/3.67) and 97 percent (2.18/2.25), whereas the retract correlation is not as good: 87 percent (1.53/1.76) and 90 percent (1.35/1.5). The reasons for these disparities are the inaccuracies in generating the curves and the interpolation difficulty, which further compounds the problem. Nevertheless, with the given tools it is remarkably close. Three additional notes here:

1. Valves are manufactured to have uniform flows to and from both ends of a cylinder. The differences in requirements of the two ends of a cylinder, e.g., times, loads are attained by compensating with flow controls, use of dual pressures, etc. Thus the $3.37C_v$ valve that was necessary for the extend stroke will render a retract-stroke time faster than required (0.50 s) at 60/60 psig (with no compensation method) namely, 0.30 s because of lesser extend-load conditions.

2. For the pneumatic sleuth there may appear to be an apparent contradiction when comparing Surveys 6-16 and 6-19. The total weights to be moved, pressures applied, and components are identical, yet the attained results in performance times are different. In reviewing them carefully, especially the retract loads, we see a 236-lb load in Survey 6-16 and only a 200-lb in Survey 6-19 (we mentioned this briefly a few pages back). The difference is due entirely to the acceleration portion of the load. In Survey 6-19 we use 0.5 s for the required time, which generates the 200-lb load, and under those conditions our attained time is 0.30 s. However, when we use a stroke time of 0.3 s, the load will be greater, and thus the attained retract time will now be longer than 0.3 s. We take this subtle condition into account in our calculations and arrive at an equalized time of 0.33 s, which generates a load of 236 lb. Now when we determine the performance time for a load of 236 lb we obtain the same time of 0.33 s. The variation is minor, approximately 10 percent (0.30 to 0.33), which in the overall picture may not be meaningful, but we would be remiss if we failed to include that facet in our program. The inconsistency of the extend time of 0.50 s in Survey 6-19 to 0.49 s in Survey 6-16 is for the identical reason but to a lesser extent because the moving loads vary only from 467 to 465 lb.

3. I am compelled, for the purist reader, to clear up the following detail, which accounts for a very minor variance (partly because the author is one, too, and desires to have a coherent picture). Earlier we solved for the retract load to be 235 lb at 0.33 s, and in Survey 6-19 we obtain 236 lb also at 0.33 s. The explanation is that the result in Survey 6-19 is based on a time of somewhat less than 0.33 s, generat-

| Survey # | Valve | $C_\nu$ | Port Size | $C_{\nu s}$ | Hose Diameter x Length | $ Cost/1000 |
|---|---|---|---|---|---|---|
| 6–13 | MK15 | 1.56 | 3/8 NPT | 1.46 | 3/4" x 1" | 17.20 |
| 6–14 | MK25 | 2.05 | 1/2 NPT | 1.88 | 3/4" x 1" | 16.79 |
| 6–15 | MK40 | 3.55 | 3/4 NPT | 2.95 | 3/4" x 1" | 16.31 |
| 6–1 | MK15 | 1.56 | 3/8 NPT | 1.46 | 3/4" x 48" | 17.98 |
| 6–2 | MK25 | 2.05 | 1/2 NPT | 1.87 | 3/4" x 48" | 17.37 |
| 6–3 | MK40 | 3.55 | 3/4 NPT | 2.90 | 3/4" x 48" | 16.67 |
| 6–7 | MK15 | 1.56 | 3/8 NPT | 1.45 | 3/4" x 96" | 18.83 |
| 6–8 | MK25 | 2.05 | 1/2 NPT | 1.86 | 3/4" x 96" | 18.01 |
| 6–9 | MK40 | 3.55 | 3/4 NPT | 2.86 | 3/4" x 86" | 17.07 |

**Figure 6.5**  Cost per 1000 versus conductor lengths.

ing a larger load, but when rounded to two decimal places, this becomes 0.33 seconds.

Figure 6.5 shows the cost per 1000 units compiled from the printouts in Surveys 6-1, 6-2, 6-3, 6-7 to 6-9, and 6-13 to 6-15.

In the comparison given in Fig. 6.5, all circuits are equipped with ¾-in rubber hose. Surveys 6-1 to 6-3 list conductor lengths of 48 in; Surveys 6-7 to 6-9, 96 in of conductor length; and Surveys 6-13 to 6-15, 1-in lengths, where the conductor span was presumably considered to be inconsequential regardless of length. Let us first examine the difference between essentially no conductor length to the 48- and 96-in lengths for the Mk-15 valve. It is clearly vital that conductor lengths must be involved in the calculations. For example, one can err in a quotation or cost estimation by $1.63 per 1000 units (18.83 for 96 in—17.20 for 1 in). In this example we are dealing with upward of 4,000,000 pieces, which means an error of over $7300. This is in excess of 9 percent (1.63/17.20) depending on the denominator one uses in the calculations. In today's market this could very well be the reason for accepting a job incorrectly estimated and being unaware of why the intended profit is so elusive. This obviously is just as true for the Mk-25 and Mk-40 examples. The other side of the coin is to reinforce the importance of keeping the conductor length to a minimum by comparing the 96-in cost per 1000 pieces to the 48 in and, if possible, to a shorter length. It should be understood that in our case it would be highly improbable for a single valve to be only 1 in (the example we used for a conductorless circuit) away from each port when used in conjunction with an actuator having a stroke of 6 in. It would be feasible if we used two valves, one at each port, to render the 1-in results, and that might very well be in the cards if the savings warranted it. Another thing to ponder are the costs per 1000 pieces if the conductor length required to bridge the distance between the valve and the actuator were 10 or perhaps even 20 ft away. The entire profit margin could be affected, and therefore the sizing and length of the conductor are as vital a component to consider as the valve and actuator.

There are many types and styles of directional air-control valves that internally conduct the air through the air passages in different manners. There are also many means for actuating them, where some are directly and others only superficially related to the $C_v$ capability of the structure. For a thorough understanding and appreciation of the wide variety and methods available, review the yearly handbook published by the editors of *Hydraulics and Pneumatics Handbook* series[1] as well as their many detailed surveys on the subject of directional air-control valves[2] and PAC II.[3]

Briefly, there is the lapped-spool type of assembly, which can float (air-bearing configuration) inside a honed sleeve, a composite-spool, or packed-spool variety (dynamic O-ring seals), which reciprocates inside a body. The other principal classification which rounds out the major group is the poppet-style valve. All can be operated directly by a solenoid, air, or a return spring or various combinations of these power sources. The method of actuation can be by a remote pilot, which in turn can be operated by a solenoid. Again there can be multiple associations of any and all of the above. In essence, there can be a direct operated valve with a solenoid on each end or a spring on one end and a solenoid on the other, and either can be plumbed to be normally passing or nonpassing. So much for the type, flow paths, and operators. Some can be of the two-position or three-position variety with two, three, four, or five ports and capable of having two, three, or four flow paths. See Chapter 8 for Figures 8.2, 8.3, 8.6, 8.7, 8.8, 8.10, 8.11, and 8.12, which are schematics of some of the values I have just described. In addition, any and all of these valves can be used singularly or in concert with other valves and devices to create very basic networks or the intricate and complex circuitry demanded in today's marketplace. We have shown a few of these possibilities for your perusal and again direct your attention to the figures cited in Chapter 8 for the specific schematics.

In all the examples that we have thus far submitted and will continue to submit to the end of the text, we will involve methods to

---

[1]*Fluid Power Handbook Engineering Data, Hydraulics and Pneumatics Handbook* series, Penton Publishing, Cleveland, Ohio, 1994/1995.

[2]*Solenoid Valves Offer Control Versatility, Hydraulics and Pneumatics Handbook* series, Penton Publishing, Cleveland, Ohio, April 1990. (Just one of many studies published by Penton Publishing, Education Division.)

[3]Henry Schlenke, *Practical Air Circuitry II* (manual), Numatics Inc. 1979.

improve the efficiency of energy usage in manufacturing because it is a critical issue not only to our industry but also to our nation at large. As I've pointed out repeatedly, it's crucial if we want to be a world player. It may even prove to be decisive in some instances. There are many areas for saving fuel that can be easily identified and can be just as easily implemented without too much capital investment and pain. Others require careful appraisal to establish their economic feasibility. One thing is certain; it is incumbent upon us to investigate all opportunities. We have the wherewithal and it would be unjustifiably negligent to do otherwise than to employ it.

*"Around what is, lies a whole mysterious world of what might be."*
HENRY WADSWORTH LONGFELLOW

```
NUMATICS NUMASIZING (R) SUMMARY SHEET                    Date:   04/10/95
NU301EED  Ver 3.01 (c) 1989 Numatics, Inc.              SURVEY # 6-1
========================================================================
Prepared for:               Prepared by:    Michael Liberty
Company:                    Company:        Numatics Inc.
Address:                    Address:        1450 N. Milford Rd.
City,State,Zip:             City,State,Zip: Highland, Mi. 48357
Telephone #                 Telephone #     (810) 887-4111
Fax #                       Fax #           (810) 887-9190
------------------------------------------------------------------------
                                    Avg/Tot/Oth    Extend      Retract
INITIAL CUSTOMER PARAMETERS:
Total weight of load (lbs)                         200.00      50.00
Angle of load from horizontal           0
Coefficient of Friction              0.33
Number of actuators                     1
Total load per actuator (lbs)                      155.19      53.68
Minimum line pressure (PSIG)          100
Design pressure used (PSIG)                        80.0        80.0
Shifts/day (1 shift=120,000 m/yr)     2.0
Cycles per year                   4499333

ACTUATOR:
Description:   Single Rod High Flow Numatics Actuator with 3/8 NPT ports
Bore/stroke/rod           2.50" bore x 12.00" stroke x 0.625" rod
Fitting                              3/4" - 3/8 NPT STR

CONDUCTOR & ASSOCIATED COMPONENTS:
Branch conductor /leg                    N/A
Branch manifold fitting /leg             N/A
Branch cond equiv ftg lg /leg (in)       N/A
Quick disconnect model /leg              N/A
In line flow control model /leg                    NONE        NONE
Main conductor           3/4" rubber hose 48" long with 0.0 elbow(s)
Main manifold fitting                    N/A
Main cond equiv ftg lg (in)               0

VALVE ASSEMBLY & ASSOCIATED COMPONENTS:
Description    2 Pos Mk 15 on 3/8 NPT base with ext reg
Fitting                                  3/4" - 3/8 NPT STR
Silencer model                           N/A

SYSTEM PERFORMANCE TIMES:
Att'n stroke time (sec)                            0.39        0.31
Required stroke time (sec)                         0.39        0.31
Stroke time @ term vel (sec)                       0.27        0.25
Att'n cyclic rate (CPM)              18.74
Required cyclic rate (CPM)           18.75
Cyclic rate @ term vel (CPM)         19.86
System delay time (sec)              0.025
Dwell time after stroke (sec)                      1.40        1.10

SYSTEM INFORMATION:
Required system Cv                                 1.53        1.54
Attained system Cv                                 1.46        1.46
Att'n system air flow (SCFM)                       46.3        54.3
Att'n branch air vel (400 FPS max)       N/A             N/A
Att'n main air vel (400 FPS max)                   45          57
Att'n % delta p (46% max)                          14          20
% Act. capacity used (75% max)                     40          15
Min pres necessary for 1d w/S.F. (PSIG)            42.2        15.6
Air per cycle (SCF)                  0.58
Att'n act leakage cost/yr @ $ 0.30 /KSCF   66      28          38
Att'n operating air cost/yr @ $ 0.30 /KSCF  787    403         384
Cost /1000 cyc @ att'n times @ $ 20.00 /hr 17.98
Att'n power input total (HP)         2.41

COMMENTS:
Using a Mk 15
```

```
NUMATICS NUMASIZING (R) SUMMARY SHEET                    Date:   04/10/95
NU301EED   Ver 3.01 (c) 1989 Numatics, Inc.            SURVEY # 6-2
==============================================================================
Prepared for:                   Prepared by:   Michael Liberty
Company:                        Company:       Numatics Inc.
Address:                        Address:       1450 N. Milford Rd.
City,State,Zip:                 City,State,Zip: Highland, Mi. 48357
Telephone #                     Telephone #    (810) 887-4111
Fax #                           Fax #          (810) 887-9190
------------------------------------------------------------------------------
                                    Avg/Tot/Oth    Extend     Retract
INITIAL CUSTOMER PARAMETERS:
Total weight of load (lbs)                         200.00      50.00
Angle of load from horizontal          0
Coefficient of Friction             0.33
Number of actuators                    1
Total load per actuator (lbs)                      181.31      70.05
Minimum line pressure (PSIG)         100
Design pressure used (PSIG)                        80.0        80.0
Shifts/day (1 shift=120,000 m/yr)    2.0
Cycles per year                  4657408

ACTUATOR:
Description:   Single Rod High Flow Numatics Actuator with 3/8 NPT ports
Bore/stroke/rod          2.50" bore x 12.00" stroke x 0.625" rod
Fitting                  3/4" - 3/8 NPT STR

CONDUCTOR & ASSOCIATED COMPONENTS:
Branch conductor /leg                N/A
Branch manifold fitting /leg         N/A
Branch cond equiv ftg lg /leg (in)   N/A
Quick disconnect model /leg          N/A
In line flow control model /leg                    NONE        NONE
Main conductor          3/4" rubber hose 48" long with 0.0 elbow(s)
Main manifold fitting                N/A
Main cond equiv ftg lg (in)            0

VALVE ASSEMBLY & ASSOCIATED COMPONENTS:
Description     2 Pos Mk 25 on 1/2 NPT base with ext reg
Fitting                              3/4" - 1/2 NPT STR
Silencer model                       N/A

SYSTEM PERFORMANCE TIMES:
Att'n stroke time (sec)                            0.34        0.26
Required stroke time (sec)                         0.34        0.26
Stroke time @ term vel (sec)                       0.21        0.20
Att'n cyclic rate (CPM)            19.41
Required cyclic rate (CPM)         19.41
Cyclic rate @ term vel (CPM)       20.65
System delay time (sec)            0.025
Dwell time after stroke (sec)                      1.40        1.10

SYSTEM INFORMATION:
Required system Cv                                 1.97        2.01
Attained system Cv                                 1.87        1.87
Att'n system air flow (SCFM)                       53.3        66.9
Att'n branch air vel (400 FPS max)     N/A         N/A
Att'n main air vel (400 FPS max)                   50          69
Att'n % delta p (46% max)                          11          18
% Act. capacity used (75% max)                     46          19
Min pres necessary for ld w/S.F. (PSIG)            49.2        20.3
Air per cycle (SCF)                 0.58
Att'n act leakage cost/yr @ $ 0.30 /KSCF    65     28          38
Att'n operating air cost/yr @ $ 0.30 /KSCF  815    417         398
Cost /1000 cyc @ att'n times @ $ 20.00 /hr  17.37
Att'n power input total (HP)        2.48

COMMENTS:
Using a Mk 25
```

```
NUMATICS NUMASIZING (R) SUMMARY SHEET                    Date:   04/10/95
NU301EED  Ver 3.01 (c) 1989 Numatics, Inc.              SURVEY # 6-3
========================================================================
Prepared for:                      Prepared by:     Michael Liberty
Company:                           Company:         Numatics Inc.
Address:                           Address:         1450 N. Milford Rd.
City,State,Zip:                    City,State,Zip:  Highland, Mi. 48357
Telephone #                        Telephone #      (810) 887-4111
Fax #                              Fax #            (810) 887-9190
------------------------------------------------------------------------
                                        Avg/Tot/Oth   Extend    Retract
INITIAL CUSTOMER PARAMETERS:
Total weight of load (lbs)                            200.00     50.00
Angle of load from horizontal              0
Coefficient of Friction                 0.33
Number of actuators                        1
Total load per actuator (lbs)                        230.30    111.80
Minimum line pressure (PSIG)             100
Design pressure used (PSIG)                           80.0      80.0
Shifts/day (1 shift=120,000 m/yr)        2.0
Cycles per year                      4854504

ACTUATOR:
Description:   Single Rod High Flow Numatics Actuator with 3/8 NPT ports
Bore/stroke/rod           2.50" bore x 12.00" stroke x 0.625" rod
Fitting                   3/4" - 3/8 NPT STR

CONDUCTOR & ASSOCIATED COMPONENTS:
Branch conductor /leg               N/A
Branch manifold fitting /leg        N/A
Branch cond equiv ftg lg /leg (in)  N/A
Quick disconnect model /leg         N/A
In line flow control model /leg                      NONE       NONE
Main conductor            3/4" rubber hose 48" long with 0.0 elbow(s)
Main manifold fitting               N/A
Main cond equiv ftg lg (in)           0

VALVE ASSEMBLY & ASSOCIATED COMPONENTS:
Description    2 Pos Mk 40 on 3/4 NPT base with ext reg
Fitting                             3/4" - 3/4 NPT STR
Silencer model                      N/A

SYSTEM PERFORMANCE TIMES:
Att'n stroke time (sec)                              0.28       0.19
Required stroke time (sec)                           0.28       0.19
Stroke time @ term vel (sec)                         0.13       0.13
Att'n cyclic rate (CPM)                20.23
Required cyclic rate (CPM)             20.23
Cyclic rate @ term vel (CPM)           21.73
System delay time (sec)                0.022
Dwell time after stroke (sec)                        1.40       1.10

SYSTEM INFORMATION:
Required system Cv                                    3.09       3.19
Attained system Cv                                   2.90       2.90
Att'n system air flow (SCFM)                         64.1       91.5
Att'n branch air vel (400 FPS max)         N/A                  N/A
Att'n main air vel (400 FPS max)                     58         89
Att'n % delta p (46% max)                            6          13
% Act. capacity used (75% max)                       58         30
Min pres necessary for ld w/S.F. (PSIG)              62.6       32.4
Air per cycle (SCF)                     0.58
Att'n act leakage cost/yr @ $ 0.30 /KSCF    65       28         37
Att'n operating air cost/yr @ $ 0.30 /KSCF 850       435        415
Cost /1000 cyc @ att'n times @ $ 20.00 /hr 16.67
Att'n power input total (HP)            2.58

COMMENTS:
Using a Mk 40
```

```
NUMATICS NUMASIZING (R) SUMMARY SHEET                      Date:    04/10/95
NU301EED  Ver 3.01 (c) 1989 Numatics, Inc.               SURVEY # 6-4
==========================================================================
Prepared for:                    Prepared by:       Michael Liberty
Company:                         Company:           Numatics Inc.
Address:                         Address:           1450 N. Milford Rd.
City,State,Zip:                  City,State,Zip:    Highland, Mi. 48357
Telephone #                      Telephone #        (810) 887-4111
Fax #                            Fax #              (810) 887-9190
--------------------------------------------------------------------------
                                       Avg/Tot/Oth     Extend      Retract
INITIAL CUSTOMER PARAMETERS:
Total weight of load (lbs)                            200.00       50.00
Angle of load from horizontal            0
Coefficient of Friction               0.33
Number of actuators                      1
Total load per actuator (lbs)                        162.75       57.40
Minimum line pressure (PSIG)           100
Design pressure used (PSIG)                           80.0        80.0
Shifts/day (1 shift=120,000 m/yr)      2.0
Cycles per year                    4546922

ACTUATOR:
Description:   Single Rod High Flow Numatics Actuator with 3/8 NPT ports
Bore/stroke/rod            2.50" bore x 12.00" stroke x 0.625" rod
Fitting                            1/2" - 3/8 NPT STR

CONDUCTOR & ASSOCIATED COMPONENTS:
Branch conductor /leg                   N/A
Branch manifold fitting /leg            N/A
Branch cond equiv ftg lg /leg (in)      N/A
Quick disconnect model /leg             N/A
In line flow control model /leg                        NONE        NONE
Main conductor              1/2" rubber hose 48" long with 0.0 elbow(s)
Main manifold fitting                   N/A
Main cond equiv ftg lg (in)              0

VALVE ASSEMBLY & ASSOCIATED COMPONENTS:
Description      2 Pos Mk 15 on 3/8 NPT base with ext req
Fitting                            1/2" - 3/8 NPT STR
Silencer model                          N/A

SYSTEM PERFORMANCE TIMES:
Att'n stroke time (sec)                                0.37        0.30
Required stroke time (sec)                             0.37        0.30
Stroke time @ term vel (sec)                           0.25        0.24
Att'n cyclic rate (CPM)               18.95
Required cyclic rate (CPM)            18.95
Cyclic rate @ term vel (CPM)          20.10
System delay time (sec)               0.025
Dwell time after stroke (sec)                          1.40        1.10

SYSTEM INFORMATION:
Required system Cv                                     1.39        1.41
Attained system Cv                                     1.33        1.33
Att'n system air flow (SCFM)                          41.3        48.7
Att'n branch air vel (400 FPS max)      N/A            N/A
Att'n main air vel (400 FPS max)                        90         115
Att'n % delta p (46% max)                               13          19
% Act. capacity used (75% max)                          41          16
Min pres necessary for 1d w/S.F. (PSIG)               44.2        16.6
Air per cycle (SCF)                    0.50
Att'n act leakage cost/yr @ $ 0.30 /KSCF   66           28          38
Att'n operating air cost/yr @ $ 0.30 /KSCF 676         347         329
Cost /1000 cyc @ att'n times @ $ 20.00 /hr 17.76
Att'n power input total (HP)           2.09

COMMENTS:
Using a Mk 15 w/optimum 1/2" hose
```

```
NUMATICS NUMASIZING (R) SUMMARY SHEET                    Date:   04/10/95
NU301EED   Ver 3.01 (c) 1989 Numatics, Inc.             SURVEY # 6-5
=========================================================================
Prepared for:                   Prepared by:    Michael Liberty
Company:                        Company:        Numatics Inc.
Address:                        Address:        1450 N. Milford Rd.
City,State,Zip:                 City,State,Zip: Highland, Mi. 48357
Telephone #                     Telephone #     (810) 887-4111
Fax #                           Fax #           (810) 887-9190
-------------------------------------------------------------------------
                                    Avg/Tot/Oth    Extend      Retract
INITIAL CUSTOMER PARAMETERS:
Total weight of load (lbs)                        200.00       50.00
Angle of load from horizontal          0
Coefficient of Friction             0.33
Number of actuators                    1
Total load per actuator (lbs)                     186.69       73.13
Minimum line pressure (PSIG)         100
Design pressure used (PSIG)                        80.0        80.0
Shifts/day (1 shift=120,000 m/yr)    2.0
Cycles per year                  4681349

ACTUATOR:
Description:   Single Rod High Flow Numatics Actuator with 3/8 NPT ports
Bore/stroke/rod              2.50" bore x 12.00" stroke x 0.625" rod
Fitting                              5/8" - 3/8 NPT STR

CONDUCTOR & ASSOCIATED COMPONENTS:
Branch conductor /leg                    N/A
Branch manifold fitting /leg             N/A
Branch cond equiv ftg lg /leg (in)       N/A
Quick disconnect model /leg              N/A
In line flow control model /leg                    NONE         NONE
Main conductor           5/8" rubber hose 48" long with 0.0 elbow(s)
Main manifold fitting                    N/A
Main cond equiv ftg lg (in)                0

VALVE ASSEMBLY & ASSOCIATED COMPONENTS:
Description    2 Pos Mk 25 on 1/2 NPT base with ext req
Fitting                                  5/8" - 1/2 NPT STR
Silencer model                           N/A

SYSTEM PERFORMANCE TIMES:
Att'n stroke time (sec)                            0.33        0.25
Required stroke time (sec)                         0.33        0.25
Stroke time @ term vel (sec)                       0.20        0.19
Att'n cyclic rate (CPM)             19.50
Required cyclic rate (CPM)          19.51
Cyclic rate @ term vel (CPM)        20.77
System delay time (sec)             0.025
Dwell time after stroke (sec)                      1.40        1.10

SYSTEM INFORMATION:
Required system Cv                                 1.89        1.92
Attained system Cv                                 1.79        1.79
Att'n system air flow (SCFM)                       49.9        63.3
Att'n branch air vel (400 FPS max)       N/A              N/A
Att'n main air vel (400 FPS max)                   67          93
Att'n % delta p (46% max)                          10          18
% Act. capacity used (75% max)                     48          20
Min pres necessary for 1d w/S.F. (PSIG)            50.7        21.2
Air per cycle (SCF)                 0.54
Att'n act leakage cost/yr @ $ 0.30 /KSCF          28          38
Att'n operating air cost/yr @ $ 0.30 /KSCF         385         366
Cost /1000 cyc @ att'n times @ $ 20.00 /hr  17.27
Att'n power input total (HP)        2.30

COMMENTS:
Using a Mk 25 w/optimum 5/8" hose
```

```
NUMATICS NUMASIZING (R) SUMMARY SHEET                   Date:    04/10/95
NU301EED  Ver 3.01 (c) 1989 Numatics, Inc.             SURVEY # 6-6
=========================================================================
Prepared for:                     Prepared by:   Michael Liberty
Company:                          Company:       Numatics Inc.
Address:                          Address:       1450 N. Milford Rd.
City,State,Zip:                   City,State,Zip: Highland, Mi. 48357
Telephone #                       Telephone #    (810) 887-4111
Fax #                             Fax #          (810) 887-9190
-------------------------------------------------------------------------
                                  Avg/Tot/Oth    Extend      Retract
INITIAL CUSTOMER PARAMETERS:
Total weight of load (lbs)                       200.00       50.00
Angle of load from horizontal         0
Coefficient of Friction            0.33
Number of actuators                   1
Total load per actuator (lbs)                    230.78      111.62
Minimum line pressure (PSIG)        100
Design pressure used (PSIG)                       80.0        80.0
Shifts/day (1 shift=120,000 m/yr)     2.0
Cycles per year                 4854890

ACTUATOR:
Description:   Single Rod High Flow Numatics Actuator with 3/8 NPT ports
Bore/stroke/rod          2.50" bore x 12.00" stroke x 0.625" rod
Fitting                  3/4" - 3/8 NPT STR

CONDUCTOR & ASSOCIATED COMPONENTS:
Branch conductor /leg                     N/A
Branch manifold fitting /leg              N/A
Branch cond equiv ftg lg /leg (in)        N/A
Quick disconnect model /leg               N/A
In line flow control model /leg                  NONE        NONE
Main conductor           3/4" rubber hose 48" long with 0.0 elbow(s)
Main manifold fitting                     N/A
Main cond equiv lg (in)                    0

VALVE ASSEMBLY & ASSOCIATED COMPONENTS:
Description    2 Pos Mk 40 on 3/4 NPT base with ext req
Fitting                  3/4" - 3/4 NPT STR
Silencer model                            N/A

SYSTEM PERFORMANCE TIMES:
Att'n stroke time (sec)                           0.28        0.19
Required stroke time (sec)                        0.28        0.19
Stroke time @ term vel (sec)                      0.13        0.13
Att'n cyclic rate (CPM)               20.22
Required cyclic rate (CPM)            20.23
Cyclic rate @ term vel (CPM)          21.73
System delay time (sec)               0.022
Dwell time after stroke (sec)                     1.40        1.10

SYSTEM INFORMATION:
Required system Cv                                3.10        3.19
Attained system Cv                                2.90        2.90
Att'n system air flow (SCFM)                      63.9        91.6
Att'n branch air vel (400 FPS max)        N/A              N/A
Att'n main air vel (400 FPS max)                   57          89
Att'n % delta p (46% max)                           6          13
% Act. capacity used (75% max)                     59          30
Min pres necessary for 1d w/S.F. (PSIG)          62.7        32.3
Air per cycle (SCF)                    0.58
Att'n act leakage cost/yr @ $ 0.30 /KSCF   65      28          37
Att'n operating air cost/yr @ $ 0.30 /KSCF 850    435         415
Cost /1000 cyc @ att'n times @ $ 20.00 /hr 16.67
Att'n power input total (HP)           2.58

COMMENTS:
Using a Mk 40 w/optimum 3/4" hose & therefore identical to 6-3
```

```
NUMATICS NUMASIZING (R) SUMMARY SHEET                 Date:    04/10/95
NU301EED  Ver 3.01 (c) 1989 Numatics, Inc.           SURVEY # 6-7
=======================================================================
Prepared for:                    Prepared by:    Michael Liberty
Company:                         Company:        Numatics Inc.
Address:                         Address:        1450 N. Milford Rd.
City,State,Zip:                  City,State,Zip: Highland, Mi. 48357
Telephone #                      Telephone #     (810) 887-4111
Fax #                            Fax #           (810) 887-9190
-----------------------------------------------------------------------
                                   Avg/Tot/Oth    Extend      Retract
INITIAL CUSTOMER PARAMETERS:
Total weight of load (lbs)                        200.00       50.00
Angle of load from horizontal          0
Coefficient of Friction                0.33
Number of actuators                    1
Total load per actuator (lbs)                     131.91       42.64
Minimum line pressure (PSIG)         100
Design pressure used (PSIG)                       80.0         80.0
Shifts/day (1 shift=120,000 m/yr)      2.0
Cycles per year                  4304868

ACTUATOR:
Description:   Single Rod High Flow Numatics Actuator with 3/8 NPT ports
Bore/stroke/rod          2.50" bore x 12.00" stroke x 0.625" rod
Fitting                  3/4" - 3/8 NPT STR

CONDUCTOR & ASSOCIATED COMPONENTS:
Branch conductor /leg                    N/A
Branch manifold fitting /leg             N/A
Branch cond equiv ftg lg /leg (in)       N/A
Quick disconnect model /leg              N/A
In line flow control model /leg                    NONE        NONE
Main conductor           3/4" rubber hose 96" long with 0.0 elbow(s)
Main manifold fitting                    N/A
Main cond equiv ftg lg (in)              0

VALVE ASSEMBLY & ASSOCIATED COMPONENTS:
Description     2 Pos Mk 15 on 3/8 NPT base with ext req
Fitting                                  3/4" - 3/8 NPT STR
Silencer model                           N/A

SYSTEM PERFORMANCE TIMES:
Att'n stroke time (sec)                            0.46        0.39
Required stroke time (sec)                         0.45        0.39
Stroke time @ term vel (sec)                       0.34        0.33
Att'n cyclic rate (CPM)               17.93
Required cyclic rate (CPM)            17.94
Cyclic rate @ term vel (CPM)          18.96
System delay time (sec)               0.025
Dwell time after stroke (sec)                      1.40        1.10

SYSTEM INFORMATION:
Required system Cv                                 1.51        1.52
Attained system Cv                                 1.45        1.45
Att'n system air flow (SCFM)                       49.8        55.9
Att'n branch air vel (400 FPS max)       N/A                N/A
Att'n main air vel (400 FPS max)                   50          61
Att'n % delta p (46% max)                          16          22
% Act. capacity used (75% max)                     34          12
Min pres necessary for ld w/S.F. (PSIG)            35.8        12.4
Air per cycle (SCF)                    0.74
Att'n act leakage cost/yr @ $ 0.30 /KSCF    66     27          38
Att'n operating air cost/yr @ $ 0.30 /KSCF 958     488         470
Cost /1000 cyc @ att'n times @ $ 20.00 /hr 18.83
Att'n power input total (HP)           2.89

COMMENTS:
Using a Mk 15 w/96" of 3/4" hose
```

```
NUMATICS NUMASIZING (R) SUMMARY SHEET              Date:    04/10/95
NU301EED  Ver 3.01 (c) 1989 Numatics, Inc.         SURVEY # 6-8
===============================================================================
Prepared for:                       Prepared by:    Michael Liberty
Company:                            Company:        Numatics Inc.
Address:                            Address:        1450 N. Milford Rd.
City,State,Zip:                     City,State,Zip: Highland, Mi. 48357
Telephone #                         Telephone #     (810) 887-4111
Fax #                               Fax #           (810) 887-9190
-------------------------------------------------------------------------------
                                           Avg/Tot/Oth   Extend    Retract
INITIAL CUSTOMER PARAMETERS:
Total weight of load (lbs)                              200.00      50.00
Angle of load from horizontal                0
Coefficient of Friction                   0.33
Number of actuators                          1
Total load per actuator (lbs)                          154.83      54.18
Minimum line pressure (PSIG)               100
Design pressure used (PSIG)                             80.0       80.0
Shifts/day (1 shift=120,000 m/yr)          2.0
Cycles per year                        4501630

ACTUATOR:
Description:   Single Rod High Flow Numatics Actuator with 3/8 NPT ports
Bore/stroke/rod                2.50" bore x 12.00" stroke x 0.625" rod
Fitting                                  3/4" - 3/8 NPT STR

CONDUCTOR & ASSOCIATED COMPONENTS:
Branch conductor /leg                   N/A
Branch manifold fitting /leg            N/A
Branch cond equiv ftg lg /leg (in)      N/A
Quick disconnect model /leg             N/A
In line flow control model /leg                        NONE       NONE
Main conductor            3/4" rubber hose 96" long with 0.0 elbow(s)
Main manifold fitting                   N/A
Main cond equiv ftg lg (in)               0

VALVE ASSEMBLY & ASSOCIATED COMPONENTS:
Description    2 Pos Mk 25 on 1/2 NPT base with ext req
Fitting                                  3/4" - 1/2 NPT STR
Silencer model                          N/A

SYSTEM PERFORMANCE TIMES:
Att'n stroke time (sec)                                 0.39       0.31
Required stroke time (sec)                              0.39       0.31
Stroke time @ term vel (sec)                           0.26       0.25
Att'n cyclic rate (CPM)                  18.75
Required cyclic rate (CPM)               18.76
Cyclic rate @ term vel (CPM)             19.88
System delay time (sec)                  0.025
Dwell time after stroke (sec)                          1.40       1.10

SYSTEM INFORMATION:
Required system Cv                                      1.95       1.97
Attained system Cv                                     1.86       1.86
Att'n system air flow (SCFM)             58.6                     69.9
Att'n branch air vel (400 FPS max)      N/A            N/A
Att'n main air vel (400 FPS max)                        57         74
Att'n % delta p (46% max)                               13         21
% Act. capacity used (75% max)                          39         15
Min pres necessary for ld w/S.F. (PSIG)                42.1       15.7
Air per cycle (SCF)                      0.74
Att'n act leakage cost/yr @ $ 0.30 /KSCF   66           28         38
Att'n operating air cost/yr @ $ 0.30 /KSCF 1001        510        491
Cost /1000 cyc @ att'n times @ $ 20.00 /hr 18.01
Att'n power input total (HP)             3.01

COMMENTS:
Using a Mk 25 w/96" of 3/4" hose
```

```
NUMATICS NUMASIZING (R) SUMMARY SHEET                    Date:    04/10/95
NU301EED  Ver 3.01 (c) 1989 Numatics, Inc.              SURVEY # 6-9
=========================================================================
Prepared for:                   Prepared by:     Michael Liberty
Company:                        Company:         Numatics Inc.
Address:                        Address:         1450 N. Milford Rd.
City,State,Zip:                 City,State,Zip:  Highland, Mi. 48357
Telephone #                     Telephone #      (810) 887-4111
Fax #                           Fax #            (810) 887-9190
-------------------------------------------------------------------------
                                        Avg/Tot/Oth    Extend     Retract
INITIAL CUSTOMER PARAMETERS:
Total weight of load (lbs)                           200.00      50.00
Angle of load from horizontal             0
Coefficient of Friction                   0.33
Number of actuators                       1
Total load per actuator (lbs)                        201.61      85.60
Minimum line pressure (PSIG)              100
Design pressure used (PSIG)                           80.0        80.0
Shifts/day (1 shift=120,000 m/yr)         2.0
Cycles per year                           4751049

ACTUATOR:
Description:    Single Rod High Flow Numatics Actuator with 3/8 NPT ports
Bore/stroke/rod                 2.50" bore x 12.00" stroke x 0.625" rod
Fitting                         3/4" - 3/8 NPT STR

CONDUCTOR & ASSOCIATED COMPONENTS:
Branch conductor /leg                       N/A
Branch manifold fitting /leg                N/A
Branch cond equiv ftg lg /leg (in)          N/A
Quick disconnect model /leg                 N/A
In line flow control model /leg                         NONE        NONE
Main conductor                  3/4" rubber hose 96" long with 0.0 elbow(s)
Main manifold fitting                       N/A
Main cond equiv ftg lg (in)                 0

VALVE ASSEMBLY & ASSOCIATED COMPONENTS:
Description     2 Pos Mk 40 on 3/4 NPT base with ext req
Fitting                                     3/4" - 3/4 NPT STR
Silencer model                              N/A

SYSTEM PERFORMANCE TIMES:
Att'n stroke time (sec)                                0.31        0.22
Required stroke time (sec)                             0.31        0.22
Stroke time @ term vel (sec)                           0.17        0.17
Att'n cyclic rate (CPM)                   19.80
Required cyclic rate (CPM)                19.80
Cyclic rate @ term vel (CPM)              21.15
System delay time (sec)                   0.022
Dwell time after stroke (sec)                          1.40        1.10

SYSTEM INFORMATION:
Required system Cv                                     3.03        3.08
Attained system Cv                                     2.86        2.86
Att'n system air flow (SCFM)                          73.1        98.9
Att'n branch air vel (400 FPS max)        N/A                N/A
Att'n main air vel (400 FPS max)                      67          100
Att'n % delta p (46% max)                             8           17
% Act. capacity used (75% max)                        51          23
Min pres necessary for 1d w/S.F. (PSIG)               54.8        24.8
Air per cycle (SCF)                       0.74
Att'n act leakage cost/yr @ $ 0.30 /KSCF             65          37
Att'n operating air cost/yr @ $ 0.30 /KSCF  1057     28          519
Cost /1000 cyc @ att'n times @ $ 20.00 /hr  17.07    538
Att'n power input total (HP)                3.17

COMMENTS:
Using a Mk 40 w/96" of 3/4" hose
```

```
NUMATICS NUMASIZING (R) SUMMARY SHEET                    Date:    04/10/95
NU301EED  Ver 3.01 (c) 1989 Numatics, Inc.              SURVEY # 6-10
========================================================================
Prepared for:                   Prepared by:    Michael Liberty
Company:                        Company:        Numatics Inc.
Address:                        Address:        1450 N. Milford Rd.
City,State,Zip:                 City,State,Zip: Highland, Mi. 48357
Telephone #                     Telephone #     (810) 887-4111
Fax #                           Fax #           (810) 887-9190
------------------------------------------------------------------------
                                     Avg/Tot/Oth   Extend     Retract
INITIAL CUSTOMER PARAMETERS:
Total weight of load (lbs)                        200.00      50.00
Angle of load from horizontal           0
Coefficient of Friction                 0.33
Number of actuators                     1
Total load per actuator (lbs)                     146.36      49.09
Minimum line pressure (PSIG)          100
Design pressure used (PSIG)                        80.0       80.0
Shifts/day (1 shift=120,000 m/yr)       2.0
Cycles per year                   4432815

ACTUATOR:
Description:    Single Rod High Flow Numatics Actuator with 3/8 NPT ports
Bore/stroke/rod           2.50" bore x 12.00" stroke x 0.625" rod
Fitting                   1/2" - 3/8 NPT STR

CONDUCTOR & ASSOCIATED COMPONENTS:
Branch conductor /leg                 N/A
Branch manifold fitting /leg          N/A
Branch cond equiv ftg lg /leg (in)    N/A
Quick disconnect model /leg           N/A
In line flow control model /leg                   NONE        NONE
Main conductor            1/2" rubber hose 96" long with 0.0 elbow(s)
Main manifold fitting                 N/A
Main cond equiv ftg lg (in)             0

VALVE ASSEMBLY & ASSOCIATED COMPONENTS:
Description     2 Pos Mk 15 on 3/8 NPT base with ext reg
Fitting                               1/2" - 3/8 NPT STR
Silencer model                        N/A

SYSTEM PERFORMANCE TIMES:
Att'n stroke time (sec)                            0.41        0.34
Required stroke time (sec)                         0.41        0.34
Stroke time @ term vel (sec)                       0.29        0.28
Att'n cyclic rate (CPM)                18.47
Required cyclic rate (CPM)             18.47
Cyclic rate @ term vel (CPM)           19.55
System delay time (sec)                 0.025
Dwell time after stroke (sec)                      1.40        1.10

SYSTEM INFORMATION:
Required system Cv                                 1.35        1.36
Attained system Cv                                 1.29        1.29
Att'n system air flow (SCFM)                       42.6        48.6
Att'n branch air vel (400 FPS max)      N/A                   N/A
Att'n main air vel (400 FPS max)                   95          116
Att'n % delta p (46% max)                          15          21
% Act. capacity used (75% max)                     37          13
Min pres necessary for 1d w/S.F. (PSIG)            39.8        14.2
Air per cycle (SCF)                     0.57
Att'n act leakage cost/yr @ $ 0.30 /KSCF  66       28          38
Att'n operating air cost/yr @ $ 0.30 /KSCF 753    385          367
Cost /1000 cyc @ att'n times @ $ 20.00 /hr 18.24
Att'n power input total (HP)            2.31

COMMENTS:
Using a Mk 15 w/96" optimum 1/2" hose
```

```
NUMATICS NUMASIZING (R) SUMMARY SHEET                    Date:    04/10/95
NU301EED  Ver 3.01 (c) 1989 Numatics, Inc.              SURVEY # 6-11
==========================================================================
Prepared for:                    Prepared by:      Michael Liberty
Company:                         Company:          Numatics Inc.
Address:                         Address:          1450 N. Milford Rd.
City,State,Zip:                  City,State,Zip:   Highland, Mi. 48357
Telephone #                      Telephone #       (810) 887-4111
Fax #                            Fax #             (810) 887-9190
--------------------------------------------------------------------------
                                 Avg/Tot/Oth    Extend       Retract
INITIAL CUSTOMER PARAMETERS:
  Total weight of load (lbs)                    200.00        50.00
  Angle of load from horizontal       0
  Coefficient of Friction             0.33
  Number of actuators                 1
  Total load per actuator (lbs)                 164.05        58.92
  Minimum line pressure (PSIG)      100
  Design pressure used (PSIG)                    80.0         80.0
  Shifts/day (1 shift=120,000 m/yr)   2.0
  Cycles per year                 4559636

ACTUATOR:
  Description:   Single Rod High Flow Numatics Actuator with 3/8 NPT ports
  Bore/stroke/rod             2.50" bore x 12.00" stroke x 0.625" rod
  Fitting                              5/8" - 3/8 NPT STR

CONDUCTOR & ASSOCIATED COMPONENTS:
  Branch conductor /leg                N/A
  Branch manifold fitting /leg         N/A
  Branch cond equiv ftg lg /leg (in)   N/A
  Quick disconnect model /leg          N/A
  In line flow control model /leg                NONE          NONE
  Main conductor              5/8" rubber hose 96" long with 0.0 elbow(s)
  Main manifold fitting                N/A
  Main cond equiv ftg lg (in)           0

VALVE ASSEMBLY & ASSOCIATED COMPONENTS:
  Description    2 Pos Mk 25 on 1/2 NPT base with ext reg
  Fitting                              5/8" - 1/2 NPT STR
  Silencer model                       N/A

SYSTEM PERFORMANCE TIMES:
  Att'n stroke time (sec)                        0.37          0.29
  Required stroke time (sec)                     0.37          0.29
  Stroke time @ term vel (sec)                   0.24          0.23
  Att'n cyclic rate (CPM)            19.00
  Required cyclic rate (CPM)         19.00
  Cyclic rate @ term vel (CPM)       20.17
  System delay time (sec)             0.025
  Dwell time after stroke (sec)                  1.40          1.10

SYSTEM INFORMATION:
  Required system Cv                             1.85          1.87
  Attained system Cv                             1.76          1.76
  Att'n system air flow (SCFM)                   53.8          65.2
  Att'n branch air vel (400 FPS max)     N/A               N/A
  Att'n main air vel (400 FPS max)               75            99
  Att'n % delta p (46% max)                      12            20
  % Act. capacity used (75% max)                 42            16
  Min pres necessary for 1d w/S.F. (PSIG)        44.6          17.1
  Air per cycle (SCF)                 0.65
  Att'n act leakage cost/yr @ $ 0.30 /KSCF       28            38
  Att'n operating air cost/yr @ $ 0.30 /KSCF    451           432
  Cost /1000 cyc @ att'n times @ $ 20.00 /hr  17.75
  Att'n power input total (HP)        2.67

COMMENTS:
  Using a Mk 25 w/96" optimum 5/8" hose
```

```
NUMATICS NUMASIZING (R) SUMMARY SHEET               Date:    04/10/95
NU301EED  Ver 3.01 (c) 1989 Numatics, Inc.         SURVEY # 6-12
=====================================================================
Prepared for:                    Prepared by:   Michael Liberty
Company:                         Company:       Numatics Inc.
Address:                         Address:       1450 N. Milford Rd.
City,State,Zip:                  City,State,Zip: Highland, Mi. 48357
Telephone #                      Telephone #    (810) 887-4111
Fax #                            Fax #          (810) 887-9190
---------------------------------------------------------------------
                                    Avg/Tot/Oth   Extend     Retract
INITIAL CUSTOMER PARAMETERS:
Total weight of load (lbs)                        200.00      50.00
Angle of load from horizontal         0
Coefficient of Friction               0.33
Number of actuators                   1
Total load per actuator (lbs)                     210.79      85.89
Minimum line pressure (PSIG)        100
Design pressure used (PSIG)                        80.0       80.0
Shifts/day (1 shift=120,000 m/yr)     2.0
Cycles per year                  4752162

ACTUATOR:
Description:  Single Rod High Flow Numatics Actuator with 3/8 NPT ports
Bore/stroke/rod          2.50" bore x 12.00" stroke x 0.625" rod
Fitting                  3/4" - 3/8 NPT STR

CONDUCTOR & ASSOCIATED COMPONENTS:
Branch conductor /leg                N/A
Branch manifold fitting /leg         N/A
Branch cond equiv ftg lg /leg (in)   N/A
Quick disconnect model /leg          N/A
In line flow control model /leg                   NONE        NONE
Main conductor           3/4" rubber hose 96" long with 0.0 elbow(s)
Main manifold fitting                N/A
Main cond equiv ftg lg (in)            0

VALVE ASSEMBLY & ASSOCIATED COMPONENTS:
Description     2 Pos Mk 40 on 3/4 NPT base with ext req
Fitting                              3/4" - 3/4 NPT STR
Silencer model                       N/A

SYSTEM PERFORMANCE TIMES:
Att'n stroke time (sec)                            0.31        0.22
Required stroke time (sec)                         0.31        0.22
Stroke time @ term vel (sec)                       0.17        0.17
Att'n cyclic rate (CPM)             19.79
Required cyclic rate (CPM)          19.80
Cyclic rate @ term vel (CPM)        21.15
System delay time (sec)             0.022
Dwell time after stroke (sec)                      1.40        1.10

SYSTEM INFORMATION:
Required system Cv                                 3.03        3.09
Attained system Cv                                 2.86        2.86
Att'n system air flow (SCFM)                       73.1        98.8
Att'n branch air vel (400 FPS max)    N/A                    N/A
Att'n main air vel (400 FPS max)                    67        100
Att'n % delta p (46% max)                            8         17
% Act. capacity used (75% max)                      51         23
Min pres necessary for 1d w/S.F. (PSIG)           54.8       24.9
Air per cycle (SCF)                   0.74
Att'n act leakage cost/yr @ $ 0.30 /KSCF  65        28         37
Att'n operating air cost/yr @ $ 0.30 /KSCF 1057    538        519
Cost /1000 cyc @ att'n times @ $ 20.00 /hr 17.07
Att'n power input total (HP)          3.17

COMMENTS:
Using a Mk 40 w/96" optimum 3/4" hose & therefore identical to 6-9
```

```
NUMATICS NUMASIZING (R) SUMMARY SHEET                    Date:    04/10/95
NU301EED  Ver 3.01 (c) 1989 Numatics, Inc.              SURVEY # 6-13
==========================================================================
Prepared for:                     Prepared by:      Michael Liberty
Company:                          Company:          Numatics Inc.
Address:                          Address:          1450 N. Milford Rd.
City,State,Zip:                   City,State,Zip:   Highland, Mi. 48357
Telephone #                       Telephone #       (810) 887-4111
Fax #                             Fax #             (810) 887-9190
--------------------------------------------------------------------------
                                       Avg/Tot/Oth    Extend      Retract
INITIAL CUSTOMER PARAMETERS:
Total weight of load (lbs)                            200.00       50.00
Angle of load from horizontal             0
Coefficient of Friction                0.33
Number of actuators                       1
Total load per actuator (lbs)                        189.52       74.28
Minimum line pressure (PSIG)            100
Design pressure used (PSIG)                           80.0         80.0
Shifts/day (1 shift=120,000 m/yr)       2.0
Cycles per year                     4691623

ACTUATOR:
Description:   Single Rod High Flow Numatics Actuator with 3/8 NPT ports
Bore/stroke/rod          2.50" bore x 12.00" stroke x 0.625" rod
Fitting                  3/4" - 3/8 NPT STR

CONDUCTOR & ASSOCIATED COMPONENTS:
Branch conductor /leg                    N/A
Branch manifold fitting /leg             N/A
Branch cond equiv ftg lg /leg (in)       N/A
Quick disconnect model /leg              N/A
In line flow control model /leg                      NONE         NONE
Main conductor           3/4" rubber hose 1" long with 0.0 elbow(s)
Main manifold fitting                    N/A
Main cond equiv ftg lg (in)               0

VALVE ASSEMBLY & ASSOCIATED COMPONENTS:
Description      2 Pos Mk 15 on 3/8 NPT base with ext req
Fitting                                  3/4" - 3/8 NPT STR
Silencer model                           N/A

SYSTEM PERFORMANCE TIMES:
Att'n stroke time (sec)                               0.33         0.24
Required stroke time (sec)                            0.32         0.24
Stroke time @ term vel (sec)                         0.20         0.18
Att'n cyclic rate (CPM)                 19.54
Required cyclic rate (CPM)              19.55
Cyclic rate @ term vel (CPM)            20.83
System delay time (sec)                 0.025
Dwell time after stroke (sec)                        1.40         1.10

SYSTEM INFORMATION:
Required system Cv                                    1.55         1.57
Attained system Cv                                   1.46         1.46
Att'n system air flow (SCFM)                         40.8         50.8
Att'n branch air vel (400 FPS max)        N/A                      N/A
Att'n main air vel (400 FPS max)                     38           52
Att'n % delta p (46% max)                            10           17
% Act. capacity used (75% max)                       48           20
Min pres necessary for 1d w/S.F. (PSIG)              51.5         21.5
Air per cycle (SCF)                     0.43
Att'n act leakage cost/yr @ $ 0.30 /KSCF  65         28           38
Att'n operating air cost/yr @ $ 0.30 /KSCF 603       311          292
Cost /1000 cyc @ att'n times @ $ 20.00 /hr 17.20
Att'n power input total (HP)             1.89

COMMENTS:
Using a Mk 15 w/1" long x  3/4" dia. hose
```

```
NUMATICS NUMASIZING (R) SUMMARY SHEET              Date:    04/10/95
NU301EED  Ver 3.01 (c) 1989 Numatics, Inc.         SURVEY # 6-14
===================================================================
Prepared for:                  Prepared by:   Michael Liberty
Company:                       Company:       Numatics Inc.
Address:                       Address:       1450 N. Milford Rd.
City,State,Zip:                City,State,Zip: Highland, Mi. 48357
Telephone #                    Telephone #    (810) 887-4111
Fax #                          Fax #          (810) 887-9190
-------------------------------------------------------------------
                                    Avg/Tot/Oth   Extend    Retract
INITIAL CUSTOMER PARAMETERS:
Total weight of load (lbs)                       200.00     50.00
Angle of load from horizontal         0
Coefficient of Friction            0.33
Number of actuators                   1
Total load per actuator (lbs)                    217.46     97.54
Minimum line pressure (PSIG)        100
Design pressure used (PSIG)                       80.0      80.0
Shifts/day (1 shift=120,000 m/yr)   2.0
Cycles per year                 4807563

ACTUATOR:
Description:   Single Rod High Flow Numatics Actuator with 3/8 NPT ports
Bore/stroke/rod            2.50" bore x 12.00" stroke x 0.625" rod
Fitting                          3/4" - 3/8 NPT STR

CONDUCTOR & ASSOCIATED COMPONENTS:
Branch conductor /leg            N/A
Branch manifold fitting /leg     N/A
Branch cond equiv ftg lg /leg (in) N/A
Quick disconnect model /leg      N/A
In line flow control model /leg                   NONE      NONE
Main conductor             3/4" rubber hose 1" long with 0.0 elbow(s)
Main manifold fitting            N/A
Main cond equiv ftg lg (in)        0

VALVE ASSEMBLY & ASSOCIATED COMPONENTS:
Description     2 Pos Mk 25 on 1/2 NPT base with ext reg
Fitting                          3/4" - 1/2 NPT STR
Silencer model                   N/A

SYSTEM PERFORMANCE TIMES:
Att'n stroke time (sec)                           0.29      0.20
Required stroke time (sec)                        0.29      0.20
Stroke time @ term vel (sec)                      0.15      0.14
Att'n cyclic rate (CPM)              20.03
Required cyclic rate (CPM)           20.03
Cyclic rate @ term vel (CPM)         21.46
System delay time (sec)             0.025
Dwell time after stroke (sec)                     1.40      1.10

SYSTEM INFORMATION:
Required system Cv                                2.00      2.05
Attained system Cv                               1.88      1.88
Att'n system air flow (SCFM)                     45.5      61.1
Att'n branch air vel (400 FPS max)   N/A          N/A
Att'n main air vel (400 FPS max)                   41        60
% Act. capacity used (75% max)                      7        14
Min pres necessary for ld w/S.F. (PSIG)            55        26
Air per cycle (SCF)                 59.1      28.3
Att'n act leakage cost/yr @ $ 0.30 /KSCF  0.43
Att'n operating air cost/yr @ $ 0.30 /KSCF  65      28        37
Cost /1000 cyc @ att'n times @ $ 20.00 /hr  618    319       299
Att'n power input total (HP)        16.79
                                     1.93

COMMENTS:
Using a Mk 25 w/1" long x  3/4" dia. hose
```

```
NUMATICS NUMASIZING (R) SUMMARY SHEET                              Date:   04/10/95
NU301EED  Ver 3.01 (c) 1989 Numatics, Inc.                       SURVEY # 6-15
==============================================================================
Prepared for:                          Prepared by:      Michael Liberty
Company:                               Company:          Numatics Inc.
Address:                               Address:          1450 N. Milford Rd.
City,State,Zip:                        City,State,Zip:   Highland, Mi. 48357
Telephone #                            Telephone #       (810) 887-4111
Fax #                                  Fax #             (810) 887-9190
------------------------------------------------------------------------------
                                                 Avg/Tot/Oth     Extend     Retract
INITIAL CUSTOMER PARAMETERS:
 Total weight of load (lbs)                                      200.00       50.00
 Angle of load from horizontal                             0
 Coefficient of Friction                                0.33
 Number of actuators                                       1
 Total load per actuator (lbs)                                   265.17      149.15
 Minimum line pressure (PSIG)                            100
 Design pressure used (PSIG)                                       80.0        80.0
 Shifts/day (1 shift=120,000 m/yr)                       2.0
 Cycles per year                                     4948417

ACTUATOR:
 Description:    Single Rod High Flow Numatics Actuator with 3/8 NPT ports
 Bore/stroke/rod                2.50" bore x 12.00" stroke x 0.625" rod
 Fitting                                       3/4" - 3/8 NPT STR

CONDUCTOR & ASSOCIATED COMPONENTS:
 Branch conductor /leg                         N/A
 Branch manifold fitting /leg                  N/A
 Branch cond equiv ftg lg /leg (in)            N/A
 Quick disconnect model /leg                   N/A
 In line flow control model /leg                           NONE        NONE
 Main conductor                    3/4" rubber hose 1" long with 0.0 elbow(s)
 Main manifold fitting                         N/A
 Main cond equiv ftg lg (in)                               0

VALVE ASSEMBLY & ASSOCIATED COMPONENTS:
 Description     2 Pos Mk 40 on 3/4 NPT base with ext req
 Fitting                                       3/4" - 3/4 NPT STR
 Silencer model                                N/A

SYSTEM PERFORMANCE TIMES:
 Att'n stroke time (sec)                                           0.25        0.16
 Required stroke time (sec)                                        0.25        0.16
 Stroke time @ term vel (sec)                                      0.10        0.09
 Att'n cyclic rate (CPM)                                20.62
 Required cyclic rate (CPM)                             20.62
 Cyclic rate @ term vel (CPM)                           22.32
 System delay time (sec)                                0.022
 Dwell time after stroke (sec)                                     1.40        1.10

SYSTEM INFORMATION:
 Required system Cv                                                3.16        3.30
 Attained system Cv                                                2.95        2.95
 Att'n system air flow (SCFM)                                      52.3        79.4
 Att'n branch air vel (400 FPS max)                          N/A         N/A
 Att'n main air vel (400 FPS max)                                    46          74
 Att'n % delta p (46% max)                                            4           9
 % Act. capacity used (75% max)                                      68          41
 Min pres necessary for ld w/S.F. (PSIG)                           72.0        43.2
 Air per cycle (SCF)                                     0.43
 Att'n act leakage cost/yr @ $ 0.30 /KSCF                  65        28          37
 Att'n operating air cost/yr @ $ 0.30 /KSCF               637       329         308
 Cost /1000 cyc @ att'n times @ $ 20.00 /hr             16.31
 Att'n power input total (HP)                            1.98

COMMENTS:
 Using a Mk 40 w/1" long x  3/4" dia. hose
```

```
NUMATICS NUMASIZING (R) SUMMARY SHEET                    Date:    04/10/95
NU301EED  Ver 3.01 (c) 1989 Numatics, Inc.              SURVEY # 6-16
=========================================================================
Prepared for:                       Prepared by:     Michael Liberty
Company:                            Company:         Numatics Inc.
Address:                            Address:         1450 N. Milford Rd.
City,State,Zip:                     City,State,Zip:  Highland, Mi. 48357
Telephone #                         Telephone #      (810) 887-4111
Fax #                               Fax #            (810) 887-9190
-------------------------------------------------------------------------
                                    Avg/Tot/Oth     Extend     Retract
INITIAL CUSTOMER PARAMETERS:
Total weight of load (lbs)                          430.00     -215.00
Angle of load from horizontal            5
Coefficient of Friction               0.85
Number of actuators                      1
Total load per actuator (lbs)                       466.80      236.16
Minimum line pressure (PSIG)            80
Design pressure used (PSIG)                          60.0        60.0
Shifts/day (1 shift=120,000 m/yr)      2.0
Cycles per year                    6212076

ACTUATOR:
Description:   Single Rod Conventional Actuator with 1/2 NPT ports
Bore/stroke/rod            4.00" bore x 6.00" stroke x 1.000" rod
Fitting                    5/8" - 1/2 NPT EL

CONDUCTOR & ASSOCIATED COMPONENTS:
Branch conductor /leg               N/A
Branch manifold fitting /leg        N/A
Branch cond equiv ftg lg /leg (in)  N/A
Quick disconnect model /leg         N/A
In line flow control model /leg                     NONE        NONE
Main conductor             5/8" rubber hose 48" long with 4.0 elbow(s)
Main manifold fitting               N/A
Main cond equiv ftg lg (in)         105

VALVE ASSEMBLY & ASSOCIATED COMPONENTS:
Description     2 Pos Mk 40 on 3/8 NPT base with sand reg
Fitting                    5/8" - 3/8 NPT EL
Silencer model                      N/A

SYSTEM PERFORMANCE TIMES:
Att'n stroke time (sec)                             0.49        0.33
Required stroke time (sec)                          0.49        0.33
Stroke time @ term vel (sec)                        0.20        0.19
Att'n cyclic rate (CPM)               25.87
Required cyclic rate (CPM)            25.88
Cyclic rate @ term vel (CPM)          31.88
System delay time (sec)               0.022
Dwell time after stroke (sec)                       0.00        1.50

SYSTEM INFORMATION:
Required system Cv                                  2.23        2.23
Attained system Cv                                  2.23        2.23
Att'n system air flow (SCFM)                        32.3        46.2
Att'n branch air vel (400 FPS max)    N/A                  N/A
Att'n main air vel (400 FPS max)                    52          78
Att'n % delta p (46% max)                            4           9
% Act. capacity used (75% max)                      62          33
Min pres necessary for ld w/S.F. (PSIG)            49.5        26.7
Air per cycle (SCF)                   0.52
Att'n act leakage cost/yr @ $ 0.28 /KSCF  101      13          88
Att'n operating air cost/yr @ $ 0.28 /KSCF 898    461         437
Cost /1000 cyc @ att'n times @ $ 20.00 /hr 13.04
Att'n power input total (HP)          2.68

COMMENTS:
```

```
NUMATICS NUMASIZING (R) SUMMARY SHEET                  Date:    04/10/95
NU301EED   Ver 3.01 (c) 1989 Numatics, Inc.           SURVEY # 6-16
========================================================================
Prepared for:                   Prepared by:     Michael Liberty
Company:                        Company:         Numatics Inc.
Address:                        Address:         1450 N. Milford Rd.
City,State,Zip:                 City,State,Zip:  Highland, Mi. 48357
Telephone #                     Telephone #      (810) 887-4111
Fax #                           Fax #            (810) 887-9190
------------------------------------------------------------------------
                                                   Extend      Retract
Cv DATA PER ACTUATOR

Actuator Fitting Cv                                 5.85         5.85
Flow Control Free Flow Cv from Chart                N/A          N/A
Flow Control Adjustable Cv from Chart               N/A          N/A
Flow Control Adjustable Cv Used                     N/A          N/A
Quick Disconnect Cv                                 N/A          N/A
Branch Conductor Cv                                 N/A          N/A
Additional Cv Due to Elbows in Branch Conductor     N/A          N/A
Branch Conductor Manifold Fitting Cv                N/A          N/A

Cv DATA - TOTAL SYSTEM

Actuator Fitting Cv                                 5.85         5.85
Flow Control Free Flow Cv from Chart                N/A          N/A
Flow Control Adjustable Cv from Chart               N/A          N/A
Flow Control Adjustable Cv Used                     N/A          N/A
Quick Disconnect Cv                                 N/A          N/A
Branch Conductor Cv                                 N/A          N/A
Additional Cv Due to Elbows in Branch Conductor     N/A          N/A
Branch Conductor Manifold Fitting Cv                N/A          N/A
Main Conductor Cv                                  10.00        10.00
Additional Cv Due to Elbows in Main Conductor       9.56         9.56
Main Conductor Manifold Fitting Cv                  N/A          N/A
Silencer Cv                                         N/A          N/A
Valve Fitting Cv                                     4.19         4.19
Valve Cv                                             3.55         3.55
Sandwich Regulator Cv                               8.00         8.00
Sandwich Speed Control Cv from Chart                N/A          N/A
Sandwich Speed Control Cv Used                      N/A          N/A
Sandwich Check Valve Cv (3 pos valve only)          N/A          N/A


Attained system Cv                                  2.23         2.23

Required system Cv                                  2.23         2.23

Flow Control Adjustable Cv Suggested                N/A          N/A
Valve Cv Suggested                                  3.56         3.56
Sandwich Speed Control Cv Suggested                 N/A          N/A
```

```
NUMATICS NUMASIZING (R) SUMMARY SHEET                Date:    04/10/95
NU301EED  Ver 3.01 (c) 1989 Numatics, Inc.          SURVEY # 6-17
===============================================================================
Prepared for:                     Prepared by:    Michael Liberty
Company:                          Company:        Numatics Inc.
Address:                          Address:        1450 N. Milford Rd.
City,State,Zip:                   City,State,Zip: Highland, Mi. 48357
Telephone #                       Telephone #     (810) 887-4111
Fax #                             Fax #           (810) 887-9190
-------------------------------------------------------------------------------
                                     Avg/Tot/Oth    Extend     Retract
INITIAL CUSTOMER PARAMETERS:
Total weight of load (lbs)                          430.00     -215.00
Angle of load from horizontal            5
Coefficient of Friction               0.85
Number of actuators                      1
Total load per actuator (lbs)                      477.99      204.40
Minimum line pressure (PSIG)            80
Design pressure used (PSIG)                         60.0        40.0
Shifts/day (1 shift=120,000 m/yr)      2.0
Cycles per year                    5969588

ACTUATOR:
Description:    Single Rod Conventional Actuator with 1/2 NPT ports
Bore/stroke/rod         4.00" bore x 6.00" stroke x 1.000" rod
Fitting                 5/8" - 1/2 NPT EL

CONDUCTOR & ASSOCIATED COMPONENTS:
Branch conductor /leg                    N/A
Branch manifold fitting /leg             N/A
Branch cond equiv ftg lg /leg (in)       N/A
Quick disconnect model /leg              N/A
In line flow control model /leg                    NONE        NONE
Main conductor          5/8" rubber hose 48" long with 4.0 elbow(s)
Main manifold fitting                    N/A
Main cond equiv ftg lg (in)              105

VALVE ASSEMBLY & ASSOCIATED COMPONENTS:
Description     2 Pos Mk 40 on 3/8 NPT base with sand req
Fitting                 5/8" - 3/8 NPT EL
Silencer model          N/A

SYSTEM PERFORMANCE TIMES:
Att'n stroke time (sec)                            0.45        0.46
Required stroke time (sec)                         0.45        0.46
Stroke time @ term vel (sec)                       0.20        0.19
Att'n cyclic rate (CPM)              24.87
Required cyclic rate (CPM)           24.87
Cyclic rate @ term vel (CPM)         31.88
System delay time (sec)              0.022
Dwell time after stroke (sec)                      0.00        1.50

SYSTEM INFORMATION:
Required system Cv                                 2.23        2.22
Attained system Cv                                 2.23        2.23
Att'n system air flow (SCFM)                       35.4        23.8
Att'n branch air vel (400 FPS max)       N/A                N/A
Att'n main air vel (400 FPS max)                   57          52
Att'n % delta p (46% max)                          5           4
% Act. capacity used (75% max)                     63          43
Min pres necessary for ld w/S.F. (PSIG)            50.7        23.1
Air per cycle (SCF)                  0.45
Att'n act leakage cost/yr @ $ 0.28 /KSCF   72      12          61
Att'n operating air cost/yr @ $ 0.28 /KSCF 750     443         307
Cost /1000 cyc @ att'n times @ $ 20.00 /hr 13.54
Att'n power input total (HP)         2.21

COMMENTS:
```

```
NUMATICS NUMASIZING (R) SUMMARY SHEET                     Date:    04/10/95
NU301EED   Ver 3.01 (c) 1989 Numatics, Inc.              SURVEY # 6-17
=============================================================================
Prepared for:                  Prepared by:      Michael Liberty
Company:                       Company:          Numatics Inc.
Address:                       Address:          1450 N. Milford Rd.
City,State,Zip:                City,State,Zip:   Highland, Mi. 48357
Telephone #                    Telephone #       (810) 887-4111
Fax #                          Fax #             (810) 887-9190
-----------------------------------------------------------------------------
                                                  Extend      Retract
Cv DATA PER ACTUATOR

Actuator Fitting Cv                               5.85        5.85
Flow Control Free Flow Cv from Chart              N/A         N/A
Flow Control Adjustable Cv from Chart             N/A         N/A
Flow Control Adjustable Cv Used                   N/A         N/A
Quick Disconnect Cv                               N/A         N/A
Branch Conductor Cv                               N/A         N/A
Additional Cv Due to Elbows in Branch Conductor   N/A         N/A
Branch Conductor Manifold Fitting Cv              N/A         N/A

Cv DATA - TOTAL SYSTEM

Actuator Fitting Cv                               5.85        5.85
Flow Control Free Flow Cv from Chart              N/A         N/A
Flow Control Adjustable Cv from Chart             N/A         N/A
Flow Control Adjustable Cv Used                   N/A         N/A
Quick Disconnect Cv                               N/A         N/A
Branch Conductor Cv                               N/A         N/A
Additional Cv Due to Elbows in Branch Conductor   N/A         N/A
Branch Conductor Manifold Fitting Cv              N/A         N/A
Main Conductor Cv                                 10.00       10.00
Additional Cv Due to Elbows in Main Conductor     9.56        9.56
Main Conductor Manifold Fitting Cv                N/A         N/A
Silencer Cv                                       N/A         N/A
Valve Fitting Cv                                  4.19        4.19
Valve Cv                                          3.55        3.55
Sandwich Regulator Cv                             8.00        8.00
Sandwich Speed Control Cv from Chart              N/A         N/A
Sandwich Speed Control Cv Used                    N/A         N/A
Sandwich Check Valve Cv (3 pos valve only)        N/A         N/A


Attained system Cv                                2.23        2.23

Required system Cv                                2.23        2.22

Flow Control Adjustable Cv Suggested              N/A         N/A
Valve Cv Suggested                                3.56        3.54
Sandwich Speed Control Cv Suggested               N/A         63.34
```

```
NUMATICS NUMASIZING (R) SUMMARY SHEET                 Date:    04/10/95
NU301EED  Ver 3.01 (c) 1989 Numatics, Inc.           SURVEY # 6-18
========================================================================
Prepared for:                    Prepared by:    Michael Liberty
Company:                         Company:        Numatics Inc.
Address:                         Address:        1450 N. Milford Rd.
City,State,Zip:                  City,State,Zip: Highland, Mi. 48357
Telephone #                      Telephone #     (810) 887-4111
Fax #                            Fax #           (810) 887-9190
------------------------------------------------------------------------
                                      Avg/Tot/Oth   Extend      Retract
INITIAL CUSTOMER PARAMETERS:
Total weight of load (lbs)                          430.00      -215.00
Angle of load from horizontal              5
Coefficient of Friction                 0.85
Number of actuators                        1
Total load per actuator (lbs)                       465.04      200.04
Minimum line pressure (PSIG)              80
Design pressure used (PSIG)                         55.5        36.3
Shifts/day (1 shift=120,000 m/yr)        2.0
Cycles per year                      5760000

ACTUATOR:
Description:   Single Rod Conventional Actuator with 1/2 NPT ports
Bore/stroke/rod             4.00" bore x 6.00" stroke x 1.000" rod
Fitting                     5/8" - 1/2 NPT EL

CONDUCTOR & ASSOCIATED COMPONENTS:
Branch conductor /leg            N/A
Branch manifold fitting /leg     N/A
Branch cond equiv ftg lg /leg (in)  N/A
Quick disconnect model /leg      N/A
In line flow control model /leg                     NONE        NONE
Main conductor              5/8" rubber hose 48" long with 4.0 elbow(s)
Main manifold fitting            N/A
Main cond equiv ftg lg (in)      105

VALVE ASSEMBLY & ASSOCIATED COMPONENTS:
Description      2 Pos Mk 40 on 3/8 NPT base with sand reg
Fitting                          5/8" - 3/8 NPT EL
Silencer model                   N/A

SYSTEM PERFORMANCE TIMES:
Att'n stroke time (sec)                             0.50        0.50
Required stroke time (sec)                          0.50        0.50
Stroke time @ term vel (sec)                        0.20        0.19
Att'n cyclic rate (CPM)                  23.93
Required cyclic rate (CPM)               24.00
Cyclic rate @ term vel (CPM)             31.88
System delay time (sec)                  0.022
Dwell time after stroke (sec)                       0.00        1.50

SYSTEM INFORMATION:
Required system Cv                                  2.23        2.23
Attained system Cv                                  2.23        2.23
Att'n system air flow (SCFM)                        29.9        20.5
Att'n branch air vel (400 FPS max)         N/A              N/A
Att'n main air vel (400 FPS max)                    51          48
Att'n % delta p (46% max)                           4           4
% Act. capacity used (75% max)                      67          47
Min pres necessary for ld w/S.F. (PSIG)             49.3        22.6
Air per cycle (SCF)                      0.42
Att'n act leakage cost/yr @ $ 0.28 /KSCF           66    12     54
Att'n operating air cost/yr @ $ 0.28 /KSCF        678   402    276
Cost /1000 cyc @ att'n times @ $ 20.00 /hr       14.03
Att'n power input total (HP)             1.99

COMMENTS:
```

```
NUMATICS NUMASIZING (R) SUMMARY SHEET              Date:    04/10/95
NU301EED  Ver 3.01 (c) 1989 Numatics, Inc.        SURVEY # 6-18
=====================================================================
Prepared for:                   Prepared by:    Michael Liberty
Company:                        Company:        Numatics Inc.
Address:                        Address:        1450 N. Milford Rd.
City,State,Zip:                 City,State,Zip: Highland, Mi. 48357
Telephone #                     Telephone #     (810) 887-4111
Fax #                           Fax #           (810) 887-9190
---------------------------------------------------------------------
                                                Extend      Retract
Cv DATA PER ACTUATOR

Actuator Fitting Cv                              5.85         5.85
Flow Control Free Flow Cv from Chart             N/A          N/A
Flow Control Adjustable Cv from Chart            N/A          N/A
Flow Control Adjustable Cv Used                  N/A          N/A
Quick Disconnect Cv                              N/A          N/A
Branch Conductor Cv                              N/A          N/A
Additional Cv Due to Elbows in Branch Conductor  N/A          N/A
Branch Conductor Manifold Fitting Cv             N/A          N/A

Cv DATA - TOTAL SYSTEM

Actuator Fitting Cv                              5.85         5.85
Flow Control Free Flow Cv from Chart             N/A          N/A
Flow Control Adjustable Cv from Chart            N/A          N/A
Flow Control Adjustable Cv Used                  N/A          N/A
Quick Disconnect Cv                              N/A          N/A
Branch Conductor Cv                              N/A          N/A
Additional Cv Due to Elbows in Branch Conductor  N/A          N/A
Branch Conductor Manifold Fitting Cv             N/A          N/A
Main Conductor Cv                               10.00        10.00
Additional Cv Due to Elbows in Main Conductor    9.56         9.56
Main Conductor Manifold Fitting Cv               N/A          N/A
Silencer Cv                                      N/A          N/A
Valve Fitting Cv                                 4.19         4.19
Valve Cv                                         3.55         3.55
Sandwich Regulator Cv                            8.00         8.00
Sandwich Speed Control Cv from Chart             N/A          N/A
Sandwich Speed Control Cv Used                   N/A          N/A
Sandwich Check Valve Cv (3 pos valve only)       N/A          N/A


Attained system Cv                               2.23         2.23

Required system Cv                               2.23         2.23

Flow Control Adjustable Cv Suggested             N/A          N/A
Valve Cv Suggested                               3.55         3.58
Sandwich Speed Control Cv Suggested              N/A          N/A
```

```
NUMATICS NUMASIZING (R) SUMMARY SHEET              Date:    04/10/95
NU301EED  Ver 3.01 (c) 1989 Numatics, Inc.        SURVEY # 6-19
================================================================
Prepared for:               Prepared by:    Michael Liberty
Company:                    Company:        Numatics Inc.
Address:                    Address:        1450 N. Milford Rd.
City,State,Zip:             City,State,Zip: Highland, Mi. 48357
Telephone #                 Telephone #     (810) 887-4111
Fax #                       Fax #           (810) 887-9190
-----------------------------------------------------------------
                                Avg/Tot/Oth    Extend     Retract
INITIAL CUSTOMER PARAMETERS:
Total weight of load (lbs)                    430.00     -215.00
Angle of load from horizontal         5
Coefficient of Friction            0.85
Number of actuators                   1
Total load per actuator (lbs)                 465.04      200.04
Minimum line pressure (PSIG)         80
Design pressure used (PSIG)                    60.0        60.0
Shifts/day (1 shift=120,000 m/yr)    2.0
Cycles per year                 5760000

ACTUATOR:
Description:  Single Rod Conventional Actuator with 1/2 NPT ports
Bore/stroke/rod         4.00" bore x 6.00" stroke x 1.000" rod
Fitting                 5/8" - 1/2 NPT EL

CONDUCTOR & ASSOCIATED COMPONENTS:
Branch conductor /leg             N/A
Branch manifold fitting /leg      N/A
Branch cond equiv ftg lg /leg (in) N/A
Quick disconnect model /leg       N/A
In line flow control model /leg                NONE        NONE
Main conductor          5/8" rubber hose 48" long with 4.0 elbow(s)
Main manifold fitting             N/A
Main cond equiv ftg lg (in)       105

VALVE ASSEMBLY & ASSOCIATED COMPONENTS:
Description    2 Pos Mk 40 on 3/8 NPT base with sand reg
Fitting                 5/8" - 3/8 NPT EL
Silencer model          N/A

SYSTEM PERFORMANCE TIMES:
Att'n stroke time (sec)                        0.49 ?     0.30 ?
Required stroke time (sec)                     0.50        0.50
Stroke time @ term vel (sec)                   0.20        0.19
Att'n cyclic rate (CPM)             26.17
Required cyclic rate (CPM)          24.00
Cyclic rate @ term vel (CPM)        31.88
System delay time (sec)             0.022
Dwell time after stroke (sec)                  0.00        1.50

SYSTEM INFORMATION:
Required system Cv                             2.18        1.35
Attained system Cv                             2.23        2.23 ?
Att'n system air flow (SCFM)                  32.5        49.7
Att'n branch air vel (400 FPS max)    N/A              N/A
Att'n main air vel (400 FPS max)               52          85
Att'n % delta p (46% max)                       4          10
% Act. capacity used (75% max)                 62          28
Min pres necessary for 1d w/S.F. (PSIG)       49.3        22.6
Air per cycle (SCF)                 0.52
Att'n act leakage cost/yr @ $ 0.28 /KSCF      101         14          88
Att'n operating air cost/yr @ $ 0.28 /KSCF    908        466         442
Cost /1000 cyc @ att'n times @ $ 20.00 /hr  12.90
Att'n power input total (HP)         2.71

COMMENTS:
```

```
NUMATICS NUMASIZING (R) SUMMARY SHEET                Date:    04/10/95
NU301EED  Ver 3.01 (c) 1989 Numatics, Inc.          SURVEY # 6-19
========================================================================
Prepared for:                    Prepared by:    Michael Liberty
Company:                         Company:        Numatics Inc.
Address:                         Address:        1450 N. Milford Rd.
City,State,Zip:                  City,State,Zip: Highland, Mi. 48357
Telephone #                      Telephone #     (810) 887-4111
Fax #                            Fax #           (810) 887-9190
------------------------------------------------------------------------
                                                 Extend      Retract
Cv DATA PER ACTUATOR

Actuator Fitting Cv                               5.85        5.85
Flow Control Free Flow Cv from Chart              N/A         N/A
Flow Control Adjustable Cv from Chart             N/A         N/A
Flow Control Adjustable Cv Used                   N/A         N/A
Quick Disconnect Cv                               N/A         N/A
Branch Conductor Cv                               N/A         N/A
Additional Cv Due to Elbows in Branch Conductor   N/A         N/A
Branch Conductor Manifold Fitting Cv              N/A         N/A

Cv DATA - TOTAL SYSTEM

Actuator Fitting Cv                               5.85        5.85
Flow Control Free Flow Cv from Chart              N/A         N/A
Flow Control Adjustable Cv from Chart             N/A         N/A
Flow Control Adjustable Cv Used                   N/A         N/A
Quick Disconnect Cv                               N/A         N/A
Branch Conductor Cv                               N/A         N/A
Additional Cv Due to Elbows in Branch Conductor   N/A         N/A
Branch Conductor Manifold Fitting Cv              N/A         N/A
Main Conductor Cv                                 10.00       10.00
Additional Cv Due to Elbows in Main Conductor     9.56        9.56
Main Conductor Manifold Fitting Cv                N/A         N/A
Silencer Cv                                       N/A         N/A
Valve Fitting Cv                                  4.19        4.19
Valve Cv                                          3.55        3.55
Sandwich Regulator Cv                             8.00        8.00
Sandwich Speed Control Cv from Chart              N/A         N/A
Sandwich Speed Control Cv Used                    N/A         N/A
Sandwich Check Valve Cv (3 pos valve only)        N/A         N/A


Attained system Cv                                2.23        2.23

Required system Cv                                2.18        1.35

Flow Control Adjustable Cv Suggested              N/A         N/A
Valve Cv Suggested                                3.37        1.53
Sandwich Speed Control Cv Suggested               10.75       1.70
```

# Accumulators, Receivers, Reservoirs, Surge Tanks, and Vessels

There is a great deal of confusion surrounding the use of a receiver. To gain some insight into where and when to use one, I will compare it to the workings of a checking account. All of the terms in the title for this chapter (above) describe similar components employed for different intentions, some subtle and some more obvious.

I have broadly placed all these vessels in the same category to explain their underlying concepts, which generally are comparable. However, there is a distinction; the vessel that is used as an accumulator is meant to absorb a shock (act as a cushioning device or dashpot) and serve as a counterbalance, tensioning device, or air spring, whereas the vessel that is utilized as a surge tank is meant to supply a sudden large demand or dampen compressor pulsations. The accumulator generally does not use air once it is charged, for the air is trapped in the system, whereas the surge tank continually dispenses air and requires continual replenishment. Interestingly, there are several types of accumulators: bladder accumulators, piston accumulators, or simply a vessel, whereas receivers are generally hollow vessels. Nonetheless, there is the same familiar thread running through all of these tanks, as will be borne out in my discussion.

Therefore, if you would apply the same logic first to surge tanks as you would to a bank account, you will have no difficulty in mastering its concept. Think of the minimum balance as the minimum pressure, something that should be avoided at all costs (pardon the pun). The large monthly mortgage payment is similar to the sudden momentary demand required once every cycle of the machine. The weekly deposits similar to bank deposits are the ongoing recharging of the tank by the compressor. One of the most fundamental and valuable concepts practiced with a checking account that should be applied to pneumatics, for it is just as crucial, is to make certain that your deposits are greater than your withdrawals. No surge tank will sustain production indefinitely if one withdraws more air than one replaces, and similar to a bank account, it will eventually be drained dry regardless of how large the initial deposit may be. By employing these tenets, one can expect to make a balloon withdrawal from a tank and still be prepared for the next large withdrawal so long as there is a sufficient amount of dwell time to recharge it. In other words, there must be periodic installments to save sufficiently for the large removal. If one happens to be in the enviable position of having on hand adequate funds for any purpose, then obviously there is no need for a checking account except for a safe location to store the funds. The corollary is if the supply for the machine is greater than the peak demand, then here, too, there is no need for a surge tank.

We must briefly bring into our discussion the compressor and its cycle time to provide further insight into the function of the receiver. The compressor cycle consists of the off time plus the on time. Small compressors will shut off completely during the off-time period, whereas large compressors will simply go into an idling mode during the off period. During this idling mode, compressor motors use only about 10 percent of the required compressing input power based on today's improved compressor efficiency. Two notes are appropriate here:

*Screw compressors:* This type of compressor modulates its air intake according to its demand. The screw compressor operates somewhat differently from other compressors, which is not the subject of this discussion. Information on this topic can be found in compressor handbooks by Ingersol-Rand, Joy, etc. The input power is a function of the demand on these compressors as well.

*Tanks:* A tank dictates the length of time the compressor rests or specifically is in the off or idling mode. The relation between the off and on times is governed by the size of the compressor. The tank does not alter this ratio.

As we've stated before, we suggest a minimum of 2:1 or, more preferably, 3:1 relationship of the off time to the on time. Looking at it from the on-time point of view, the compressor should run 25 percent (3:1) of the total time or at a maximum of 33 percent (2:1) of the total time. This should be checked with the manufacturers. Another rule of thumb, which should be cleared with the compressor manufacturers, is the length of time the compressor should be in a run mode before it proceeds to an off or idling mode. We have used the two-minute rule for this aspect. However, there is so broad a spectrum of compressors and manufacturers that what may be applicable for a 100-hp unit may be totally out of range for a <1-hp unit, and the same applies for similar-hp units of different brands.

The following is a partial list intended to facilitate determination of when to specify a tank for a pneumatic system:

1. When there is a sudden demand for a large withdrawal of compressed air and the existing drop line cannot supply it

2. To dampen pulsations from the compressor so as to maintain constant pressure

3. To provide emergency standby power, such as during a breakdown, to have an adequate amount of air to operate enough cycles to clear the work in process

4. To store power for intermittent cycling of equipment

5. To compensate for leakage

6. To act as an air spring (cushioning device, counterbalance, or dashpot)

Actuators having no or small retract loads often use mechanical springs to return the piston. Since mechanical springs have a finite life, designers prefer, where possible, to replace them with equivalent air springs which are not afflicted with this malady. The prime advantage of using any type of a spring for the retract stroke is that it basically does not use any energy. The suggested method for the design of an air spring is as follows. Let us assume that we require a retract force of 100 lb on the rod (0.625-in) end of a 2.5-in-bore × 3-in-stroke actuator:

The effective area is 4.60 in$^2$ [(2.5$^2$ − 0.625$^2$)0.7854].

The actuator volume is 13.8 in$^3$ (4.60 × 3).

The conductor between the rod end and the tank is ½-in nylon, ⅜-in ID × 36 in long, with 4.0-in$^3$ volume (0.375$^2$ × 0.7854 × 36).

The total system volume without a tank is 17.8 in$^3$ (13.8 + 4.0).

The required retract pressure based on the effective area (4.6 in$^2$) and force (100 lb) is 22 psig (100/4.6). We will assume 25 psig to compensate for any unanticipated extraneous loads. Let us further assume that we do not wish to drop below this 25 psig when the piston is fully extended nor have it exceed 28 psig when the piston is fully retracted. According to this information, we will solve for an accumulator tank that will serve as an air spring. We will first use Boyle's law to deter-

mine the tank size (assumes movement at constant temperature—
isothermal process):

$$p_{1a}V_1 = p_{2a}V_2$$

where $V_T$ = tank volume, expressed in $in^3$ (throughout, in the formulas and text that follow in this section)

$p_{1a}$ = pressure, expressed in absolute terms and equal to initial
condition with piston fully extended = 25.0 + 14.7 = 39.7
psia

$V_1$ = total volume, expressed in $in^3$ at initial conditions = $V_T$ +
17.8

$p_{2a}$ = pressure, expressed in absolute terms and equal to final
condition with piston fully retracted = 28.0 + 14.7 = 42.7
psia

$V_2$ = total volume, expressed in $in^3$ at final conditions = $V_T$ +
4.0

Using these figures in Boyle's law, we obtain

$$39.7(V_T + 17.8) = 42.7(V_T + 4); \qquad 3V_T = 535.86; \qquad V = 178.6 \text{ in}^3$$

$$7.48 \text{ gal} = 1 \text{ ft}^3 \text{ (also } 231 \text{ in}^3 = 1 \text{ gal)}$$

$$\frac{178.6}{1728} = 0.10 \text{ ft}^3 \quad \text{or} \quad 0.77 \text{ gal}$$

We will, however, use the more appropriate equation which applies to
a tank used as an air spring as it more accurately reflects what is
occurring rather than what is expressed by the ideal-gas or perfect-
gas relationships. We derived the exponent value for $\eta$ to be 1.35
(polytropic process); the detailed discussion and the derivation for $\eta$
can be found near the end of Chap. 2):

$$p_{1a}V_1^{\eta} = p_{2a}V_2^{\eta}$$

$$p_{1a}V_1^{1.35} = p_{2a}V_2^{1.35}$$

$$39.7(V_T + 17.8)^{1.35} = 42.7(V_T + 4)^{1.35}$$

$$\left(\frac{V_T + 17.8}{V_T + 4}\right)^{1.35} = \frac{42.7}{39.7}$$

$$\frac{V_T + 17.8}{V_T + 4} = \left(\frac{42.7}{39.7}\right)^{0.741}; \quad V_T = 244.8 \text{ in}^3 \quad \text{or} \quad 0.142 \text{ ft}^3 \quad \text{or} \quad 1.06 \text{ gal}$$

[where $V$ is in $in^3$ (throughout this section)]. There will be a regulator set at 25 psig supplying this tank to maintain the pressure to make up for any loss due to leakage.

As you can see, the tank size would have been too small using Boyle's law, for the pressure would have reached 29.1 psig instead of the maximum of 28.0 psig:

$$p_{1a}(V_T + 17.8)^{1.35} = p_{2a}(V_T + 4)^{1.35}$$

$$39.7(178.6 + 17.8)^{1.35} = p_{2a}(178.6 + 4)^{1.35}$$

$$49,491.6 = 1129.9p_{2a}$$

$$p_{2a} = 43.8 \text{ psia} = 29.1 \text{ psig}$$

While we are on the subject of the exponent $\eta$, it is worthwhile to point out that it can be used to check the velocity of sound within a gas. In our case the gas is principally air, and experiments have shown the velocity to be approximately 1120 ft/s depending on temperature. Boyle's law has an assumed exponent value equal to 1.00, and if we apply the formula for the velocity of sound ($v_c$), which is equal to $(\eta P/\rho)^{0.5}$, we find the result to be 947 ft/s since $P_a$ = pressure expressed in psfa (14.7 psia $\times$ 144 = 2116 psfa) and $\rho$ = density, expressed in slugs/ft$^3$ = $w/g$ [weight per unit volume or specific weight expressed in pounds per cubic foot at 68°F (see Chap. 3)/acceleration due to gravity, expressed in feet per second per second] = 0.076/32.2 = 0.00236 slugs/ft$^3$ at 68°F. If $P$, $g$, and $w$ were taken to more significant decimal places, the results would be altered slightly. In our case it would not have any relevance because we predict to only two decimal places. However, if $w$ were taken at 60°F, it would have an impact. I am delving into more detail on this subject for those students who require greater accuracy and desire to know the method of solution and derivation. Also, $\rho$ at 60°F = 0.0765/32.2 = 0.00237. Therefore $v_c$ = (2116/0.00237)$^{0.5}$ = 944 ft/s. (As mentioned above, if the figures were taken to more significant decimal places, this would not have the same effect as the temperature variation on the density as indicated above.)

This value is substantially less than the recorded velocity of 1116 ft/s at 60°F arrived at experimentally.[1] The reason for this large variance is because the actual compressed air temperature and other ambient conditions do not remain constant and, as stated before, more closely reflect a polytropic process (see Chap. 2). Let us therefore solve for $\eta$ in the equation by using 1116 ft/s for the velocity of sound; 1116 = $(\eta P/\rho)^{0.5}$ = $(\eta 2116/0.00237)^{0.5}$; 1,245,000 = $\eta 2116/0.00237$; $\eta$ = (1,245,000 $\times$

---

[1]Most basic texts in elementary physics.

0.00237)/2116; $\eta$ = 1.39. If one would calculate the velocity based on a value for $\eta$ of 1.35, the speed of sound would be closer to 1098 ft/s at a temperature of 60°F.[2] We do have this slight variation, which could be attributed to the method of reading temperatures, rounding of numbers, as well as using imprecise figures for $g$ (32.2 ft/s), the specific weight $w$ based on temperature, etc. The problem which is confusing is that fluid-dynamic engineers use as a standard temperature 68°F (20°C), whereas aeronautical engineers and physicists use 60°F (15.56°C) or 32°F (0°C); chemists use still another base temperature, and perhaps electrical engineers employ still another, and therefore there is virtually no agreed-on standard temperature. Nevertheless, 1.35 is what we've been using and is suggested by many other manufacturers in the pneumatics field. I would be remiss if I did not point out these inconsistencies. All our performance-time readings were recorded to two decimal places, and thus the predicted survey figures are printed to the same accuracy. Thus, you can readily concede that these deviations would play no substantial role in the outcome of our calculations as the variances occur in the third significant decimal places. For the pragmatic engineering student, this is more than adequate.

Even within the narrow spectrum of air temperatures ranging from 30 to 90°F, the velocity of sound can vary by as much as 64 ft/s (1065 to 1129 ft/s) by using the velocity formula with an $\eta$ coefficient of 1.35. The same 64-ft/s spread exists from 30 to 90°F if we use 1.40 as the specific-heat ratio as well as other different vital values which generate velocities ranging from 1085 to 1149 ft/s.[3] It is abundantly obvious from these and the other sources that dissimilar results are disseminated, and, I might add, all correct, due to the various disciplines using different reference points. As we've mentioned several times, for our purposes these variations play an insignificant role. They are mentioned and discussed in order to acquaint the serious student with the implications. We round our figures because we are pragmatic and our designs demand a reasonable value.

I have come across the following formula, which also expresses the speed of sound using different terms which some of you may be more familiar with

$$v_c = 223\left(\frac{\eta\Gamma_a}{M}\right)^{0.5}$$

---

[2]The general accepted approximate norm at 60°F is 1100 ft/s.

[3]Physical properties of air at standard atmospheric pressure (English; i.e, British units). Based on data from R. D. Blevins, *Applied Fluid Dynamics Handbook,* Van Nostrand Reinhold, New York, 1984.

Careful scrutiny reveals this formula to be identical to the original formula for $v_c$, where it is equal to $= (\eta P/\rho)^{0.5}$. Since everything is expressed per cubic foot, then $V$ (volume expressed in cubic feet) is equal to one:

$$w = \frac{PV}{R_a \Gamma_a}; \quad R_a = \frac{R}{M} = \frac{1544}{M}; \quad w = \frac{PM}{1544\Gamma_a};$$

$$\rho = \frac{w}{g} = \frac{PM}{1544\Gamma_a g}$$

(where $V$ is volume in ft$^3$ and $R$ is the universal gas constant). Let us substitute into the original equation for $\rho$

$$v_c = \left( \frac{\eta P 1544 \Gamma_a g}{PM} \right)^{0.5} = \left( \frac{49{,}717 \eta \Gamma_a}{M} \right)^{0.5} = 223 \left( \frac{\eta T_a}{M} \right)^{0.5}$$

We thus have complete agreement.

Since we are on the topic of directing your attention to minor variances, allow me to refer to an additional one. We have been espousing the use of the figure 0.533 as the critical ratio (minimum downstream pressure in relationship to the upstream pressure) to render maximum flow, up to this point in our text. The formula for determining the critical flow ratio $\gamma$ is

$$\gamma = \left( \frac{2}{k+1} \right)^{k/(k-1)}$$

The only time we should be using $k$ is when it is equal to $c_p/c_v$, which for air is 1.4 (depending on temperature: within the range of $-40°$ to $+120°$F it is extremely stable, for the variation is from 1.401 to 1.400 (see footnote 3), and thus for our purposes it has very little significance). These temperatures are well within the range that we encounter. Since we are using a figure other than 1.4, we should replace $k$ with $\eta$ in the equation. If we use the value of 1.35 for $\eta$, then $\gamma$ becomes 0.537, which is slightly different from the 0.533 we have been using. However, the use of 1.39 for the value of $\eta$ would render a $\gamma$ of 0.531.[4] This would almost confirm the result we arrived at earlier by solving for $\eta$ using the velocity of 1116 ft/s for sound. Now we arrive at the purpose for this entire exercise. If we use 1.37 (which would render the desired solution of 0.533) instead of 1.35, we would have an accumulator solution for the air spring of 1.076 instead of 1.060 gal. Since it is customary to select the nearest-higher

---

[4]See Fig. 2.12 (in Chap. 2).

standard tank size, it is quite obvious that this has no impact of any extent on our choice. The option to utilize a standard 1-gal vessel may very well be an appropriate selection as we are within 7 percent of the target. Another criterion to factor into the equation may be space, as that always is hard to come by. However, for the curious, purist, and serious pneumatics student, this should be an area to be investigated in order to eventually arrive at an appropriate, universally accepted figure to be used for industry at large. Figure 7.1 is a chart based on the Blevins data, which indicates the different velocities we've been discussing.

A tank is unnecessary if it is designed for the specific purpose of supplying a momentary demand that is less than the ongoing supply. In fact, it is a detriment, as there will be losses due to sudden diameter changes (large increase as air enters the larger vessel diameter and large decrease as air discharges to the smaller exiting conductor). This was reviewed in Chap. 4, on fittings.

A tank is beneficial when the drop line, for whatever reason, cannot adequately supply the flow requirements of a piece of equipment. This may be the case even though the header has a sufficient supply available. The reservoir can augment the drop for peak demands. However, it is imperative to ascertain that there be ample recharge time between cycles. If not, the drop will have to be replaced with a larger conductor. Since the idea of increasing the conductor size is being entertained at this juncture, it may be wise to also calculate and submit to the customer how large a drop-line size would be required to supply the sudden instantaneous demand so as to entirely avoid the use of a tank. A careful diagnosis can be conducted to include costs, labor, and essentially all aspects of a circuit to determine which choice would best benefit the customer.

Let us review such a field problem with all its ramifications which would very likely be encountered at almost any plant site (see Fig. 7.2). The following complaints are most frequently voiced by production people and epitomize the problems associated with this area:

Why is it so difficult to obtain the 3 cpm consistently that I require?

At times we come very close to the desired cyclic rate, and at other times during the day we are miles away!

If we could dependably maintain the 3-cpm output at this specific location, we would be able to increase the productivity of the entire line by over 6 percent.

Because of this one application, which is the slowest operation, we must reduce our cyclic rate for the complete line, or else the entire process will be out of synchronization.

| Temp. $\tau$ ($^\circ$F) | Specific Weight w(lbm/ft3) | Kinematic Viscosity, $v$ (ft2/sec) | Ratio of Specific Heats (k) | Speed of Sound, $v_c$ (ft/sec) |
|---|---|---|---|---|
| -100 | 0.1103 | $0.907 \times 10^{-4}$ | 1.402 | 930.1 |
| -80 | 0.1045 | 0.998 | 1.402 | 955.6 |
| -60 | 0.09929 | 1.09 | 1.402 | 980.5 |
| -40 | 0.09456 | 1.12 | 1.401 | 1004 |
| -20 | 0.09026 | 1.19 | 1.401 | 1028 |
| 0 | 0.08633 | $1.26 \times 10^{-4}$ | 1.401 | 1051 |
| 10 | 0.08449 | 1.31 | 1.401 | 1062 |
| 20 | 0.08273 | 1.36 | 1.401 | 1074 |
| 30 | 0.08104 | 1.42 | 1.401 | 1085 |
| 40 | 0.07942 | 1.46 | 1.401 | 1096 |
| 50 | 0.07786 | $1.52 \times 10^{-4}$ | 1.401 | 1106 |
| 60 | 0.07636 | 1.58 | 1.401 | 1117 |
| 70 | 0.07492 | 1.64 | 1.401 | 1128 |
| 80 | 0.07353 | 1.69 | 1.400 | 1138 |
| 90 | 0.07219 | 1.74 | 1.400 | 1149 |
| 100 | 0.07090 | $1.79 \times 10^{-4}$ | 1.400 | 1159 |
| 120 | 0.06846 | 1.89 | 1.400 | 1180 |
| 140 | 0.06617 | 2.01 | 1.399 | 1200 |
| 160 | 0.06404 | 2.12 | 1.399 | 1220 |
| 180 | 0.06204 | 2.25 | 1.399 | 1239 |
| 200 | 0.06016 | $2.40 \times 10^{-4}$ | 1.398 | 1258 |
| 250 | 0.05592 | 2.80 | 1.396 | 1304 |
| 300 | 0.05224 | 3.06 | 1.394 | 1348 |
| 350 | 0.04901 | 3.36 | 1.391 | 1390 |
| 400 | 0.04616 | 3.65 | 1.389 | 1431 |
| 450 | 0.04361 | 4.13 | 1.386 | 1471 |
| 500 | 0.04135 | $4.51 \times 10^{-4}$ | 1.383 | 1509 |
| 550 | 0.03929 | 4.91 | 1.380 | 1546 |
| 600 | 0.03744 | 4.99 | 1.378 | 1583 |
| 650 | 0.03575 | 5.76 | 1.374 | 1618 |
| 700 | 0.03420 | 6.22 | 1.370 | 1651 |
| 750 | 0.03280 | $6.68 \times 10^{-4}$ | 1.367 | 1685 |
| 800 | 0.03149 | 7.15 | 1.364 | 1717 |
| 850 | 0.03029 | 7.76 | 1.361 | 1749 |
| 900 | 0.02918 | 8.25 | 1.358 | 1780 |
| 950 | 0.02814 | 8.76 | 1.355 | 1811 |
| 1000 | 0.02717 | $9.30 \times 10^{-4}$ | 1.351 | 1839 |
| 1100 | 0.02543 | 10.4 | 1.346 | 1898 |
| 1200 | 0.02390 | 11.5 | 1.341 | 1954 |
| 1300 | 0.02255 | 12.6 | 1.337 | 2009 |
| 1500 | 0.02024 | 15.1 | 1.329 | 2114 |

Density $\varrho = W/g$

**Figure 7.1**   Physical properties of air at standard atmospheric pressure (English units). (*Based on data from R. D. Blevins, Applied Fluid Dynamics Handbook, Van Nostrand Reinhold, New York, 1984.*)

Eventually the following is requested: "What is necessary to improve productivity with the minimum of interruption, effort, and cost?" In our case the schematic of the circuit is shown in Fig. 7.2, with the specifications for the new performance times listed as well. Essentially, they desire to know what would be required to satisfy the new 3-cpm requirements. The first order of business would be to determine whether the existing components, such as valves, are capable of obtaining the requisite flow.

See Fig. 7.2 for configuration. *Given:*

1. Five (5) 6-in-bore × 12-in-stroke cylinders, vertically oriented in a circle, with rods facing up and tied together by a platform so that they act in unison—a pair of flow controls is currently used for each cylinder.

2. New desired extend and retract time = 1 s each.

3. Dwell time for each direction remains at 9 s, thus rendering a new cycle time of 20 s or 3 cpm.

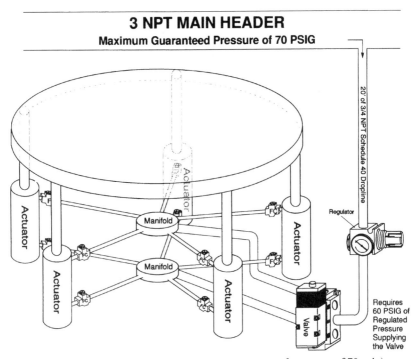

## 3 NPT MAIN HEADER
### Maximum Guaranteed Pressure of 70 PSIG

**Figure 7.2**  3-NPT main header (with maximum guaranteed pressure of 70 psig).

4. Upstream supply pressure varies between a minimum of 70 to a maximum of 80 psig from a compressor source having a kick-in point of 100 psig.

5. We will use the worst-case scenario of 70 psig emanating from the header to supply the drop.

6. We require a continual regulated downstream pressure of 60 psig to supply the valve which ultimately feeds the five cylinders.

7. The $\frac{3}{4}$-NPT Schedule 40 pipe drop line has a length of 20 ft with no elbows originating at the header and terminating via a regulator into the valve pressure entry port.

8. The main conductor between the valve and the manifold is a $1\frac{1}{2}$-NPT nipple 6 in long—from the manifold to the cylinders are the branch conductors, each $\frac{3}{4}$-NPT Schedule 40 pipe and 60 in long.

9. The main header is a 3-NPT Schedule 40 pipe which circles the plant.

10. Extend weight = 3000 lb; retract weight = 1000 lb.

From our initial survey, Survey 7-1 at the end of the chapter, we can readily conclude that the components selected originally are not restricting at all. In fact, they are capable of generating 3.09 cpm with no difficulty (Survey 7-1a), and without the FCs they can generate 3.15 cpm (Survey 7-1b). Let us therefore work our way upstream to the next item, which is the drop line supplying the valve, and determine whether it can accommodate the sudden surge and if not, what size of reservoir is needed, or how large a drop is required without the use of a reservoir. If we find that the drop line is capable of supplying the necessary flow, we will continue upstream to the next device to determine whether it is the restraining member and proceed in this fashion until we locate the restricting component(s). We then correct the situation by either the elimination or replacement process. This process should continue even if the initial plugged artery is discovered because there may be an additional one further upstream, and what may turn out to be the most disturbing condition is that supplementary compressor capacity may be needed.

Ergo, the first item on the agenda is to determine what the $\frac{3}{4}$-NPT drop line can manage. The most stringent peak demand (extend stroke) is 328 scfm, based on the survey results. Let us quickly verify how we arrived at the 328 scfm from Survey 7-1. We have five cylinders having 6-in bores and 12-in strokes. There are five $\frac{3}{4}$-NPT branch conductors, each 60 in in length, commencing at the manifold and ending at the cylinders. In addition, we have a $1\frac{1}{2}$-NPT main conductor with a length of 6 in originating at the valve and terminating at the manifold. The main conductor can be considered to be divided into five imaginary sectors where each is supplying via the manifold one of the branches leading to its mating cylinder. The same logic applies to the valve where it is hypothetically divided into five equal parts, where each is supplying one sector of the main conductor:

| | |
|---|---|
| Cylinder extend volume | $0.1964 \text{ ft}^3$ |
| Branch conductor extend volume | $0.0185 \text{ ft}^3$ |
| Main conductor extend volume | $0.0014 \text{ ft}^3$ |
| Total extend volume per cylinder | $0.2163 \text{ ft}^3$ |
| $0.2163 \times 74.7/14.7$ | $1.099 \text{ scf}$ |
| $1.099 \times 5 \text{ cylinders}$ | $5.496 \text{ scf}$ |

There is 5.496 scf demanded in 1 s of extend time, which is translated into 330 scfm ($5.49 \times 60$). This corresponds with the 328 scfm determined in Survey 7-1 and indicates good correlation. This implies that once we know the extend time, we can easily solve for the scfm. The key ingredient is that we have no way of knowing beforehand that a 6-in-bore cylinder under a pressure of 60 psig is capable of moving the specified mechanical load and exhaust the 60 psig representing the exhaust-pressure load within the allotted time of one second. The calculation is possible only from the information available to us as a result of all the tests we conducted. Let us return now to the qualification of the $\frac{3}{4}$-NPT drop:

Drop flow rate = $Q_D$ (to be calculated)

Peak system flow rate demanded = $Q_s$ (328 scfm)

Makeup flow rate = $Q_M = Q_s - Q_D$

$d$ = ID of drop line = 0.824 in

$a$ = area of drop line = 0.533 in$^2$

$l$ = drop-line length = 240 in

$f$ = 0.0265

$T_e$ = extend time in seconds = 1 s

$V_M$ = makeup volume expressed in cubic feet (will vary depending on options)

$V_T$ = tank volume expressed in cubic feet (will vary depending on options).

pressure $p_1$ is assumed to be 70 psig (84.7 psia), allowing for a 5-psi drop ($\Delta p$) in the line to bring $p_2$ down to 65 psig (79.7 psia) entering the regulator, thus leaving a 5-psi adjustment to be made by it so as to realize the 60 psig required as the regulated output pressure. One of our recommendations, which we've emphasized in Chap. 5 (on conductors), is a maximum pressure drop of 2 psi in a drop line. Despite arguments to the contrary, this particular customer originally insisted on using a 5-psi pressure drop in the line for varied reasons, and thus our survey is based on that number. As we've mentioned before, some end users adopt a 10-psi pressure drop or larger as a standard for the sake of expediency (we do not agree).

In this instance we cannot permit the pressure drop to assume whatever is dictated by the circuit requirements because we do not have that luxury in a drop line. In a drop line we must not fall below a certain pressure tier as we must maintain enough pressure to regulate to a specific level, or we would be starving the system. If we drop below the required pressure level, we would be unable to supply the specific $Q$ (in scfm) to render the performance-time constraints. This is different from the needs of the conductor between the valve and the actuator, which is continually charged and discharged and has a greater latitude. The pressure upstream of the valve must be sustained, whereas downstream of the valve all that is required is for the initial pressure to be at a specific level which can drop to whatever is dictated to achieve smooth cylinder piston movement at the desired performance time. All our tests were conducted on the basis of this premise. We observed the initial pressure and clocked the cylinder's stroke time, making certain that it traveled smoothly and uniformly (the CRT chart recordings were inspected for any abnormal or inconsistent trajectory). We took Polaroid shots of any potentially suspect test firings for careful scrutiny. As soon as any erratic behavior was evident, we documented it to establish our limiting condition. Obviously the faster the cylinder was required to move, the greater this pressure drop was observed to be. The corollary is the slower the cylinder speed requirements were, the smaller the pressure drops were. Let us return to the drop-line calculations:

$$C_v = 33.2d^2\left(\frac{d}{fl}\right)^{0.5} = 8.12 \quad \text{for the drop line}$$

$$Q_D = 0.978C_v(\Delta pp_{2a})^{0.5} = 159 \text{ scfm} \quad \text{for the drop line}$$

As an interesting side issue, this 159 scfm would render an extend time of 2.06 s (328/159) and a retract time of 1.98 s (315/159). The total cycle time would then be the summation of 2.06 + 1.98 + 9.0 (dwell time) = 22.04 s or 2.72 cpm, which is far short of the desired 3 cpm. This piece of equipment, however, was operating at 2.83 cpm [1.6 s extend and 1.6 s retract (Survey 7-5), and thus the entire line was synchronized to it]. It may appear to be impossible to achieve 3 cpm in the light of the 2.72 cpm just calculated. However, we will resolve this apparent enigma in Surveys 7-1 to 7-5. (*Note:* The 2.72 cpm is based on 159 scfm, which in turn is based on an assumed $\Delta p$ of 5 psi, which obviously was not the case.)

Since we require 328 scfm, it is necessary to either increase the size of the existing drop line or use a surge tank if replacing the line is not a practical alternative. We will evaluate all the alternatives. First let us determine the size of a replacement drop line to determine whether it is a viable option (maintaining a $\Delta p$ of 5 psi): $C_v = Q_p/0.978(\Delta pp_{2a})^{0.5} = 328/0.978(5 \times 79.7)^{0.5} = 16.8$ ($Q$ in scfm). This is the $C_v$ required for a drop line to support the flow without the need of a surge tank. We will try the next-larger pipe size above $^3/_4$ NPT, which is 1 NPT, and determine whether its $C_v$ is sufficient to supply the required 328 scfm: $d = 1.049$ in; $f = 0.0248$; $C_v = 15.3$. This $d$ is still too small, for it can supply only 299 scfm. The customer requested, since we are rather close, us to determine the exact pressure drop and evaluate whether the $p_2$ available to the regulator would present a regulation problem since the two pressures (upstream to downstream of the regulator) may not have a sufficient spread for stable regulation:

$$\Delta p = \frac{p_{1a} - [(p_{1a})^2 - 4.18(Q_p/C_v)^2]^{0.5}}{2} = 6.1 \text{ psi}$$

($Q$ in scfm). This means that we have only 63.9 psig available to the pressure regulator to regulate down to 60 psig. The customer felt that the possibility exists, no matter how remote, that the dependable upstream pressure of 70 psig may be breached sometime; this would leave the customer with a very slim safety margin. Even if the customer were able to maintain the 70 psig, we felt it was still calling it too close to the vest. If a replacement was being considered, it made more sense to increase the drop line one more size. The object is to supply as many options as possible to customers for a thorough review of the pros and cons of each option and let them make the decision.

We will continue to use a maximum pressure drop of 5 psi for a $1^1/_4$-NPT pipe, which is the next-larger size available, since the customer elects to remain with this specification. A $1^1/_4$-NPT pipe has a $d$ of 1.38 in (its ID) and an $f$ equal to 0.0232. Therefore, its $C_v$ is equal to 31.5 and thus more than enough to supply the needs of the machine. In fact, it can supply, if necessary, 615 scfm at the 5-psi pressure drop. At the demand of 328 scfm, the pressure drop will be only 1.4 psi; therefore, the regulator will have an incoming pressure of 68.6 psig. The adjusting range will be increased to 8.6 psi (68.6 − 60 psig). This now satisfies as well our maximum recommendation of no more than a 2 psi loss through the drop line.

An interesting exercise is to calculate the $\Delta p$ with the $\frac{3}{4}$-NPT conductor to determine the consequences. Using the same formula we obtain a pressure drop of 32.9 psi or having a pressure entering the regulator of only 37.1 psig. Obviously 37.1 psig cannot be regulated up to the unit's set pressure of 60 psig, and thus will supply only whatever the downstream pressure happens to be. The least pressure at which the system will properly operate in its present configuration is 60 psig (in this instance, the regulator will not hunt and thus will be open continually and just fall with the incoming pressure if it is below the setpoint). The maximum we can muster for a pressure drop is 10 psi (70 − 60). With a 10-psi difference, we can expect only 217 scfm:

$$Q_D = 0.978C_v(\Delta pp_{2a})^{0.5} = 0.978 \times 8.12(10 \times 74.7)^{0.5} = 217 \text{ scfm}$$

This means we are still shy by 111 scfm, and therefore the cylinders will not conclude their task within the allotted time of one second (1 s). In fact the $T_e$ would be 1.51 s (328/217) and the $T_r$ would be 1.45 s for a total cycle time of 20.96 s resulting in a 2.86 cpm. You may recall that we had a 2.72 cpm when using a $\Delta p$ of 5 psi. (*Note:* This in no way implies that the system cannot operate properly with lower pressures. We soon will see another approach which will indicate that with the elimination of certain components, we can operate at lower pressures and still have ample safety to move the loads.)

Let us assume now that the customer may decide to keep the $\frac{3}{4}$-in NPT drop and go with a surge tank as there may be too much effort involved as well as lost time due to shutdown so as to be able to tap into the 3-NPT main header with a larger-size drop line. Therefore, the crucial element to determine is the amount of makeup air that will be necessary to import each cycle into an added tank so that it will be able to supply each and every machine cycle the required 328 scfm. To review, we wish to have no less than 65 psig at the pressure regulator, thus leaving the remaining 5 psi as the permissible pressure drop to be distributed between the other components that lie between the regulator and the header ($\frac{3}{4}$-NPT drop, sudden enlargement in diameter and tank and sudden reduction in diameter). The $\frac{3}{4}$-NPT fitting entering the tank, a device we discussed in Chap. 4, carries a $K$ (loss coefficient for a fitting) value of 1 (sudden enlargement) and thus adds an additional equivalent length of 2.59 ft (31 in) to the already actual length of 240 in, for a total of 271 in. It is important to recognize, and is quite obvious, that a regulator works best when its incoming or upstream pressure is in the order of 50 percent above its outgoing or downstream pressure. In this case since we require a downstream pressure of 60 psig, we would suggest the necessary input pressure into the regulator to be 90 psig or better. However, the real world does not function that way, and with respect to our immediate problem, if we would be assured of 90 psig, we obviously wouldn't have the need for an intermediate surge tank to store a quantity of air to handle the peak demand in the first place. It is precisely for that reason that we require a device to supplement the air supply. We are thus left with a situation that at best is not favorable but from which we cannot escape. Unfortunately in many applications we are called on to supply regulated pressures where the regulating window is only 10 or 5 psi, as in this case. For that reason we try to arrange and design minimum pressure drops upstream of the regulator to allow the maximum possible pressure procurable for regulation. The regulator will respond faster if the differential between the incoming and outgoing air has a 50 percent spread. If we have an approximate spread of only 8 percent, as in this case, we can experience a slower response time as compared to a spread of 50 percent. The problem is compounded further by the capability of the regulator and its relation to what is demanded to be drawn from it. A selection of a weak upstream mating component, an unusually large demand, or a small differential across the regulator all adversely effect the regulator's performance.

We will assume, for a moment, that we did in fact have 90 psig available to us on a continuous basis and will determine the outcome with the original $\frac{3}{4}$-NPT conductor. This will serve as an excellent academic exercise. Assume we allowed a $\Delta p$ through the drop line of 20 psi (90 − 70), leaving a regulating window for the pressure regulator of 10 psi. With the $\Delta p$ of 20 psi, the $p_2$ becomes 84.7 (70 + 14.7) and the flow capable under these conditions is 327 scfm (the original requirement was 328 scfm). As an end user, I would be tempted to select this solution and monitor the efficiency of the equipment if I can consistently maintain the necessary 3 cpm. If, on the other hand, we allowed a $\Delta p$ of 25 psig, and leaving only 5 psig for regulation, we can expect to flow 354 scfm. All these suppositions are based on the ability of the regulator to flow the designated quantity of air in each case.

Confirmation for the preceding equivalent-length figure of 31 in:

$$L_e = \frac{KD}{f} = \frac{1 \times 0.824}{12 \times 0.0265} = 2.59 \text{ ft} \quad \text{or} \quad 31 \text{ in}$$

(where $K$ = fitting loss coefficient; $L$ = length in feet). We obtain a result of 36 in (equivalent length) by applying the same formula for the $1\frac{1}{2}$-NPT fitting (1.61 in ID) exiting the tank, which carries a $K$ loss value of 0.5 (sudden reduction):

$$L_e = \frac{0.5 \times 1.61}{12 \times 0.0223} = 3.0 \text{ ft} \quad \text{or} \quad l = 36 \text{ in}$$

(where $L$ is length, expressed in feet). With all this in mind, we will continue to allocate the entire pressure drop of 5 psi to the drop line, which now includes the entering fitting, 0 psi for the tank (it is essentially a short, fat conductor, as stated earlier, and effectively has a very large $C_v$ and therefore an infinitesimal pressure drop, thus having a negligible impact on the system) and 0 psi for the exiting fitting (same reasoning as applies to the tank but to a lesser degree). We will evaluate different assigned pressure drops to the ³⁄₄-NPT drop line and trace their impact on the resulting tank sizes. The 271-in line length, including the ³⁄₄-NPT inlet fitting and the 1½-NPT exit fitting (36 in), are fixed, leaving the assignable pressure drop to the drop line as the only variable available to govern the tank size. It is not necessary for the pressure regulator (1½ NPT) to be close-coupled to the tank. We have close-nippled (6 in) the manifold to the valve, which in turn is directly mated to the regulator and in succession to the tank. It's wisest to store as much air at the highest possible pressure and then regulate immediately downstream of the regulator directly into a valve. The 1½-NPT pressure regulator should be able to supply approximately 400 scfm under the specified flow conditions. If there is a desire for further improving future cycle times, it would be wise to select one capable of supplying 500 scfm under these same operating conditions, or, to make a selection on the basis of whatever is deemed appropriate for future productivity. The flow $Q$ that the 271-in ³⁄₄-NPT pipe will permit with a pressure drop of 5 psi is 149 scfm:

$$C_v = 33.2d^2 \left( \frac{d}{fl} \right)^{0.5} = 33.2 \times 0.824^2 \left( \frac{0.824}{0.0265 \times 271} \right)^{0.5} = 7.64$$

$$Q_D = 0.978 C_v (\Delta pp_{2a})^{0.5} = 0.978 \times 7.64(5 \times 79.7)^{0.5} = 149 \text{ scfm}$$

(*Note:* The $C_v$ of the 31-in length of the ³⁄₄ NPT entering enlarging fitting is 22.6 and, when combined with the $8.12C_v$ of the drop line, results in a $C_v$ for the combination of the same 7.64. We will see that the $C_v$ of the 1½-NPT reduction fitting exiting the tank is considerably larger and thus would have a negligible effect on the overall system.)

The entering pressure into the tank at the start of the cycle is now considered to be 84.7 psia with a designed pressure drop of 5 psi. The reason for this is that the tank's volume and pressure are integral with those of the conductor's; at the start of any cycle they are one. The exiting pressure will be 79.7 psia. In summary, we have assumed that the drop line is composed of four conductors in series, of which the entire pressure drop is assigned to the ³⁄₄-NPT drop. The ³⁄₄-NPT fitting was folded into this drop line. The other two contributed so little to the pressure drop that we are able to discard them entirely, as we will prove shortly.

The makeup flow rate $Q_M$ that must be supplied by the tank is equal to 179 scfm (328 − 149). A suggested approach to understand the concept of how we size a tank is to view it with the $1\frac{1}{2}$-NPT exiting fitting and regulator having invisible boundary lines down their length (as described previously for the main conductor emanating from the valve), where one sector is fed continually by the $\frac{3}{4}$-NPT conductor contributing a flow of 149 scfm and the remaining larger sector is fed a flow of 179 scfm from the tank. Or if you prefer, the entire combination can be viewed as a doughnut where the hole is feeding the equivalent of the $\frac{3}{4}$-NPT conductor and the larger body of the torus is feeding the remaining flow. Obviously the $\frac{3}{4}$ NPT has to have ample time during the dwell portion of the cycle to recharge the tank in order for it to be prepared for the ensuing cycle:

$$\text{Makeup volume } V_M = \frac{Q_M T_e}{60} = \frac{179 \times 1}{60} = 2.98 \text{ scf}$$

$$\text{Tank volume } V_T = \frac{14.7 \times V_M}{\Delta p} = \frac{14.7 \times 2.98}{5} = 8.76 \text{ ft}^3 \text{ or } 65.5 \text{ gal}$$

$$\text{as } 7.48 \text{ gal} = 1 \text{ ft}^3$$

($Q$ in scfm; $V$ in ft³). You may observe that the formula for sizing this tank does not include the 1.35 exponent (polytropic process) that we derived and discussed earlier. This is because there is a distinct difference in the flow characteristics between the two tanks. The one earlier was used strictly as an accumulator or, so to speak, a single-deposit annuity where there are essentially no withdrawals or deposits. Once a single lump sum is deposited, it is trapped in the system. As a result, there are changes which create both temperature fluctuations (isothermal if there is no temperature change) and heat-flow variations (isentropic if there is no heat-flow change) as the accumulator is operating, and therefore it follows a polytropic process, carrying an exponent value of 1.35. The system consists of the accumulator and associated piping into the rod-end section of the cylinder. The system therefore has either a larger volume and thus lower pressure when the piston is fully retracted, or smaller volume and higher pressure when the piston is fully extended. The cylinder's rod-end volume and accumulator volume remain trapped, and thus there are no withdrawals or deposits. It is used strictly to retract the piston. It is an air-spring application with temperature fluctuations and heat exchanges. The cylinder that we are currently evaluating behaves in a different fashion in that its (extend and retract) air masses are completely purged and filled each cycle. The tank we are sizing here is open at both ends and continually being replenished as fresh compressed air is repeatedly supplied and only momentarily halted in its progress (as a checking account) as it courses ultimately to the atmosphere. Functionally, it is essentially a short, squat conductor in series with other conductors, and as such is primarily an isothermal process carrying an exponent value of 1.00 and treated as dynamic flow through conductors. We treated this subject extensively in Chap. 5. There are undoubtedly some slight temperature and heat flow exchanges, but they are minor (and very difficult to determine) and thus can for all intents and purposes be discarded for our practical applications.

The selected closest standard size vessel would be a tank having a volumetric capacity of 10 ft$^3$ or 75 gal. Therefore, the $\Delta p$ would actually be 4.4 psi making the exiting pressure from the 1½-NPT fitting 65.6 psig (80.3 psia).

The following calculations will establish why we can neglect the 1½-NPT fitting pressure drop and, to an even greater extent, the pressure drop in the tank. The equivalent length of the fitting was found to be 36 in, and the $C_v$ of the fitting is equal to 121.9.

$$\text{Proof: } C_v = 33.2d^2\left(\frac{d}{fl}\right)^{0.5} \quad 33.2 \times 1.61^2\left(\frac{1.61}{0.02223 \times 36}\right)0.5 = 121.9$$

The $\Delta p = 0.09$ psi is rather small, and if we added it to the pressure drop sustained in the drop line of 4.4 psi, it would bring the total to 4.5 psi. The pressure entering the regulator would then be 80.2 psia instead of 80.3 psia (65.5 psig). The calculations for the pressure drop in the tank would produce an even smaller number. Therefore, in any further calculations we may contemplate, the pressure drops will be considered to be zero through this fitting and the tank.

$$\text{Proof: } \Delta p = \frac{p_{1a} - [(p_{1a})^2 - 4.18(Q_p/C_v)^2]^{0.5}}{2}$$

$$\Delta p = \frac{84.7 - [(84.7)^2 - 4.18(328/121.9)^2]^{0.5}}{2} = 0.09 \text{ psi}$$

Viewing this in terms of $C_v$ obviously will yield the same results and conclusion. We will perform the operations only to indicate another approach. The effect of the 121.9$C_v$ on the drop line $C_v$ of 7.64 reduces it to 7.63, and the impact of a much larger $C_v$ for the tank would not even be evident to two decimal places.

Assume we allow the drop in pressure for the drop line with fitting this time to be 3 psi and determine the effect on the tank size. The drop-line flow is reduced to 117 scfm (1.95 scfs). The makeup volume that must be supplied by the tank is increased to 3.52 scf (211 scfm/60). The tank-size requirement now becomes 17.25 ft$^3$ (14.7 × 3.52 × 7.48/3 = 129 gal), or using a standard 130-gal tank, which has a volume of 17.4 ft$^3$ and will have an overall $\Delta p$ of essentially the same 3 psi, making the entry pressure into the regulator somewhat higher than the first attempt or 67 psig. This allows for 7 psi above the regulated pressure of 60 psig.

Let us reassign a pressure drop once more, this time using the recommended 2 psi for the drop line and associated hardware and review the results. The flow through the drop line under these new conditions is 96 scfm (1.58 scfs) of air. The makeup volume is now 3.87 scf (232 scfm/60) because the duration of the stroke time is 1 s. This new apportionment of pressure drops necessitates a tank size of 28.44 ft$^3$ (213 gal) or using a standard 225-gal capacity which is 30 ft$^3$. The $\Delta p$ will be somewhat less than 2 psi (specifically 1.9 psi), but for purposes of discussion is regarded to be 2. Thus, the entering pressure into the pressure regulator will be somewhat more than 68 psig, allowing for a more comfortable spread through the regulator.

Two additional questions must be considered: (1) whether there is ample time for the drop line to recharge the tank within 9 s (specified dwell time between strokes) and (2) in case of a catastrophic compressor failure, whether there is enough air in the system to operate the machine the required number of cycles to clear the work in process. More often than not, this last specification is not requested, but if it is, it must be examined, and we will review the method to deal with it.

The answer to the first question is 2.4 s for the initial $\Delta p$ of 4.5 psi for the 75-gal (10-ft$^3$) reservoir tank. This is more than adequate because we have a 9.0-s dwell time. Before we delve into the supporting calculations, it would behoove us to consider the different flow rates and pressure drops during the operating and nonoperating cylinder cycle times. We must keep in mind that the $\Delta p$ is approaching zero as we are filling the reservoir with 70 psig from the 65.5-psig point after the extend stroke is concluded and there is no demand on it, as is the case during the dwell period. Thus the flow of 149 scfm is continually dwindling to eventually reaching zero as well. By contrast, the $\Delta p$ suddenly increases, calling for a flow demand which remains reasonably constant at 149 scfm while the cylinders are operating, as there is no throttling effect during this period of the cycle. For this reason the general practice is to compensate by averaging the flow at the outset of the fill cycle (149 scfm) with the flow at the conclusion of the fill cycle (0 scfm) during the dwell period. This averaging implies that the rate of approach is linear, which it obviously isn't, for it follows more closely an exponential curve approaching the available pressure asymptotically. We will compare these results in Chap. 9 with the tests we have conducted for correlation.

The supporting math follows. We must recover a volume of 2.98 scf (makeup volume calculated earlier; $Q_M T_e/60 = 179$ scfm $\times$ 1/60). The drop line supplies 149 scfm or 2.48 (149/60) standard cubic feet per second (scfs); the average is 1.24 scfs. Therefore, it will take 2.40 s (2.98 scf/1.24 scfs). The answer to the 3-psi drop having a 130-gal tank (17.4 ft$^3$) is 3.62 s (3.52/1.95). The answer to the 2-psi drop having a 225-gal tank is 4.84 s (3.87/1.6). As you can see, all the suggested circuits fulfill the 9-s dwell. Let us for a moment also explore what avenue would be available to us if the dwell time after the extend-stroke time were 1 s. Obviously we would have had no choice but to replace the ¾-NPT drop line, for even under the maximum of a 5-psi pressure drop requiring the smallest tank it was impossible to refill the tank within a 1-s allotted time. Let us explore the possibility for a requested dwell time or 2.5 s. Continuing with this logic, the only available choice would be the 10-ft$^3$ tank with its associated 5-psi pressure drop, which is contrary to our recommendation of a 2-psi maximum pressure drop. We now have a conflict as to whether to proceed with replacing the drop or going with the 5-psi pressure-drop solution. My personal choice would be to convince the customer to go with the replacement drop line and if so, go with one large enough so as to eliminate the need for the surge tank entirely. However, the final decision rests with the customer. We are not completely through, as we still have to answer the second question (whether there is enough air in the system to operate the machine the required number of cycles to clear the work in process, in the event of a compressor failure). The answer to this question deals with the number of charges necessary to clear a press. The answer is dependent on how much air we must store in the chamber to achieve that end, which obviously negates the possibility of designing a tank-free circuit. The 10-ft$^3$ tank has less than one cycle, specifically 0.63 cycle.

The argument is as follows. We see from Survey 7-1 that we use 10.73 scf per cycle and we have at any one time 6.80 scf available for use once the 10-ft$^3$ tank has been recharged to 70 psig (prior to going into the cylinder operating mode). The lowest it can drop to is the minimum operating pressure of 60 psig, which renders a 10-psi $\Delta p$ in the tank at the specified speeds. Under these conditions we have 0.63 cycles (6.80/10.73) available.

Backup documentation is as follows. We require 328 scfm or 5.47 scfs to operate the extend stroke, and since the duration of the stroke is 1 s, we need 5.47 scf. Similarly, we need 315 scfm or 5.15 scf per retract stroke for a total of 10.72 scf (a result somewhat different from the 10.73 determined in the Survey 7-1, due to rounding off). We have at the outset in the tank 70 psig, and since the equipment is nonfunctional at 60 psig or less, we have only a 10-psi working window available to us. In the 10-ft$^3$ tank we have 6.80 scf, or [(70 psig − 60 psig)/14.7] × 10$^3$ available. Two additional notes here:

1. As far as subtracting the pressures, it makes no difference whether one utilizes psig (70 − 60) or psia (84.7 − 74.7); the difference is identical (expressed as psi) as long as similar units are subtracted.

2. It is vital that there be a check valve just upstream of the tank so that none of the air in the tank will bleed back into the upstream system where the failure has occurred. In this way all the available air stored in the tank will be directed for its intended purpose, namely, to have sufficient air for the required number of cycles to clear the equipment.

The result for the 17.4-ft$^3$ tank is 1.10 cycles. We have 11.84 scf amassed in the tank, which is enough air to operate 1.10 (11.84/10.73) cycles. The result for the 30.0-ft$^3$ tank is 1.90 cycles. We have 20.41 scf amassed in the tank, which is enough air to operate 1.90 (20.42/10.73) cycles.

Whenever one specifies a certain amount of cycles needed to clear a press, one can automatically assume that a reservoir tank is necessary. It is highly improbable that there will be enough air in the lines feeding the equipment to support such a request. In this instance there was no specification delineating the cycles required to use in the event of a major problem with the air service. It could have been specified that at least 1 cycle be available for clearance of parts still in the machine. In that event the 10-ft$^3$ reservoir, as we've just seen, would have been inadequate, and a tank somewhat less than the 17.4 ft$^3$ would have been required. However, if it would have been specified that even 40 psig would be adequate to operate the machine (obviously not at the one second stroke times) for purposes of clearing all the in-process parts, we would be back to the 10-ft$^3$ tank size. One could have requested that the tank be not full, and only large enough to assure an adequate air supply available to clear the equipment in the event of a catastrophe coinciding with the end of the stroke. Here, as in most cases, there is more than meets the eye, and therefore the need exists for a comprehensive survey where every eventuality is considered.

I would like to briefly review the preceding math in light of my original analogy, of viewing a surge-tank problem as a monetary checking service and examining each transaction and its effect on the overall account. We will review the checking account of the 10-ft$^3$

tank. The audit will be run with the original solution of the 8.76-ft$^3$ unit prior to selecting the 10-ft$^3$ standard-size receiver. We are continually depositing compressed air [2.48 scfs (149 scfm/60) at the start of the dwell gradually dwindling to zero prior to the end of the dwell period] into the bank until we fill it to the brim at 50.47 (at 70 psig; 8.76 × 84.7/14.7). We remove in a single withdrawal 5.47 scf (328/60) in a 1-s timeframe from the account while at the same time, during this same 1-s timespan, we deposit 2.48 scf (with no tapering off during this portion of the operating cycle). At the end of this 1-s period we are left with 47.48 scf in the account (50.47 + 2.48 − 5.47). We have a net reduction of 2.99 scf (50.47 − 47.48; previously we calculated the makeup volume to be 2.98 scf) at the end of 1 s, which must be replaced by the continuous curtailing supply of 2.48-scfs (average of 1.24 scfs) deposits before we commence with the next peak removal. We can replace the 2.99 scf in 2.40 (2.99/1.24) s, which leaves us ample time before the next major withdrawal in 9.0 s. When we are at the 47.48-scf level, as we must maintain this minimum balance, it is at 65 psig. This gives us a good opportunity to check our figures. The scf in the tank at 65 psig (79.7 psia) is 47.49 scf (8.76 × 79.7/14.7): good correlation. Some of these figures as well as those solved for previously may be off in the second decimal place simply because of rounding. (*Note:* The volume in the ¾-NPT drop line is only 0.07 ft$^3$; therefore, it is not taken into account for it is so negligible. Any amount that it does possess is simply an additional reservoir and thus adds to our safety margin.)

An interesting side issue that I would like to briefly discuss is the current method some individuals use to size a tank. They will take 10 times the volume displacement of one stroke of the cylinder and use that as a reservoir. The stroke time, dwell time, conductor size and length, and pressures are all irrelevant in this technique. Let us apply this rule of thumb and check how closely this approximates our results. It should be borne in mind that the purpose of this exercise for these designers is to satisfy a demand for a specific number of complete cycles to clear a press in the event of a major breakdown of the compressed-air service. Let us assume that one complete cycle is required to clear the press. We have the five cylinders, each having 6-in bores and 12-in strokes. The blind-end volume of one stroke of a cylinder is 339 in$^3$ or 0.196 ft$^3$. The volumes of the five cylinders are 0.98 ft$^3$, and 10 times that quantity is 9.8 ft$^3$. By happenstance, the result is amazingly close to the smallest tank we arrived at previously. However, you may recall that we only had 0.63 cycles possible to clear the in-process parts with a 10-ft$^3$ tank.

At this point I would like to derive the tank-sizing formula, for although it is quite simple, it warrants some discussion so that you can appreciate the basic concept. Assume that a tank is charged up to the upper pressure, which we will consider to be the operating pressure within the system ($p_{1a}$). In our case it was assumed to be the minimum available or 70 psig (84.7 psia). We also invoked a minimum pressure ($p_{2a}$) below which we should not enter the regulator which was 65 psig (79.7 psia). The difference between the two we called the *designed pressure drop* ($\Delta p$). The purpose of the surge tank expressed in cubic feet ($V_T$) is to make up a specific volume ($V_M$) that was required during a peak period which the drop line leading into the tank was unable to supply on its own. We have at the outset a fixed amount of air confined in a chamber ($V_T p_{1a}/14.7$) ($V$ in ft$^3$ throughout here, except $V_g$ in gallons as indicated below). At the end of the demand period we have a lesser fixed amount of air confined in the same chamber ($V_T p_{2a}/14.7$) by the amount removed that has to be made up ($V_M$):

$$\frac{V_T p_{1a}}{14.7} - \frac{V_T p_{2a}}{14.7} = V_M$$

$$\Delta p = p_{1a} - p_{2a}$$

$$\frac{V_T \Delta p}{14.7} = V_M$$

$$V_T = \frac{V_M 14.7}{\Delta p} \quad \text{(the form we use in our calculations)}$$

The tank-sizing formula can be combined and stated in gallons ($V_g$) by the following expression: $1.83 \times Q_M T/\Delta p$ ($Q$ ins cfm), where $T$ represents either extend or retract time in seconds depending on which accompanying $Q_M$ is the greatest (most stringent condition).

When the tank size is solved for required clearing cycles, it is compared to the result based on peak demand if that, too, was necessary and it goes without saying that the one entailing the most severe need would be selected.

In all our reasoning we have assumed that the main header would have no difficulty in supplying a consistent supply of air even up to and perhaps beyond the stated demand of 328 scfm. This meant that if we desired and if it was not explicitly requested, we could have designed our circuit without a tank and just used a 1¼-NPT drop line. However, there are those times where the most one can expect from the header on a consistent basis would still be insufficient to supply the instantaneous peak demand. In that event even if the drop line was properly designed for the entire flow rate, it still would necessitate the use of a tank and be solved for in the same fashion as an inadequate drop line. In addition, we would calculate for the magnitude of the minimum flow to satisfactorily refill the tank during the dwell period. If this flow would be insufficient to recharge the tank, which is a distinct possibility, one must then use either a dedicated compressor for this application or provide for additional compressor capacity to be tied into the existing plant's pneumatic facility. To repeat, this added tank serves the same function, namely, to handle peak demands, for an inadequate supply as it does for an undersized drop line. The tank in this instance is not intended to supply several cycles for clearing equipment, although it is available for that purpose. It is thus necessary to solve for size and recharge time only.

You may have concluded by now that in certain instances the requirements dictate not only the incorporation of a reservoir tank into the circuit but also the upsizing of the drop line. In our problem we had a maximum of 10 psi available at most for the $\Delta p$, which is a far cry from a comfortable situation. The objective is always to use as much of this $\Delta p$ as possible for the regulator and assign or design as little of it as possible to be used for the other components. This may involve the upsizing of the drop line. If it is not possible to cut into the header with a larger conductor, it may entail cutting the existing restricting ¾-NPT conductor as short as possible and marrying it into a larger-diameter drop line which will then proceed to the tank. Emanating from the tank through a large port would be a short nipple tied directly into the regulator, or in some instances the regulator would be mated directly to the tank's port. From the regulator we would proceed as previously into the valve. Or it may prove to be more practical to locate the tank close to the header and then proceed in succession to the regulator, larger drop line, valve, etc. An examination would be undertaken to determine which of these options would be the most practical to install and maintain. Many firms prefer the regulator to be inaccessible to the operator; however, this makes legitimate adjusting less convenient.

We also urged the customer to review the drop-line and tank solutions using the dual-pressure technique (this is what we were alluding to earlier). As we proceed, it will be evident that this provides us with yet another advantage over the conventional method of using flow controls. We will examine its impact on costs and sizes and perhaps be able to alleviate some of the dilemmas that we encountered with the other potential solutions.

Again the first task is to obtain a revised survey having the same requirements but solving it using dual pressures with the restricting flow controls removed (see Survey 7-2). We find we need only 238 scfm ($Q_p$) for our new peak demand at 40 psig (39.3 psig specifically) to satisfy the most rigorous requirement. We will first examine the capability of the $\frac{3}{4}$-NPT drop under these new conditions. If we continue to use the $\Delta p$ of 5 psi with a $p_1$ of 70 psig, our $Q_D$ would remain at 159 scfm. This would be shy by the additional 79 scfm (238 − 159) required to meet our performance-time specification. To satisfy the condition we must again either upsize the drop line or add a tank. Before we do that, let us calculate the $\Delta p$ across the conductor as if we attempted to flow the entire 238 scfm through it:

$$\Delta p = \frac{p_{1a} - [(p_{1a})^2 - 4.18(Q_p/C_v)^2]^{0.5}}{2}$$

$$= \frac{84.7 - [(84.7)^2 - 4.18(238/8.12)^2]^{0.5}}{2} = 12.4 \text{ psi}$$

This would mean that we have 57.6 psig (70 − 12.4) entering the regulator and 40 psig (39.3 psig specifically) exiting the regulator. This essentially accomplishes the recommendation of having a 50 percent safety factor for the incoming pressure to be greater than the exiting pressure (57.6 − 39.3 = 18.3: 18.3/39.3 = 47 percent). This total package is not one that we would suggest, for it still falls short in the category of the $\Delta p$ we recommend for the drop. Therefore, let us determine whether a 1-NPT satisfies the recommended pressure drop. A 1-NPT conductor has a $C_v$ of 15.3 (solved for earlier), and if we substitute that figure into the equation for $\Delta p$, it amounts to 3 psi. The customer may be inclined to settle for this solution. Let us now determine the tank size, assuming that the upsizing would not be a practical solution.

We established earlier that using the existing $\frac{3}{4}$-NPT conductor in conjunction with an added tank would render a $C_v$ for the drop line of 7.64. Allowing our maximum of 2 psi for the $\Delta p$, we find that the line can accommodate 96 scfm. This means that our $Q_M$ would factor out to be 142 scfm (238 − 96). The makeup volume ($V_M$, in ft$^3$) becomes 2.36 scf ($Q_M T_e/60$; $Q$ in scfm). We desire to exit the tank with 60 psig (50 percent safety factor), and since we enter the system with 70 psig, we have 10 psi available to expend for the tank system. The tank size $V_T$ then becomes 3.4 ft$^3$ or 25 gal, a far cry from the original requirement of 65 gal in both cost and space. The refill or recharge time is 2.95 s, which is certainly within the 9-s dwell time allowed in the window. The supporting proof is as follows. The drop supplies 96 scfm or 1.6 scfs (96 × 1/60), which amounts to 0.8 scfs as the average, which is what we use for our calculations. Since we must recoup 2.36 scf, it will take 2.95 (2.36/0.8) s. We also have 6.94 scf stored in the tank in the event of a compressor failure. The window we now have is 30 psi, which is a result of the maximum 70 psig available to us and the minimum 40 psig we can supply and still remain functional. The total scf is therefore 6.94 [(30/14.7) × 3.4 ft$^3$]. We require 5.14 scf per cycle, essentially half that needed at the elevated pressures we used earlier of 60/60 psig. The number of cycles available for clearing in-process material is 1.35 (6.94/5.14), considerably more than the 0.63 cycle available to us with the larger 10-ft$^3$ tank. In summary, not only do we experience over a 50 percent drop in operating costs (Survey 7-1, $2185 (1738 + 447) compared to Survey 7-2, $952 (833 + 119)], but the tank requirement, with its consequent capital expense, is substantially reduced. Finally, even with the smaller tank, we can supply more air for clearing product and better fulfill all the recommended design considerations. As a side benefit, the dual-pressure approach calls for a smaller regulator if desired. It also readily supplies the 50 percent over the 40-psig design criterion required to leave the regulator with the 60 psig of upstream pressure entering the regulator from the tank.

There are additional points that require some discussion dealing with the seeming contradictions encountered earlier: (1) the ability to almost reach 3 cpm and (2) the capability to sustain 2.83 cpm under present conditions. We will first explore the 3-cpm riddle, where the production supervisor stated that when the pressure in the header is up to 80 psig and the flow controls are at their maximum openings the equipment comes very close to realizing the 3 cpm. Therefore, let us calculate the flow that can be achieved at this pressure if the flow controls are in their full-open mode and the limitation is the $^3/_4$-NPT drop line:

$$Q_D = 0.978 C_v (\Delta p p_{2a})^{0.5}$$

where $\Delta p$ = 15 psi (80 − 65 psig)
$\quad p_{2a}$ = 65 psig (79.7 psia) (the entering regulator pressure set at the customer's establishment as stated in the original specifications)
$\quad C_v$ = 8.12 (determined earlier)

and

$$Q_D = 0.978 \times 8.12(15 \times 79.7)^{0.5} = 275 \text{ scfm}$$

$Q_D$ required for a 1-s extend time is 328 scfm and 315 scfm for a 1-s retract time. The 275 scfm will extend the cylinder in 1.19 s (328/275) and will retract the cylinder in 1.15 s (315/275). The total cycle time is 20.34 s (1.19 + 1.15 + dwells totaling 18.0) or 2.95 cpm. This is close to the 3 cpm, but still not what the machine was actually operating at on the floor with the flow controls wide open. The $\Delta p$ cannot be the assumed 15 psi but must be somewhat greater, which leads us into the resolution of this dilemma. A regulator in a circuit is such that only the outgoing pressure is regulated. The incoming pressure cannot be regulated unless one has another regulator located directly upstream of it set at the customer's prescribed 65 psig. What was actually occurring, since the equipment necessitates and is capable of using 328 scfm, was that it was drawing everything it could to reach it. The system was unable to supply it. This is very similar to an electrical circuit's inability to furnish the required current $I$ (pneumatic counterpart to $Q$ scfm) through an inadequate supplying conductor. The wire will be overloaded creating heat and a dangerous situation, thus blowing a fuse which is rated at the safest maximum current that the conductor can handle without overheating it. A pneumatic system has no comparable hazardous equivalent, and thus no safety device is necessary. The equipment will just not cycle the anticipated rate. The circuit paid no attention to the customer's stipulation of the incoming requirement of 65 psig, and thus the pressure going into the regulator was very close to the set pressure of 60 psig and attempting to regulate itself to 60 psig. The regulator simply serves as a device attempting to regulate the incoming pressure to a set pressure of 60 psig (if incoming pressure is above 60 psig), which is the precise purpose of a regulator. (*Note:* If the upstream pressure drops below the intended regulated pressure of 60 psig, the regulator acts as a passage way for the flow of air at the reduced air pressure through its air paths.)

Under these conditions the flow was up to 307 scfm with a $\Delta p$ of 20 psi, and thus $p_{2a}$ was down to 74.7 psia:

$$Q_D = 0.978C_v(\Delta p p_{2a})^{0.5} = 0.978 \times 8.12(20 \times 74.7)^{0.5} = 307 \text{ scfm}$$

The extend time was 1.07 s (328/307), and the retract time was 1.03 s (315/307) for a total time of 20.1 s or 2.99 cpm, which is truly very close to the 3 cpm desired.

Now for the explanation of the second riddle. At 70 psig the best that could be expected would be 217 scfm (as determined earlier), which would generate only a 1.51-s extend time and a 1.45-s retract time for a total of 20.96 s or 2.86 cpm (as determined earlier). This, too, is based on a $p_2$ of 60 psig, with the ensuing $\Delta p$ now only 10 psi. The customer, as we stated earlier, had the flow controls set so that the extend time and retract time were both 1.6 s for a cyclic rate of 2.83 cpm, which they found from experience to be continuously maintainable. On the basis of these 1.6-s performance times, the flow rates required by these simple calculations are 205 (328/1.6) and 197 (315/1.6) scfm. Obviously the available 217 scfm is more than sufficient to supply these needs, and consequently the flow controls were cranked down to render the 1.6-s performance times. There is one fallacy to this quick calculation, as was pointed out in Chap. 3, on cylinders. We assume the dynamic load to be the same at 1.07 s as it is for the example of 1.00 s, which obviously it isn't, as we've stated so often. The acceleration load portion of the total dynamic load varies, as we know, with time. Therefore, the uncorrected flow of 328 scfm, which is based on a 1-s time, carries a slightly larger acceleration load than is required to raise the same weight in 1.07 s. This would reduce the required flow for the 1.07-s time by somewhat less than the flow of 307 scfm (328/1.07). In this particular instance the acceleration contribution is small and the differences small as the time demands are relatively slow, and thus the variations from the straight ratio are almost insignificant but nevertheless exist, as we will prove shortly. Another way of viewing it is that the available 307 scfm will render a slightly faster time than 1.07/1.03 s, which would bring the machine cycle even closer to the 3 cpm during the period when the pressure was up to 80 psig. The survey results taking into consideration these conditions are presented in Surveys 7-3 to 7-5 and summarized in the following list:

1. The 80-psig survey solution having 307 scfm available rendered times of 1.07/1.02 s (Survey 7-3). There was a very slight difference from 1.07/1.03 because of the minute reduction in loads from those generated at 1.00/1.00 s.

2. The 70-psig survey solution having 217 scfm available rendered times of 1.50/1.43 s (Survey 7-4). These time differences were somewhat more perceptible as the acceleration portion of the load had a slightly greater disparity due to a larger time variation from the base of 1.00/1.00-s performance times.

3. The flow requirements calculated for the 1.6/1.6-s performance times via the quick method indicated 205/197 scfm, whereas the results obtained using the detailed method came to 203/194 scfm (Survey 7-5). These variations resulted because the acceleration loads are different; this disparity was explained in detail earlier.

Here, as in the previous chapters, we arrive at a similar conclusion; namely, the established tactics are no longer the appropriate passageways to profits, efficiency, and energy conservation in today's world economic order.

There are two additional subtle points that dictate some elaboration and clarification. The first is that since the demand for the retract stroke is only 315 scfm as opposed to 328 scfm for the extend stroke, it does not seem necessary for the drop line to resupply the tank back up to the brink after the machine has concluded its extend stroke. The rationale is that the demand will not be as great and will therefore drain less from the tank and still not dip below the minimum. However, after the retract stroke, the drop line will need greater capability, for it now will require to fully recharge the tank as it now has to be up to maximum in order to handle the more stringent extend-stroke demand. Consequently, this makes no difference when one solves for the maximum case. A valid case can be proposed and can be calculated in similar fashion to recharge the vessel with an intermediate drop line which supplies a makeup flow between the two demands, which presents the potential for reducing the drop-line size. This is possible and useful when there is a large disparity between the two demands. The reasoning is that it will supply more than required for the succeeding minor stroke demand, thus not emptying the vessel to the lower limit, and after the minor drain is complete, it supplies an equivalent amount to bring the vessel up to capacity for the major requirement. This average supply may call for a smaller drop line than would be required if the drop were designed to handle the larger demand after each stroke. Obviously, following that concept would generate a resultant size which is unnecessarily large in one direction. I must emphasize that a meaningful variance between the two demands must exist so that it can render a different-size conductor for the drop line using the averaging method.

The other point warranting discussion is that in all the demand flow computations that we have evaluated we have never included leakage, which rightly should be encompassed in the calculations. I must hasten to state that actuator leakage of new units is negligible. As time progresses, the leakage becomes more profound, and as such we should have a means for considering it so that it can be represented in the analysis. Cylinders leak primarily around the rod bushing. In our tests we have found that after approximately 50,000 cycles (considered relatively new) under a cantilever load in a moderately clean factory environment, the leak around a 1-in rod is the equivalent of a hole having a diameter of 0.045 in (smaller rod diameters carry smaller equivalent leakage orifices). This is comparable to a radial clearance of 0.0005 in around a 1-in rod (which appears to be very little). The torus at this stage is converted to a 0.045-in pinhole having a $C_v$ of 0.046 ($23d^2$). This is somewhat of an oversimplification of the leakage investigation; nevertheless it allows one to grasp the magnitude even for a relatively new actuator. All the leakages we state are based on cylinders having sequenced approximately 50,000 cycles in an average factory environment with some reasonable side loading. We also take into account piston-seal leakage. It is well to bear in mind that if the actuator has an abnormally high cantilever load, is subjected to excessive amounts of grit, lacks lubricity, is exposed to prevailing high temperatures, and most importantly has acquired a good many cycles, the leakage can only degenerate from the initial conditions for which we calculate. For example, assume that we have a 4-in-bore cylinder with a 1-in rod operating under 100 psig (114.7 psia) where the sequence is 1 s to extend, 0 second dwell, 1 second to retract, and a final 0-s dwell before commencing the cycle. Essentially it is acting as a continuous positive-displacement pump and operating for two shifts for 4000 h per year. The loss of air occurs strictly by leaking around the rod only, is based on essentially a new cylinder, and is calculated to be $92.90.

The cost of air at 100 psig is currently at $0.30 per 1000 scf (we are assuming for simplicity that the compressor is operating the pump directly). The flow $Q$ for air at 100 psig having a $C_v$ of 0.046 is

$$Q = 0.489C_v p_{1a}$$

$$= 0.489 \times 0.046 \times 114.7 = 2.58 \text{ scfm}$$

The total amount leaking at the rod end occurs only when the rod end is subjected to 100 psig and that transpires 1 s out of very 2-s cycle. Therefore, the rod end is subjected to 100 psig for 2000 h during the year, or for 120,000 minutes. Thus, $2.58 \times 120,000 = 309,600$ scf lost per year and at $0.30/1000 scf, this amounts to $92.90. (*Note:* The leakage emanating from the blind end is less as it must cross the piston-seal barrier first and then leak out the rod bushing.)

Consequently, the next time you are told it's only a pinhole leak and nothing to be concerned about, you will know better. Tally all the cylinders in a plant plus all the threaded connections, and this amounts to one-third to one-half of a compressor's output time devoted to simply feeding leaks. Time will only intensify this waste unless one takes corrective measures to arrest or at least decrease this condition.

*"It is always the adventurers who accomplish great things."*
MONTESQUIEU

*"He that will not apply new remedies must expect new evils; for time is the greatest innovator."*
SIR FRANCIS BACON

```
NUMATICS NUMASIZING (R) SUMMARY SHEET                       Date:    04/10/95
NU301EED  Ver 3.01 (c) 1989 Numatics, Inc.                 SURVEY # 7-1
==============================================================================
Prepared for:                       Prepared by:    Michael Liberty
Company:                            Company:        Numatics Inc.
Address:                            Address:        1450 N. Milford Rd.
City,State,Zip:                     City,State,Zip: Highland, Mi. 48357
Telephone #                         Telephone #     (810) 887-4111
Fax #                               Fax #           (810) 887-9190
------------------------------------------------------------------------------
                                          Avg/Tot/Oth    Extend      Retract
INITIAL CUSTOMER PARAMETERS:
Total weight of load (lbs)                              3000.00     -1000.00
Angle of load from horizontal               90
Coefficient of Friction                   0.00
Number of actuators                          5
Total load per actuator (lbs)                           651.10      -173.77
Minimum line pressure (PSIG)               100
Design pressure used (PSIG)                              60.0        60.0
Shifts/day (1 shift=120,000 m/yr)          1.5
Cycles per year                         540000

ACTUATOR:
Description:   Single Rod High Flow Numatics Actuator with 3/4 NPT ports
Bore/stroke/rod              6.00" bore x 12.00" stroke x 1.375" rod
Fitting                      3/4 NPT - 3/4 NPT STR

CONDUCTOR & ASSOCIATED COMPONENTS:
Branch conductor /leg         3/4 NPT pipe 60" long with 1.0 elbow(s)
Branch manifold fitting /leg        3/4 NPT - 3/4 NPT EL
Branch cond equiv ftg lg /leg (in)       25
Quick disconnect model /leg         N/A
In line flow control model /leg                  5FC3B        5FC3B
Main conductor               1-1/2 NPT pipe 6" long with 0.0 elbow(s)
Main manifold fitting        1-1/2 NPT - 1-1/2 NPT STR
Main cond equiv ftg lg (in)          0

VALVE ASSEMBLY & ASSOCIATED COMPONENTS:
Description    2 Pos 12J on 1-1/2 NPT base with ext reg
Fitting                      1-1/2 NPT - 1-1/2 NPT STR
Silencer model               N/A

SYSTEM PERFORMANCE TIMES:
Att'n stroke time (sec)                                 1.00        1.00
Required stroke time (sec)                              1.00        1.00
Stroke time @ term vel (sec)                           0.66        0.97
Att'n cyclic rate (CPM)                    3.00
Required cyclic rate (CPM)                 3.00
Cyclic rate @ term vel (CPM)               3.06
System delay time (sec)                   0.090
Dwell time after stroke (sec)                          9.00        9.00

SYSTEM INFORMATION:
Required system Cv                                      14.09       9.04
Attained system Cv                                     13.78       8.92
Att'n system air flow (SCFM)                           328.2       315.4
Att'n branch air vel (400 FPS max)                     66          89
Att'n main air vel (400 FPS max)                       87          117
Att'n % delta p (46% max)                              12          37
% Act. capacity used (75% max)                         38          -11
Min pres necessary for ld w/S.F. (PSIG)                30.7        -8.6
Air per cycle (SCF)                       10.73
Att'n act leakage cost/yr @ $ 0.30 /KSCF     447       167         280
Att'n operating air cost/yr @ $ 0.30 /KSCF  1738       890         848
Cost /1000 cyc @ att'n times @ $ 20.00 /hr 115.16
Att'n power input total (HP)               8.22

COMMENTS:
Single pressure approach using FC's for zeroing in on the required times
```

```
NUMATICS NUMASIZING (R) SUMMARY SHEET                Date:    04/10/95
NU301EED   Ver 3.01 (c) 1989 Numatics, Inc.          SURVEY # 7-1a
=====================================================================
Prepared for:                    Prepared by:    Michael Liberty
Company:                         Company:        Numatics Inc.
Address:                         Address:        1450 N. Milford Rd.
City,State,Zip:                  City,State,Zip: Highland, Mi. 48357
Telephone #                      Telephone #     (810) 887-4111
Fax #                            Fax #           (810) 887-9190
---------------------------------------------------------------------
                                    Avg/Tot/Oth   Extend    Retract
INITIAL CUSTOMER PARAMETERS:
Total weight of load (lbs)                        3000.00  -1000.00
Angle of load from horizontal         90
Coefficient of Friction             0.00
Number of actuators                    5
Total load per actuator (lbs)                     651.10   -173.77
Minimum line pressure (PSIG)         100
Design pressure used (PSIG)                        60.0      60.0
Shifts/day (1 shift=120,000 m/yr)    1.5
Cycles per year                   540000

ACTUATOR:
Description:   Single Rod High Flow Numatics Actuator with 3/4 NPT ports
Bore/stroke/rod          6.00" bore x 12.00" stroke x 1.375" rod
Fitting                  3/4 NPT - 3/4 NPT STR

CONDUCTOR & ASSOCIATED COMPONENTS:
Branch conductor /leg        3/4 NPT pipe 60" long with 1.0 elbow(s)
Branch manifold fitting /leg       3/4 NPT - 3/4 NPT EL
Branch cond equiv ftg lg /leg (in)       25
Quick disconnect model /leg              N/A
In line flow control model /leg                5FC3B      5FC3B
Main conductor           1-1/2 NPT pipe 6" long with 0.0 elbow(s)
Main manifold fitting              1-1/2 NPT - 1-1/2 NPT STR
Main cond equiv ftg lg (in)         0

VALVE ASSEMBLY & ASSOCIATED COMPONENTS:
Description     2 Pos 12J on 1-1/2 NPT base with ext reg
Fitting                           1-1/2 NPT - 1-1/2 NPT STR
Silencer model                    N/A

SYSTEM PERFORMANCE TIMES:
Att'n stroke time (sec)                           0.86 ?    0.55 ?
Required stroke time (sec)                        1.00      1.00
Stroke time @ term vel (sec)                      0.56      0.54
Att'n cyclic rate (CPM)               3.09
Required cyclic rate (CPM)            3.00
Cyclic rate @ term vel (CPM)          3.14
System delay time (sec)             0.090
Dwell time after stroke (sec)                     9.00      9.00

SYSTEM INFORMATION:
Required system Cv                               14.09      9.04
Attained system Cv                              16.03     16.03 ?
Att'n system air flow (SCFM)                    382.9     574.9
Att'n branch air vel (400 FPS max)                 77       171
Att'n main air vel (400 FPS max)                  101       224
Att'n % delta p (46% max)                          12        40
% Act. capacity used (75% max)                     38       -11
Min pres necessary for ld w/S.F. (PSIG)          30.7      -8.6
Air per cycle (SCF)                 10.73
Att'n act leakage cost/yr @ $ 0.30 /KSCF   445    170       275
Att'n operating air cost/yr @ $ 0.30 /KSCF 1791   917       874
Cost /1000 cyc @ att'n times @ $ 20.00 /hr  111.84
Att'n power input total (HP)          8.41

COMMENTS:
Capability of components with the FC's in the full open mode is 3.09 CPM.
```

```
NUMATICS NUMASIZING (R) SUMMARY SHEET                         Date:   04/10/95
NU301EED  Ver 3.01 (c) 1989 Numatics, Inc.                   SURVEY # 7-1b
===============================================================================
Prepared for:                      Prepared by:    Michael Liberty
Company:                           Company:        Numatics Inc.
Address:                           Address:        1450 N. Milford Rd.
City,State,Zip:                    City,State,Zip: Highland, Mi. 48357
Telephone #                        Telephone #     (810) 887-4111
Fax #                              Fax #           (810) 887-9190
-------------------------------------------------------------------------------
                                        Avg/Tot/Oth   Extend      Retract
INITIAL CUSTOMER PARAMETERS:
Total weight of load (lbs)                           3000.00     -1000.00
Angle of load from horizontal             90
Coefficient of Friction                 0.00
Number of actuators                        5
Total load per actuator (lbs)                         651.10     -173.77
Minimum line pressure (PSIG)             100
Design pressure used (PSIG)                            60.0        60.0
Shifts/day (1 shift=120,000 m/yr)        1.5
Cycles per year                       540000

ACTUATOR:
Description:    Single Rod High Flow Numatics Actuator with 3/4 NPT ports
Bore/stroke/rod            6.00" bore x 12.00" stroke x 1.375" rod
Fitting                    3/4 NPT - 3/4 NPT STR

CONDUCTOR & ASSOCIATED COMPONENTS:
Branch conductor /leg        3/4 NPT pipe 60" long with 1.0 elbow(s)
Branch manifold fitting /leg          3/4 NPT - 3/4 NPT EL
Branch cond equiv ftg lg /leg (in)        25
Quick disconnect model /leg           N/A
In line flow control model /leg                       NONE        NONE
Main conductor              1-1/2 NPT pipe 6" long with 0.0 elbow(s)
Main manifold fitting                 1-1/2 NPT - 1-1/2 NPT STR
Main cond equiv ftg lg (in)            0

VALVE ASSEMBLY & ASSOCIATED COMPONENTS:
Description       2 Pos 12J on 1-1/2 NPT base with ext reg
Fitting                               1-1/2 NPT - 1-1/2 NPT STR
Silencer model                        N/A

SYSTEM PERFORMANCE TIMES:
Att'n stroke time (sec)                                0.65 ?      0.41 ?
Required stroke time (sec)                             1.00        1.00
Stroke time @ term vel (sec)                          0.43        0.41
Att'n cyclic rate (CPM)                   3.15
Required cyclic rate (CPM)                3.00
Cyclic rate @ term vel (CPM)              3.18
System delay time (sec)                  0.090
Dwell time after stroke (sec)                          9.00        9.00

SYSTEM INFORMATION:
Required system Cv                                    14.09        9.04
Attained system Cv                                   20.99 ?     20.99 ?
Att'n system air flow (SCFM)                          504.6       760.5
Att'n branch air vel (400 FPS max)                     102         239
Att'n main air vel (400 FPS max)                       134         312
Att'n % delta p (46% max)                               12          44
% Act. capacity used (75% max)                          38         -11
Min pres necessary for 1d w/S.F. (PSIG)  10.73         30.7        -8.6
Air per cycle (SCF)
Att'n act leakage cost/yr @ $ 0.30 /KSCF   445         169         276
Att'n operating air cost/yr @ $ 0.30 /KSCF 1823        934         889
Cost /1000 cyc @ att'n times @ $ 20.00 /hr 109.93
Att'n power input total (HP)             8.53

COMMENTS:
Capability of components without the FC's is 3.15 CPM.
```

```
NUMATICS NUMASIZING (R) SUMMARY SHEET                Date:   04/10/95
NU301EED  Ver 3.01 (c) 1989 Numatics, Inc.          SURVEY # 7-2
========================================================================
Prepared for:              Prepared by:      Michael Liberty
Company:                   Company:          Numatics Inc.
Address:                   Address:          1450 N. Milford Rd.
City,State,Zip:            City,State,Zip:   Highland, Mi. 48357
Telephone #                Telephone #       (810) 887-4111
Fax #                      Fax #             (810) 887-9190
------------------------------------------------------------------------
                                    Avg/Tot/Oth    Extend      Retract
INITIAL CUSTOMER PARAMETERS:
  Total weight of load (lbs)                      3000.00    -1000.00
  Angle of load from horizontal         90
  Coefficient of Friction             0.00
  Number of actuators                    5
  Total load per actuator (lbs)                    651.10    -173.77
  Minimum line pressure (PSIG)         100
  Design pressure used (PSIG)                        39.3       2.0
  Shifts/day (1 shift=120,000 m/yr)    1.5
  Cycles per year                   540000

ACTUATOR:
  Description:   Single Rod High Flow Numatics Actuator with 3/4 NPT ports
  Bore/stroke/rod          6.00" bore x 12.00" stroke x 1.375" rod
  Fitting                  3/4 NPT - 3/4 NPT STR

CONDUCTOR & ASSOCIATED COMPONENTS:
  Branch conductor /leg       3/4 NPT pipe 60" long with 1.0 elbow(s)
  Branch manifold fitting /leg        3/4 NPT - 3/4 NPT EL
  Branch cond equiv ftg lg /leg (in)       25
  Quick disconnect model /leg          N/A
  In line flow control model /leg                  5FC3B       5FC3B
  Main conductor           1-1/2 NPT pipe 6" long with 0.0 elbow(s)
  Main manifold fitting               1-1/2 NPT - 1-1/2 NPT STR
  Main cond equiv ftg lg (in)           0

VALVE ASSEMBLY & ASSOCIATED COMPONENTS:
  Description    2 Pos 12J on 1-1/2 NPT base with ext reg
  Fitting                             1-1/2 NPT - 1-1/2 NPT STR
  Silencer model                       N/A

SYSTEM PERFORMANCE TIMES:
  Att'n stroke time (sec)                           1.00        1.00
  Required stroke time (sec)                        1.00        1.00
  Stroke time @ term vel (sec)                      0.56        0.54
  Att'n cyclic rate (CPM)              3.00
  Required cyclic rate (CPM)           3.00
  Cyclic rate @ term vel (CPM)         3.14
  System delay time (sec)             0.090
  Dwell time after stroke (sec)                     9.00        9.00

SYSTEM INFORMATION:
  Required system Cv                               16.32       16.26
  Attained system Cv                               16.03       16.03
  Att'n system air flow (SCFM)                    238.3        70.5
  Att'n branch air vel (400 FPS max)                 64          61
  Att'n main air vel (400 FPS max)                   84          79
  Att'n % delta p (46% max)                           9           8
  % Act. capacity used (75% max)                     59        -321
  Min pres necessary for ld w/S.F. (PSIG)          30.7        -8.6
  Air per cycle (SCF)                  5.14
  Att'n act leakage cost/yr @ $ 0.30 /KSCF          119           9
  Att'n operating air cost/yr @ $ 0.30 /KSCF        833         190
  Cost /1000 cyc @ att'n times @ $ 20.00 /hr     112.85
  Att'n power input total (HP)         3.58

COMMENTS:
```

```
NUMATICS NUMASIZING (R) SUMMARY SHEET                  Date:    04/10/95
NU301EED  Ver 3.01 (c) 1989 Numatics, Inc.            SURVEY # 7-3
=======================================================================
Prepared for:                    Prepared by:     Michael Liberty
Company:                         Company:         Numatics Inc.
Address:                         Address:         1450 N. Milford Rd.
City,State,Zip:                  City,State,Zip:  Highland, Mi. 48357
Telephone #                      Telephone #      (810) 887-4111
Fax #                            Fax #            (810) 887-9190
-----------------------------------------------------------------------
                                 Avg/Tot/Oth    Extend      Retract
INITIAL CUSTOMER PARAMETERS:
  Total weight of load (lbs)                    3000.00    -1000.00
  Angle of load from horizontal       90
  Coefficient of Friction           0.00
  Number of actuators                  5
  Total load per actuator (lbs)                 647.60     -174.82
  Minimum line pressure (PSIG)       100
  Design pressure used (PSIG)                     80.0        80.0
  Shifts/day (1 shift=120,000 m/yr)  1.5
  Cycles per year                 537319

ACTUATOR:
  Description:   Single Rod High Flow Numatics Actuator with 3/4 NPT ports
  Bore/stroke/rod          6.00" bore x 12.00" stroke x 1.375" rod
  Fitting                           3/4 NPT - 3/4 NPT STR

CONDUCTOR & ASSOCIATED COMPONENTS:
  Branch conductor /leg     3/4 NPT pipe 60" long with 1.0 elbow(s)
  Branch manifold fitting /leg      3/4 NPT - 3/4 NPT EL
  Branch cond equiv ftg lg /leg (in)     25
  Quick disconnect model /leg       N/A
  In line flow control model /leg                5FC3B       5FC3B
  Main conductor            1-1/2 NPT pipe 6" long with 0.0 elbow(s)
  Main manifold fitting             1-1/2 NPT - 1-1/2 NPT STR
  Main cond equiv ftg lg (in)        0

VALVE ASSEMBLY & ASSOCIATED COMPONENTS:
  Description    2 Pos 12J on 1-1/2 NPT base with ext reg
  Fitting                           1-1/2 NPT - 1-1/2 NPT STR
  Silencer model                    N/A

SYSTEM PERFORMANCE TIMES:
  Att'n stroke time (sec)                         1.07        1.02
  Required stroke time (sec)                      1.07        1.02
  Stroke time @ term vel (sec)                    0.70        0.90
  Att'n cyclic rate (CPM)            2.99
  Required cyclic rate (CPM)         2.99
  Cyclic rate @ term vel (CPM)       3.05
  System delay time (sec)           0.090
  Dwell time after stroke (sec)                   9.00        9.00

SYSTEM INFORMATION:
  Required system Cv                             13.04        8.80
  Attained system Cv                             12.87        8.68
  Att'n system air flow (SCFM)                   307.0       307.0
  Att'n branch air vel (400 FPS max)                62          87
  Att'n main air vel (400 FPS max)                  81         114
  Att'n % delta p (46% max)                         12          37
  % Act. capacity used (75% max)                    38         -11
  Min pres necessary for ld w/S.F. (PSIG)         30.5        -8.7
  Air per cycle (SCF)               10.70
  Att'n act leakage cost/yr @ $ 0.30 /KSCF   445    167       279
  Att'n operating air cost/yr @ $ 0.30 /KSCF 1726   884       842
  Cost /1000 cyc @ att'n times @ $ 20.00 /hr 115.66
  Att'n power input total (HP)       8.17

COMMENTS:
  Anticipated performance times with 307 SCFM available if the 3/4 NPT drop
  line is supplied with 80 PSIG.
```

```
NUMATICS NUMASIZING (R) SUMMARY SHEET                    Date:    04/10/95
NU301EED  Ver 3.01 (c) 1989 Numatics, Inc.              SURVEY # 7-4
==========================================================================
Prepared for:                    Prepared by:    Michael Liberty
Company:                         Company:        Numatics Inc.
Address:                         Address:        1450 N. Milford Rd.
City,State,Zip:                  City,State,Zip: Highland, Mi. 48357
Telephone #                      Telephone #     (810) 887-4111
Fax #                            Fax #           (810) 887-9190
--------------------------------------------------------------------------
                                     Avg/Tot/Oth    Extend      Retract
INITIAL CUSTOMER PARAMETERS:
Total weight of load (lbs)                        3000.00    -1000.00
Angle of load from horizontal            90
Coefficient of Friction                0.00
Number of actuators                       5
Total load per actuator (lbs)                     636.87     -182.23
Minimum line pressure (PSIG)            100
Design pressure used (PSIG)                        60.0        60.0
Shifts/day (1 shift=120,000 m/yr)       1.5
Cycles per year                      515786

ACTUATOR:
Description:   Single Rod High Flow Numatics Actuator with 3/4 NPT ports
Bore/stroke/rod            6.00" bore x 12.00" stroke x 1.375" rod
Fitting                    3/4 NPT - 3/4 NPT STR

CONDUCTOR & ASSOCIATED COMPONENTS:
Branch conductor /leg      3/4 NPT pipe 60" long with 1.0 elbow(s)
Branch manifold fitting /leg         3/4 NPT - 3/4 NPT EL
Branch cond equiv ftg lg /leg (in)       25
Quick disconnect model /leg          N/A
In line flow control model /leg                  5FC3B       5FC3B
Main conductor             1-1/2 NPT pipe 6" long with 0.0 elbow(s)
Main manifold fitting                1-1/2 NPT - 1-1/2 NPT STR
Main cond equiv ftg lg (in)           0

VALVE ASSEMBLY & ASSOCIATED COMPONENTS:
Description    2 Pos 12J on 1-1/2 NPT base with ext reg
Fitting                              1-1/2 NPT - 1-1/2 NPT STR
Silencer model                       N/A

SYSTEM PERFORMANCE TIMES:
Att'n stroke time (sec)                            1.50        1.43
Required stroke time (sec)                         1.50        1.43
Stroke time @ term vel (sec)                       0.99        1.39
Att'n cyclic rate (CPM)                2.87
Required cyclic rate (CPM)             2.87
Cyclic rate @ term vel (CPM)           2.94
System delay time (sec)               0.090
Dwell time after stroke (sec)                      9.00        9.00

SYSTEM INFORMATION:
Required system Cv                                 9.15        6.21
Attained system Cv                                 9.06        6.14
Att'n system air flow (SCFM)                      217.0       217.0
Att'n branch air vel (400 FPS max)                  44          62
Att'n main air vel (400 FPS max)                    57          80
Att'n % delta p (46% max)                           12          37
% Act. capacity used (75% max)                      38         -11
Min pres necessary for 1d w/S.F. (PSIG)            30.0        -9.1
Air per cycle (SCF)                   10.61
Att'n act leakage cost/yr @ $ 0.30 /KSCF          165         276
Att'n operating air cost/yr @ $ 0.30 /KSCF        841         802
Cost /1000 cyc @ att'n times @ $ 20.00 /hr  120.34
Att'n power input total (HP)           7.84

COMMENTS:
Anticipated performance times with 217 SCFM available if the 3/4 NPT drop
line is supplied with 70 PSIG.
```

```
NUMATICS NUMASIZING (R) SUMMARY SHEET              Date:   04/10/95
NU301EED  Ver 3.01 (c) 1989 Numatics, Inc.         SURVEY # 7-5
====================================================================
Prepared for:              Prepared by:      Michael Liberty
Company:                   Company:          Numatics Inc.
Address:                   Address:          1450 N. Milford Rd.
City,State,Zip:            City,State,Zip:   Highland, Mi. 48357
Telephone #                Telephone #       (810) 887-4111
Fax #                      Fax #             (810) 887-9190
--------------------------------------------------------------------
                                    Avg/Tot/Oth   Extend    Retract
INITIAL CUSTOMER PARAMETERS:
Total weight of load (lbs)                       3000.00   -1000.00
Angle of load from horizontal          90
Coefficient of Friction              0.00
Number of actuators                     5
Total load per actuator (lbs)                     635.61   -183.69
Minimum line pressure (PSIG)          100
Design pressure used (PSIG)                         60.0      60.0
Shifts/day (1 shift=120,000 m/yr)     1.5
Cycles per year                    509292

ACTUATOR:
Description:   Single Rod High Flow Numatics Actuator with 3/4 NPT ports
Bore/stroke/rod         6.00" bore x 12.00" stroke x 1.375" rod
Fitting                 3/4 NPT - 3/4 NPT STR

CONDUCTOR & ASSOCIATED COMPONENTS:
Branch conductor /leg       3/4 NPT pipe 60" long with 1.0 elbow(s)
Branch manifold fitting /leg          3/4 NPT - 3/4 NPT EL
Branch cond equiv ftg lg /leg (in)       25
Quick disconnect model /leg           N/A
In line flow control model /leg                   5FC3B      5FC3B
Main conductor        1-1/2 NPT pipe 6" long with 0.0 elbow(s)
Main manifold fitting                 1-1/2 NPT - 1-1/2 NPT STR
Main cond equiv ftg lg (in)            0

VALVE ASSEMBLY & ASSOCIATED COMPONENTS:
Description    2 Pos 12J on 1-1/2 NPT base with ext reg
Fitting                               1-1/2 NPT - 1-1/2 NPT STR
Silencer model                        N/A

SYSTEM PERFORMANCE TIMES:
Att'n stroke time (sec)                            1.60       1.60
Required stroke time (sec)                         1.60       1.60
Stroke time @ term vel (sec)                       1.05       1.55
Att'n cyclic rate (CPM)               2.83
Required cyclic rate (CPM)            2.83
Cyclic rate @ term vel (CPM)          2.91
System delay time (sec)              0.090
Dwell time after stroke (sec)                      9.00       9.00

SYSTEM INFORMATION:
Required system Cv                                 8.55       5.54
Attained system Cv                                 8.48       5.49
Att'n system air flow (SCFM)                      203.0      194.0
Att'n branch air vel (400 FPS max)                  41         55
Att'n main air vel (400 FPS max)                    54         72
Att'n % delta p (46% max)                           12         37
% Act. capacity used (75% max)                      38        -11
Min pres necessary for 1d w/S.F. (PSIG)  10.58
Air per cycle (SCF)                                30.0       -9.2
Att'n act leakage cost/yr @ $ 0.30 /KSCF    441    165        276
Att'n operating air cost/yr @ $ 0.30 /KSCF 1618    828        789
Cost /1000 cyc @ att'n times @ $ 20.00 /hr 121.81
Att'n power input total (HP)              7.74

COMMENTS:
SCFM required to operate the actuator at 1.6/1.6 seconds with a 3/4 NPT drop
line having a supply of 70 PSIG.
```

# Air Motors, Flow Controls, and Quick-Exhaust Valves

## Air Motors

The key to appropriately sizing the components to supply and operate an air motor is to understand the terminology used to delineate it. A designer who requires an air motor contacts the manufacturers and delves through their catalogs to determine the flow necessary at a certain pressure and RPM to generate the required torque which will properly perform the task at hand within a specified time. Size, shape, performance, and efficiency are of equal importance but do not play a significant role to this point in the selection process. The problem that I have heard repeated time and again is that many of the air-motor manufacturers avoid stating whether the flow requirement is in cfm or scfm. By now we are thoroughly versed in the fact that there is a profound difference between the two. Perhaps the manufacturers feel they may be misleading the designer if they state the flow in scfm [applicable to New York City (NYC)] and the customer finds that the air motor is not delivering the designated torque in Denver, which is 5000 ft above sea level. The end user interpreted the air to mean the same regardless of elevation; after all, aren't the manufacturer and the customer breathing the same air? The atmospheric conditions in Denver are erroneously assumed to be identical to those in NYC, which is essentially at sea level. Therein lies the rub, for pressure conditions in Denver are far from those in NYC. The word *standard* in scientific terms as we use it is intended to mean the atmosphere at sea level at a specific temperature and pressure and not the general surrounding air at any other elevation. Thus the atmospheric pressure around NYC is essentially at 14.7 psia, whereas in Denver it is only 12.23 psia. Therefore the word *standard* should not apply for any altitude above sea level but rather should be reserved only for those locations at sea-level pressure, temperature, and humidity. One cubic foot of air in NYC (which is essentially at standard conditions) weighs approximately 0.076 lb, while in Denver it weighs only 0.064 lb. Even if both are assumed to be at the same temperature (68°F) and humidity conditions, the pressure is substantially different. Thus if one would state the required flow in scfm, this value would not apply universally to any altitude. If per chance one would use the unit in Denver, since it is not at standard conditions, a correction would be necessary.

Using our previous formula for the weight of 1 ft$^3$ of air, we have

$$w = p \times 144/R_a \Gamma_a = \frac{14.7 \times 144}{53.3(68 + 460)} = 0.76 \text{ lb} \quad (\text{NYC})$$

$$= \frac{12.23 \times 144}{53.3(60 + 460)} = 0.064 \text{ lb} \quad (\text{Denver})$$

Therefore if 80 scfm is specified in the catalog and assumed, and one understands it to mean the flow at 14.7 psia, a rectification would have to be performed for the difference in altitude for Denver. Denver would require under the same temperature conditions 96.2 cfm (80 × 14.7/12.23) to generate the same torque (as 96.2 cfm at a pressure of 12.23 psia is equivalent to 80 scfm at 14.7 psia, since the "s" in scfm signifies that the pressure is at 14.7 psia). If there is only 80 cfm delivered in Denver, then it would generate only 83 percent of the needed torque and thus fall far short of its expected mark.

Another problem is that the phrase "cfm of free air" is used. The air in Denver is just as free as in NYC, except it doesn't weigh as much, and thus more cfm is required in Denver than in NYC to perform the comparable function. The problem arises because the word *free* in pneumatic parlance is intended to mean something very specific rather than general, which the world normally implies. For our purposes it is synonymous with the word *standard*. People unfortunately interpret it as the surrounding free air at any altitude. The terminology should be very specific. To clarify this ambiguity the flow can be designated in either scfm or cfm in association with altitudes and a very carefully worded statement describing the applicable atmospheric temperature and pressure. Perhaps the criteria for an air motor should be specified in terms of so many pounds of air per minute, and thus all the uncertainty could be avoided. Unfortunately, that would mean an entirely new educational program. I hope we haven't lost sight of the fact that it is not necessary to select a different air motor. It is vital, however, that we supply it with sufficient air to complete its task successfully. The point of this entire discussion is to enable us to understand the distinctions and then determine the needed flow.

The aeronautics industry has adopted, out of necessity for comparing performance of equipment, a very specific definition for the term *standard air.* Many other disciplines and professions have also developed definitions for standard air. The aeronautical engineer's version of *standard air* is air at 50°F under a pressure of 29.92 in or 760 mm of mercury (mmHg) (2116 lb/ft$^2$; psF). (*Note:* They make no mention of any humidity prerequisites; as we've noted, its function is very insignificant.)

Under these conditions air exhibits the following properties:

Specific weight ($w$) = 0.0765 lbf/ft$^3$. (At the 68°F temperature we've been using as our standard the specific weight is obviously less, and thus we have employed the 0.076-lb figure.)

Specific volume $v'(1/w)$ = 13.1 ft$^3$/lbf

Density $\rho$ = 0.00238 slugs per cubic foot ($w/g$). (This is at 59°F and we used 0.00233 for our calculations; here again at 68°F the figure should be less than 0.0238, and we've assigned 0.00233.)

Absolute viscosity $\mu$ = 0.3723 × 10$^{-6}$ lbf•s/ft$^2$. (In our calculations we use 0.375 × 10$^{-6}$, which is an appropriate figure for 68°F.)

Figure 8.1 indicates the atmospheric pressure versus temperature and altitude.

It's interesting to note that the temperature gradient is practically constant to an altitude of somewhat over 35,000 ft. At this altitude the temperature stabilizes at −70°F and remains constant for a considerable distance. The lower atmosphere in which the temperature varies at an average rate of 3.57°F per thousand feet is known as the *troposphere.* The upper stratum where the temperature stays reasonably uniform is known as the *stratosphere.* The change from one to the other is gradual.

Now that we have cleared up the terminology problem, let us size a valve and its associated piping to turn an automatic nutrunner on and off. It applies a specified torque at an rpm within a stipulated time to assemble a wheel to a housing. An air motor was selected requiring 80 scfm at 59°F and a pressure of 70 psig ($p_2$) having a ½-NPT port. The engineering requirement for delivering this times the inch-pounds of torque is guaranteed if the unit is supplied with 80 scfm or its equivalent at any other elevation. The machine will be operating in Mexico City, which is 6000 ft above sea level (11.78 psia), and the operating-air temperature will average about 70°F at point of use. We will determine the required flow under these conditions, which require corrections for both pressure and temperature. We will not concern ourselves with humidity conditions. The temperature difference will not affect the end result appreciably as it is expressed in absolute terms. Nevertheless, we will correct for both conditions:

| Boiling Point Water °F | Altitude Above Sea Level | | | Temperature | | Barometer | | Atmospheric Pressure | |
|---|---|---|---|---|---|---|---|---|---|
| | Feet | Miles | Meters | °F | °C | Inches Hg Abs. | mm Hg Abs. | PSIA | Kg/sq cm Abs. |
| 220.9 | -5000 | ----- | -1526 | 77 | 25 | 35.58 | 903.7 | 17.48 | 1.229 |
| 220.0 | -4500 | ----- | -1373 | 75 | 24 | 35.00 | 889.0 | 17.19 | 1.209 |
| 219.1 | -4000 | ----- | -1220 | 73 | 23 | 34.42 | 874.3 | 16.90 | 1.188 |
| 218.3 | -3500 | ----- | -1068 | 71 | 22 | 33.84 | 859.5 | 16.62 | 1.169 |
| 217.4 | -3000 | ----- | -915 | 70 | 21 | 33.27 | 845.1 | 16.34 | 1.149 |
| 216.5 | -2500 | ----- | -763 | 68 | 20 | 32.70 | 830.6 | 16.06 | 1.129 |
| 215.6 | -2000 | ----- | -610 | 66 | 19 | 32.14 | 816.4 | 15.78 | 1.109 |
| 214.7 | -1500 | ----- | -458 | 64 | 18 | 31.58 | 802.1 | 15.51 | 1.091 |
| 213.8 | -1000 | ----- | -305 | 63 | 17 | 31.02 | 787.9 | 15.23 | 1.071 |
| 212.9 | -500 | ----- | -153 | 61 | 16 | 30.47 | 773.9 | 14.96 | 1.052 |
| 212.0 | 0 | ----- | 0 | 59 | 15 | 29.92 | 760.0 | 14.696 | 1.0333 |
| 211.1 | 500 | ----- | 153 | 57 | 14 | 29.38 | 746.3 | 14.43 | 1.015 |
| 210.1 | 1000 | ----- | 305 | 55 | 13 | 28.86 | 733.0 | 14.16 | .996 |
| 209.2 | 1500 | ----- | 458 | 54 | 12 | 28.33 | 719.6 | 13.91 | .978 |
| 208.3 | 2000 | ----- | 610 | 52 | 11 | 27.82 | 706.6 | 13.66 | .960 |
| 207.4 | 2500 | ----- | 763 | 50 | 10 | 27.32 | 693.9 | 13.41 | .943 |
| 206.5 | 3000 | ----- | 915 | 48 | 9 | 26.82 | 681.2 | 13.17 | .926 |
| 205.6 | 3500 | ----- | 1068 | 47 | 8 | 26.33 | 668.8 | 12.93 | .909 |
| 204.7 | 4000 | ----- | 1220 | 45 | 7 | 25.84 | 656.3 | 12.69 | .892 |
| 203.8 | 4500 | ----- | 1373 | 43 | 6 | 25.37 | 644.4 | 12.46 | .876 |
| 202.9 | 5000 | 0.95 | 1526 | 41 | 5 | 24.90 | 632.5 | 12.23 | .860 |
| 201.0 | 6000 | 1.1 | 1831 | 38 | 3 | 23.99 | 609.3 | 11.78 | .828 |
| 199.2 | 7000 | 1.3 | 2136 | 34 | 1 | 23.10 | 586.7 | 11.34 | .797 |
| 197.3 | 8000 | 1.5 | 2441 | 31 | -1 | 22.23 | 564.6 | 10.91 | .767 |
| 195.5 | 9000 | 1.7 | 2746 | 27 | -3 | 21.39 | 543.3 | 10.50 | .738 |
| 193.7 | 10,000 | 1.9 | 3050 | 23 | -5 | 20.58 | 522.7 | 10.10 | .710 |
| 184.5 | 15,000 | 2.8 | 4557 | 6 | -14 | 16.89 | 429.0 | 8.29 | .583 |
| 175.3 | 20,000 | 3.8 | 6102 | -12 | -24 | 13.76 | 349.5 | 6.76 | .475 |
| 166.0 | 25,000 | 4.7 | 7628 | -30 | -34 | 11.12 | 282.4 | 5.46 | .384 |
| 156.6 | 30,000 | 5.7 | 9153 | -48 | -44 | 8.903 | 226.1 | 4.37 | .307 |
| | 35,000 | 6.6 | 10,679 | -66 | -79 | 7.060 | 179.3 | 3.47 | .244 |
| 138.0 | 40,000 | 7.6 | 12,204 | -70 | -57 | 5.558 | 141.2 | 2.73 | .192 |
| | 45,000 | 8.5 | 13,730 | -70 | -57 | 4.375 | 111.1 | 2.15 | .151 |
| 120.0 | 50,000 | 9.5 | 15,255 | -70 | -57 | 3.444 | 87.5 | 1.69 | .119 |
| | 55,000 | 10.4 | 16,781 | -70 | -57 | 2.712 | 68.9 | 1.33 | .0935 |
| 103.3 | 60,000 | 11.4 | 18,306 | -70 | -57 | 2.135 | 54.2 | 1.05 | .0738 |
| 88.8 | 70,000 | 13.3 | 21,357 | -67 | -55 | 1.325 | 33.7 | .651 | .0458 |
| 73.0 | 80,000 | 15.2 | 24,408 | -62 | -52 | $8.273^{-1}$ | 21.0 | .406 | .0285 |
| 60.0 | 90,000 | 17.1 | 27,459 | -57 | -49 | $5.200^{-1}$ | 13.2 | .255 | .0179 |
| 48.0 | 100,000 | 18.9 | 30,510 | -51 | -46 | $3.290^{-1}$ | 8.36 | .162 | .0144 |
| | 120,000 | 22.8 | 36,612 | -26 | -32 | $1.358^{-1}$ | 3.45 | ----- | ----- |
| | 140,000 | 26.6 | 42,714 | 4 | -16 | $5.947^{-2}$ | 1.51 | ----- | ----- |
| | 160,000 | 30.4 | 48,816 | 28 | -2 | $2.746^{-2}$ | $6.97^{-1}$ | ----- | ----- |
| | 180,000 | 34.2 | 54,918 | 19 | -7 | $1.284^{-2}$ | $3.26^{-1}$ | ----- | ----- |
| | 200,000 | 37.9 | 61,020 | -3 | -19 | $5.846^{-3}$ | $1.48^{-1}$ | ----- | ----- |
| | 220,000 | 41.7 | 67,122 | -44 | -42 | $2.523^{-3}$ | $6.41^{-2}$ | ----- | ----- |
| | 240,000 | 45.5 | 73,224 | -86 | -66 | $9.955^{-4}$ | $2.53^{-2}$ | ----- | ----- |
| | 260,000 | 49.3 | 79,326 | -129 | -90 | $3.513^{-4}$ | $8.92^{-3}$ | ----- | ----- |
| | 280,000 | 53.1 | 84,428 | -135 | -93 | $1.143^{-4}$ | $3.67^{-3}$ | ----- | ----- |
| | 300,000 | 56.9 | 91,530 | -127 | -88 | $3.737^{-5}$ | $9.49^{-4}$ | ----- | ----- |
| | 400,000 | 75.9 | 122,040 | --- | --- | $6.3^{-7}$ | $1.60^{-5}$ | ----- | ----- |
| | 500,000 | 94.8 | 152,550 | --- | --- | $1.4^{-7}$ | $3.56^{-6}$ | ----- | ----- |
| | 600,000 | 114.0 | 183,060 | --- | --- | $5.9^{-8}$ | $1.50^{-6}$ | ----- | ----- |
| | 800,000 | 152.0 | 244,080 | --- | --- | $1.6^{-8}$ | $4.06^{-7}$ | ----- | ----- |
| | 1,000,000 | 189.0 | 305,100 | --- | --- | $5.1^{-9}$ | $1.30^{-7}$ | ----- | ----- |
| | 1,200,000 | 228.0 | 366,120 | --- | --- | $2.0^{-9}$ | $5.08^{-8}$ | ----- | ----- |
| | 1,400,000 | 266.0 | 427,140 | --- | --- | $8.2^{-10}$ | $2.08^{-8}$ | ----- | ----- |
| | 1,600,000 | 304.0 | 488,160 | --- | --- | $3.8^{-10}$ | $9.65^{-9}$ | ----- | ----- |
| | 1,800,000 | 342.0 | 549,180 | --- | --- | $1.8^{-10}$ | $4.57^{-9}$ | ----- | ----- |
| | 2,000,000 | 379.0 | 610,200 | --- | --- | $9.2^{-11}$ | $2.34^{-9}$ | ----- | ----- |

**Figure 8.1**    Altitude, temperature, and atmospheric pressures. (*Data from NASA Standard Atmosphere, 1962.*)

$$\frac{80 \times 14.7(70 + 460)}{11.78(59 + 460)} = 102 \text{ cfm}$$

As you can see, the temperature contribution accounts for very little, and therefore designers often disregard it entirely.

Assume that we can depend on a steady regulated pressure of 80 psig ($p_1$). A valve will be located 36 in from the air motor via a hose. We desire to know the size of the valve and hose that will deliver the 102 cfm at a local atmospheric pressure of 11.78 psia:

$$\Delta p = p_1 - p_2 = 80 - 70 = 10 \text{ psi}$$

$$p_{2a} = 84.7(70 + 14.7)$$

$$Q = 0.978 C_{vs} (\Delta p \, p_{2a})^{0.5}; \qquad 102 = 0.978 C_{vs}(10 \times 84.7)^{0.5};$$
$$\text{required } C_{vs} = 3.58$$

(where $Q$ is in scfm). We will select a standard valve having a $C_v$ of 5.73 with a ½-NPT port. We chose a valve to have a $C_v$ somewhat larger than 3.58 so that when it combines with its fitting, conductor, and air-motor fitting, it will be reduced to approximately the desired $C_{vs}$ or somewhat better. We will also select as our first choice a ½-in hose. A ½-NPT to ½-in fitting is required to mate the valve to the hose and has an ID of 0.406 in. It happens to be the smallest ID of the three components, namely, the inside gallery of the valve, the ID of the hose, and the ID of the fitting. The ID of 0.406 in was selected to represent both the valve and the air-motor fitting because of similar physical conditions. The corresponding $C_v$ for the 0.406-in ID is 3.79, and the hose carries a $C_v$ of 6.48. The system $C_{vs}$ is 2.27, which is obviously too small. If we select a ¾-in hose, its $C_v$ becomes 18.46 and the two fittings become 7.26 each (minimum diameter is still the fitting, which is now 0.5627 in). The total $C_{vs}$ becomes 3.74, which is somewhat more than the required 3.58. A ⅝-in hose would render a $C_{vs}$ of only 3.42 and would thus prove to be inadequate. We would therefore select the ¾-in hose with its respective fittings to mate to ½-NPT ports for the circuit.

Let us briefly review the rationale of the previous problem. We were given the scfm ($Q$) and entry pressure required ($p_{2a}$) to generate the torque at a specific rpm to tighten a nut on to a threaded shaft assembly. We had a specific upstream pressure ($p_{1a}$) available, which obviously was required to be greater than the necessary $p_{2a}$. If we did not have a $p_{1a}$ pressure that was more than the entry air-motor pressure of $p_{2a}$, we would have been unable to reach the required torque regardless of the size of the valve and its associated components. Every device, as we've learned, regardless of size has some internal resistance and thus experiences a pressure loss or drop as the air courses through it. It is imperative, therefore, to allow for it in the circuit. Pressure loss is identical to electricity in this respect. We use this pressure drop or differential pressure ($\Delta p$) in conjunction with the air-motor entry pressure $p_{2a}$ and $Q$ (in scfm) for Mexico City in the formula

$$Q = 0.978C_{vs} (\Delta pp_{2a})^{0.5}$$

to solve for a $C_{vs}$ that would fulfill the task.

Let us investigate the method for determining the size of valve and conductor to operate several air motors in parallel. Assume that we have three air motors identical to the one used in the last problem. We require three nuts to be threaded onto their respective shafts simultaneously. We will assume for simplicity that the manifold for distributing the air to the three air motors is close-coupled to the valve via a 4-in × ½-NPT nipple. Emanating from the manifold are three ¾-in branch conductor hoses, 36 in long, each feeding an air motor. The valve for this circuit would therefore require a $C_v$ value of approximately 17.2 (5.73 × 3). If we select a standard valve having a $C_v$ of 16.9 on a 1½-NPT port, the amount assignable to each motor would be 5.63. Let us go through the calculations and determine whether they are adequate. The $C_v$ of the nipple would be 365.6 ($d$ = 1.61, $f$ = 0.0223, $l$ = 4 in) or an assignable 121.9/air motor (365.6/3). The fitting $C_v$ at each end would be 59.6, thus rendering a 19.9 $C_v$/air motor. In that event the $C_{vs}$ available to each air motor would be 3.59 (combination of 18.46—branch conductor, 7.26—each branch fitting, 121.9—main conductor, 19.9—each main fitting, and finally terminating at the valve whose assignable $C_v$ is 5.63), which is somewhat greater than the dictated 3.58. This is barely over the minimum requirement which solves the problem, but leaves no margin for future expansion. It is interesting to note that the relationships are not linear, and thus the 16.9$C_{vv}$ was all that was necessary in this case. The moral is not to be hesitant in attempting to solve a problem with a figure somewhat less than that originally perceived to be correct as many other aspects are involved.

Let us expand the problem somewhat by introducing a main conductor length longer than the 4-in nipple, between the valve and the manifold. Assume that it will be 96 in long. The issue is what conductor diameters and materials we should select and what the modus operandi is for determining their sizes.

(*Note:* Again, a cursory deduction from the preceding solution would lead one to believe that a length not very much over 4 in for the main conductor in conjunction with the other selected components would be the maximum capable of supplying the necessary capacity to the air motor. Anything much longer would be detrimental to the needs of the air motor as the $C_{vs}$ would drop below the necessary 3.58. We will calculate for this length shortly to see how close to the 4 in the eventual answer actually is.)

In solving for this 96-in solution we will have to reevaluate our components except for the valve, for it would be economically advantageous to remain with the $16.9C_v$ valve. Increasing the valve to the next size will prove to be very expensive. We should bear in mind that we are not entirely tied into the stated port sizes of the air motors, manifolds, and valve. Oversized ports in some models can be supplied and should be requested of the manufacturers as many offer them as options. This is an often overlooked feature which can resolve a flow problem will little or no pain. Also

1. Our required $C_{vs}$ per air motor is still 3.58.

2. We already have an individual branch conductor whose $C_v$ is 18.46, and for the time being let us remain with it.

3. We have two branch fittings whose $C_v$ values are 7.26 each (one in the cylinder and one in the manifold).

4. We have a valve $C_v$ available to each unit of 5.63.

5. We will require two fittings (one in the valve and one in the manifold) and one conductor, and their combined $C_{vs}$ cannot be less than 13.17 per air motor.

6. Our main conductor and two fittings must have a combined total $C_{vs}$ of 39.5 ($13.17 \times 3$).

[*Note:* Combining 18.46, 7.26, 7.26, and 5.63 (items 2 to 4, above) for a total of 3.72—removing that from the required $C_{vs}$ of 3.58—renders our result of 13.17 (item 5).]

We have accumulated sufficient information to this point and thus will take the opportunity to establish the longest length of $1\frac{1}{2}$-NPT pipe that is possible to fulfill the requirements before proceeding to solve the 96-in length problem. We will essentially back into the solution. We know we need a combined total of 39.5. Let us remove the two similar main fitting $C_v$ values (19.9) from the required figure (13.17) for the maximum allowable main conductor $C_v$ on an individual basis. The outcome of this calculation is 37.4. The combination of 37.4, 19.9, and 19.9 renders the 13.17 resultant. We can now apply the following formula for determining the length, which should render a $C_v$ of 37.4 individually and 112.2 collectively (we will use the collective approach; the identical solution can be determined by using the individual figures and then multiplying the result by 3):

$$C_v = 33.2d^2 \left( \frac{d}{fl} \right)^{0.5}$$

$$l = 33.2^2 d^5 / C_{v2} f$$

$$l = \frac{33.2^2 \times 1.61^5}{112.2^2 \times 0.0223} = 42.5 \text{ in}$$

Interestingly, when we examined the initial results, since the $C_{vs}$ was off by only 0.01 of a $C_v$, the perception was that the maximum length was just somewhat over 4 in. It's wise never to prejudge, as the answer is one order of magnitude more than the original length and probably two orders of magnitude greater than the surmised difference.

Returning now to the $1\frac{1}{2}$-NPT pipe conductor whose length is 96 in and which has a $C_v$ of 74.6 or 24.9 per air motor. Each fitting termination $C_v$ would be 59.6, identical to the value given above as we are using the same threaded connections as the nipple. The available $C_v$ for each air motor would be 19.9. The combination of the three components is 12.3, which is a far cry from 13.17 and corroborates our original contention just verified.

The total $C_{vs}$ would be 3.56, which is somewhat less than the needed 3.58. It can be viewed as minor, but we will be purists so that we can proceed to solve for the minimum of 3.58. One possibility is to determine from the air-motor manufacturer whether they can increase the port size to $\frac{3}{4}$ NPT. There would be no problem in increasing the port to $\frac{3}{4}$ NPT in the manifold. If so, that would increase the branch fittings $C_v$ to 9.9 ($23d^2$ or $23 \times 0.656^2$) each from 7.26 and bring the resultant up to 4.03 (18.46, 9.9, 9.9, 5.63, 24.9, 19.9, 19.9), which certainly satisfies the situation. Let us assume that we were unable to obtain air motors with larger ports. We would, though, be able to obtain $\frac{3}{4}$-NPT ports with no difficulty in the manifold. Under these circumstances our total $C_{vs}$ would drop down to 3.77, which is still more than adequate. Beyond this point, increasing the conductor sizes would not benefit us very much as the weak links in the system are the branch fittings and the valve. If we were unable to improve the ports, our last resort would have been to increase the size of the valve.

There is another interesting element that can be taken advantage of if the designer is dealing with a five-ported four-way valve. The meaning of *five-ported* is fairly obvious; the valve has five ports. *Four-way* means that there are four distinctly different paths for the passage of air in the valve body. See Fig. 8.2 for an assortment of two-position four-way five-ported valve styles.

The significance of the type of arrangement shown in Fig. 8.2 is that the valve can flow air molecules through two distinct flow paths simultaneously as shown in Fig. 8.3. Essentially, the valve's $C_v$ is doubled. Thus, the designer in this instance can utilize a standard valve having a $C_v$ of only 8.67 to accomplish a task normally requiring a valve twice its size. The flow paths will total 17.34. The two flow paths can feed the manifold via two separate $1\frac{1}{4}$-in conductors. Calculations can be performed to determine the $C_{vs}$ and evaluated for

| | DIRECT SOLENOID | SOLENOID PILOT | AIR PILOT |
|---|---|---|---|
| TWO POSITION VALVES | 12    2 4    3 1 5    14 | 12    2 4    3 1 5    14 | 12    2 4    3 1 5    14 |
| TWO POSITION VALVES | 12    2 4    3 1 5    14 | 12    2 4    3 1 5    14 | 12    2 4    3 1 5    14 |
| THREE POSITION VALVES | 12    2 4    3 1 5    14 | 12    2 4    3 1 5    14 | 12    2 4    3 1 5    14 |
| THREE POSITION VALVES | 12    2 4    3 1 5    14 | 12    2 4    3 1 5    14 | 12    2 4    3 1 5    14 |
| THREE POSITION VALVES | 12    2 4    3 1 5    14 | 12    2 4    3 1 5    14 | 12    2 4    3 1 5    14 |

**PORT CONNECTION**

1 — Normally associated as inlet pressure port
2 — One end port of cylinder
3 — Exhaust port for #2 cylinder end
4 — Other end port of cylinder
5 — Exhaust port for #4 cylinder end
12 — Pilot pressure port -- where applicable
14 — Pilot pressure port -- where applicable

**Figure 8.2** ANSI symbols.

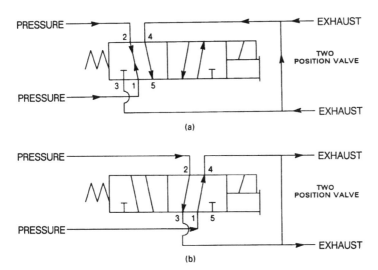

(a)

(b)

**Figure 8.3** ANSI symbology for dual-pressure arrangement. This system can pipe the flow paths to obtain either dual pressure and single exhaust as shown here or dual exhaust and single pressure in either starting position.

weak links as we did above. Obviously we would be better off with a $C_v$ of 17.34 than one with 16.9.

In reviewing the flow paths you will notice that the flow in the other direction has only a single path, which means there is no problem if time and/or torque is not critical in that direction. However, if it is, one cannot utilize this unique advantage.

Let us apply the same logic to the single-air-motor application we solved for earlier. A standard-size valve of 2.86 (5.73/2) is all that would be necessary. In this instance the two pressure conductors can be mated to two inlet ports in the air motor for ease of installation. One can ask the air-motor manufacturers to supply an additional inlet. If that is not possible, an alternative would be to feed the two lines into a tee with the outgoing member sized to accommodate the two incoming lines and in turn mating it to an appropriate air-motor inlet port. One must ascertain that the inlet port in question is not the weak link.

## Flow Controls

Flow controls (also referred to as *metering valves, speed controls,* etc.) are often misused in pneumatic circuits. There are several reasons for this misapplication. The first, mentioned earlier in Chap. 3, deals with the natural human propensity for desiring symmetry: a trait which should not be taken for granted as it is not suitable in all cases. As we will see, when dealing with flow controls this can prove to be a handicap. The second reason is a derivative of the first, which is the prevailing mind-set of automatically specifying a pair of flow controls (whether they are necessary or not) for each double-acting air cylinder ordered: one for each end port (a habit). This is excellent for the sales engineer, but in too many cases is counterproductive for the end user. It's worthwhile to explore the impact of this convention on a cylinder's stroke time and investigate alternatives. As we've mentioned before, the overwhelming number of cylinder applications require overcoming a major load on only one end. However, as we all know, the same high pressure is used for both ends, resulting in a high impact force on the minor load end. To prevent this, the traditional method of reducing the speed is employed, and that is accomplished with the aid of a flow control. Enter the symmetry syndrome. A flow control is now installed on the major-load end as well, even though none is needed (unknowingly and unfortunately). The major-load end is already burdened with a large load and is now further encumbered with a flow control. Even in the wide-open mode the flow control represents an added resistance. The valve by itself may have an adequate $C_v$ to render the required performance times, but in concert with the added resistance of the flow control, the net $C_v$ may be deficient. Therefore, in instances such as these, larger valves are required in order to compensate for the unnecessary restriction imposed on the circuit by the addition of the flow control. Consequently, there is nothing wrong in using only one flow control; in fact, in many situations it's the wisest solution in terms of performance, capital expenditure, and overhead. It should not be perceived as something that someone either failed to purchase or install.

Let us briefly return to review the minor-load end. Typically, to reduce impact, one reduces speed. This is accomplished by means of the flow control, where one is trading impact reduction for speed. If full-line pressure is essential for a clamp load at the end of the stroke (welding, heat sealing, etc.) and speed is critical, obviously the flow-control method is not the way to proceed. We will review several alternative circuits shortly which do not sacrifice speed at the expense of terminal impact. If speed is not crucial, a flow control is a very effective, efficient, and economical method of achieving the specified performance time.

If a clamp load or large final pressure is not a requirement but speed is, we can remove the single installed flow control on the minor-load end and replace it with a pressure regulator. This will permit us to reduce the pressure on this end, thereby reducing impact. We are assuming that we still have a major load on the other end and determined that the situation did not warrant a flow control; in fact, it actually was a hindrance. We are utilizing some of the tenets we have already learned (dual-pressure approach) on the minor-load end. If we were at a pressure on the minor-load end which was beyond that required to generate terminal velocity, then reducing the pressure might not impair productivity. Several benefits are simultaneously achieved by virtue of this reduced pressure on one end of the cylinder and thus bear repeating. Energy is conserved, the life of the cylinder is extended without the use of a cushioning device, and the stroke carrying the major load is accelerated as a portion of the load dealing with exhausting the air from the opposite end has been reduced. If, on the other hand, the pressure on the minor-load end is below that required to generate terminal velocity and impact is still a problem, we can further reduce the pressure. We can calculate how low we can go so that the net effect of the slower minor-load stroke time and improved faster major-load stroke time on the opposite end renders the same cyclic rate without losing productivity.

Let us continue to another aspect now, of which we have acquired a basic understanding: when to use a flow control—namely, how to integrate it into the circuit for maximum benefit, once we determined that we have an appropriate application. Here we encounter a classic example of not being able to tell a book by its cover. The external impression of a flow control is very misleading in that it appears to

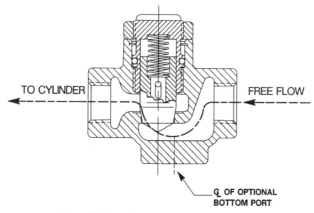

**Figure 8.4**  Air path through an inline flow control.

have the most direct compressed-air route when going from the right inlet port to the left outlet port as seen on Fig. 8.4.

With an external elbow to achieve a 90° entry to the cylinder in order to reduce the overall silhouette, we would have a minimum of five 90° bends encountered by the surging air. When viewing the design in the cutaway version as seen in Fig. 8.5, it becomes quite evident that the least restrictive path is from the bottom entry port to the left outlet port. There are flow controls that are manufactured which contain this design advantage. I am indicating the cross section of such a design in Fig. 8.5.

By bottom-porting, we achieve a smaller envelope at the desired 90° entry to the cylinder and the surging air is subjected to only one bend, thereby reducing the number of restrictions and consequently improving the $C_v$.

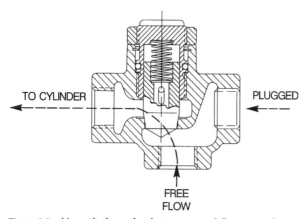

**Figure 8.5**  Air path through a bottom-ported flow control.

A very common piping practice necessitates the air lines leading to an actuator to assume 90° bends at their entry locations so as to present as small an envelope as possible. This is done for convenience, cosmetics, lack of space, or difficulty in snaking the conductors around the machine frame. To achieve this result, an elbow is threaded into the entry port. When a flow control is used, the convention is to join its exit port to the cylinder's entry port and then mate an elbow to its inlet port. This now presents five 90° deflections in the flow passage through the flow control representing a substantial restriction. By employing the bottom port of the flow control, we enjoy two simultaneous effects which are distinct advantages: (1) a smaller silhouette is created and (2) the designed flow path has only one 90° twist with all its attended benefits. It's always wise to review the internal routes of any device, for its outward image can be deceiving.

Now that we have an appreciation of the inner workings of a flow control, let us ascertain when it is in our best interests to use them:

1. Applications which require them for safety

2. Applications where slow speeds are required of the actuators and pressures cannot be reduced to accomplish them

3. Applications where time is not critical and there is a need to reduce the impact

4. Applications which require controlling the speed in only one direction of an actuator's movement

In the latter event (item 4, above) only one flow control should be used. To repeat, there is no need to invoke the symmetry rule. Introducing a flow control for the other direction penalizes the flow in that direction. Even if the flow control were opened to its fullest (wide-open mode), it would still represent a restriction. This may require the need for a larger valve to compensate for the added hindrance. Following are some general recommendations on flow controls:

1. When using flow controls always install them so as to control the exhausting air (the cylinder end which is evacuating its air). This will assure consistency of speed, smoothness, and uniformity of the stroke movement. Attempting to control the incoming air will result in a staccato motion, which is obviously undesirable.

2. The more desirable flow controls have two distinct flow paths for the aforementioned reason. This will permit as unobstructed an air passage as possible for the incoming air which pressurizes that specific actuator end and thus usually carries a larger $C_v$ value. The other air passage is the controlling end and can be adjusted to restrict the airflow; thus its path originates with a smaller $C_v$. The *free-flow pas-*

*sage,* as it is called, should be unaffected by the controlling needle. When calculating the system $C_{vs}$, if two flow controls are used, both the free-flow and controlled-flow ends are included in the computations as both are involved in the flow paths. If a single flow control is used, the free-flow $C_v$ is used to determine the uncontrolled $C_{vs}$ end and the controlled or adjusted flow $C_v$ is used to determine the controlled $C_{vs}$ end.

3. Some flow controls are merely needle valves and therefore carry the same $C_v$ in both directions. They are thus restricting in both directions, even though one may be interested only in restraining the evacuating air and not the inrushing air; thus, use of the needle-valve-type FCs is not advisable.

The question often arises as to the optimum placement of the flow control vis-à-vis the cylinder. From a purist point of view, the closer one locates the flow control to the cylinder, the better the control. By moving farther away from the cylinder, one attempts to manage the air masses which are trapped in both the conductor and the cylinder. This may contribute to a spongy cylinder action as the air in the conductor is behaving like a cushion.

Invariably a cylinder is located in the bowels of the machine, making it very difficult and hazardous to adjust integrated flow controls. Therefore, from a practical point of view, the flow control should be located remote from the cylinder. There is an additional reason why the flow control should be placed adjacent to the valve, which is usually some distance away from the cylinder. The optimum method of adjusting a flow control is while the cylinder is cycling. Obviously, if it is situated in a dangerous area, one cannot adjust it while it is cycling. Thus, a vital consideration, which is the next logical phase we will discuss, is the effect of conductor length between flow control and cylinder on the stroke-time consistency, especially at slow speeds. The ability to maintain consistency in cylinder stroke time depends principally on the ratio of the cylinder volume to the conductor volume.

(*Note:* Length, load, temperature, etc. also have roles in flow control, but the major player is volume ratio. If this volume ratio is 10:1 or less, it is difficult to discern variations in time taken to two decimal places. This is not a hard-and-fast rule, but it is a reasonably good rule of thumb. If this ratio is less and approaches a 2:1 or 1:1, the flow control is now controlling the evacuating time of the conductor. If the variations are objectionable, then under these conditions it is wise to locate the flow control as close to the cylinder port as is practical.)

We mentioned earlier that in most applications the flow control must be located remote from the cylinder, in spite of the aforementioned disadvantage, and for that reason the market pressure has spawned a sandwich-type flow control. The sandwich speed control is placed between the valve and its base, making it very convenient to adjust the speed of the cylinder from the valve location, and has the extra benefit of not requiring any piping to install it. This sandwich approach has been extended to include regulators (both single- and dual-pressure) and check valves for these very same benefits.

Flow controls restrict the flow of air for the entire stroke. The major reason for its use, to repeat, is to reduce piston impact. Obviously, piston impact contributes to an early demise of the cylinder. The conventional practice, however, is still to use flow controls. Because of this inherent flow-control characteristic, the penalty of restraining flow is loss of productivity. The ideal situation would be to allow for the major portion of the stroke, full air evacuation of the cylinder end whose air is being exhausted, to accomplish maximum speed. When the piston approaches the end of the stroke, then and only then can the speed be reduced. The net result would be increased productivity without the negative impact effect of shortening the life of the cylinder; Figs. 8.6 to 8.8 depict various deceleration circuits which accomplish just that. The initial method (Fig. 8.6) is a circuit using two valves in series. The economic feasibility can readily be determined with respect to how long it would take to recover the additional capital outlay as a result of the increased productivity.

Another approach, which avoids the drawback of having two valves in series (reducing the overall $C_{vs}$) is the scheme depicted in Fig. 8.7.

[*Note:* You may recall that the combination of the two valves' $C_v$ values is less than the smaller of the two. If one combines two valves with identical $C_v$ values, the resultant $C_v$ is 0.707 ($2^{0.5}/2$) of the original valve $C_v$ for a net loss of 30.3 percent; when three identical $C_v$ val-

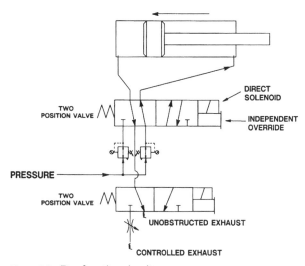

**Figure 8.6**  Deceleration circuit.

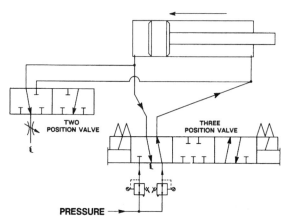

**Figure 8.7**  Deceleration circuit.

ues are combined, the result is 0.577 ($3^{0.5}$/3) of the original $C_v$ for a net loss of 42.3 percent; when four identical $C_v$ values are combined, the result is 0.5 ($4^{0.5}$/4) of the original $C_v$ for a net loss of 50 percent, etc. The circuit still requires two valves, but if space and circuitry allow, it makes for better use of the available $C_v$ values as the valve $C_v$ is not diminished by being in series with any other component.]

In the next arrangement (Fig. 8.8) a single valve is used in conjunction with the strategic placement of a sensor for each direction. This can be broken down into three cases: (1) where the cylinder cycles continuously without a dwell period at either end of the cylinder, (2) where a dwell period occurs at the end of each stroke time, and (3)

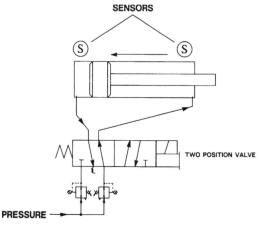

**Figure 8.8**  Deceleration circuit.

arrangements 1 and 2 combined. Figure 8.8 is a schematic of the components and their approximate locations.

Dwell-time conditions can be summarized as follows:

Condition 1: *No dwell time at the termination of either stroke:* Essentially, a rapidly moving cylinder, if allowed, would normally impact the end block. However, with the aid of the sensor(s), prior to reaching the end of the stroke the piston's presence would be detected, thereby signaling the valve to shift, causing airflow to reverse directions. Instead of air escaping from one end, there is now a sudden inrush of air and vice versa for the opposite end. This action rapidly slows the speed of the oncoming piston and shortly thereafter reverses its direction. By strategically locating the sensors, in concert with a programmable logical controller (PLC) and associated timer, it is possible to continuously cycle the cylinder without the piston ever contacting either cylinder end block. Or, the sensor's position can be adjusted with or without a timer so that the piston will gently kiss the end blocks.

Condition 2: *Dwell time at the termination of each stroke:*  If it is desirable to dwell at the end of either stroke time, because of process requirements, the piston, once it leaves the sensor, can return the valve to its original condition; this brings the piston to the end of the stroke with a diminished propelling force. This can be accomplished again with sensors and with or without the use of a timer, depending on the stroke length and total cycle time required. At the first reversal of the flow of air, when the sensor first sensed the piston's presence, the steam was literally taken out of the piston's kinetic energy. Immediately thereafter at the second air reversal (when the piston left the sensor), the flows in the air paths were returned to their original directions, which in turn reenergized the piston and continued it to the end of the stroke. At this moment in time there wasn't enough distance left to acquire a propelling force sufficient to create any impact, much less damage. The stroke time was minutely increased, and if there was a hesitation, it was imperceptible. The life of the cylinder is obviously extended. Interestingly, here, as in the case of condition 1, with the strategic placement of the sensors, with or without the aid of a PLC timer, the propelling force can be dissipated to the point where we end up with the piston gently kissing the cylinder end blocks. This is very similar to the method used for braking an automobile where the driver brakes hard at the outset and then relents momentarily before reapplying the brakes. In this fashion the major momentum has been dissipated initially, leaving only a fraction to be taken care of in the second application. Thus neither passengers, nor their pneumatic counterparts, suffer any discomfort. This method of decelerating and finally halting is commonly referred to as *dynamic braking.*

Condition 3: *Combination of dwell time at the end of one stroke and immediate reversal at the end of the other stroke:*   The approaches to follow are condition 1 for the end of one stroke and condition 2 for the other.

This appears to be an ideal solution for all impact problems. The fact of the matter is that all the techniques mentioned that do not use flow controls have shortcomings, which is true for most pneumatic concepts. Specifically, this routine is most effective when the slenderness ratio (essentially length to diameter) of the cylinder is 12:1 or higher. This allows ample time for the sensor to react and send a signal, etc. Between 12:1 and 6:1 one is approaching a questionable range. Below 6:1 there is usually an insufficient amount of time available to allow for the necessary sensor and other component response times. These reservations apply when the stroke times are in the order of 100 ms or less. If the desired stroke times are greater, even a 4:1 ratio will perform satisfactorily. If the loads occupy at least 25 percent of the cylinder's capacity, then, too, a 4:1 ratio may also function well. As we've seen all along, the best approach is to perform the survey calculations and review the results to determine whether the response times are beyond the capability of any of the elements selected. The point is that one does not have to settle for slower speeds because of fear of impact. There are alternatives, however. One further aspect to keep in mind is that if high speeds are demanded, they are probably characterized by short strokes and carry small loads; otherwise they could not even contemplate high speeds. If that is the case, the impact of the propelling force would not be sufficient to damage the cylinder via impact. Furthermore, one can always exercise the reduction of pressure concept if the pressure is above that needed to reach terminal velocity.

### Quick-Exhaust Valves

There is one additional approach that is reasonably effective in increasing speed if impact is ostensibly not a problem. There is a device on the market which rapidly exhausts the air from the evacuating end of the cylinder. It is quite properly called a *quick-exhaust valve* (QEV) and is depicted in Fig. 8.9.

The rationale behind a QEV is that wherever it is located, it will evacuate all the air upstream of its exhaust port. This flow path has direct access to the atmosphere and thus bypasses the fittings, conductor, and valve which is downstream of this exit port. It would thus

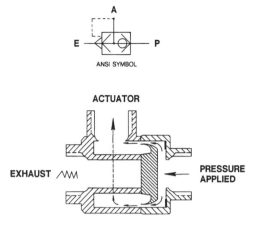

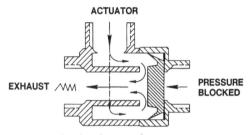

**Figure 8.9**  Quick-exhaust valve.

behoove the pipefitter to install it immediately adjacent to the cylinder port, for optimum location, so as to avoid all the other components. The trapped air in the cylinder will thus be exhausted via a large opening (large $C_v$) in the QEV. The remaining air downstream of the QEV will exhaust through the normal flow path consisting of the conductor, fittings, valve, etc. By comparison, it normally represents only a small percentage of the entire air mass to be exhausted and thus presents no problem. This evacuation takes place following activation of the device, which is triggered when the directional air-control valve operating the cylinder is fired. The pressure on the check is thus released, allowing an internal shuttle apparatus to direct the air from the upstream cylinder to the atmosphere. This obviously improves the stroke time for, as we've stated all along, the important aspect is to evacuate the air-opposing motion as rapidly as possible. This exhausting air represents an added time-delay burden on the cylinder, which in some extreme cases is greater than the time it takes for the cylinder to move the mechanical load.

Long line lengths which contain volumes larger than those of the cylinder, or restrictive-diameter conductors, represent added freight, which increases the waiting period or delay time of the actuator piston prior to motion commencing. It reflects adversely on the total stroke time. In extreme cases, as cited previously, the delay time can be longer than the piston movement time.

This confirms the need for a QEV or equivalent if time is important, which in the majority of instances it is. The closer the QEV is situated to the cylinder port, the less unnecessary air is required to be expelled via the conductor and valve; ergo, thread the QEV into the cylinder port. Since the piston stroke time is a direct function of the cylinder air to be exhausted, it would behoove one to evacuate this air by the shortest possible route as that usually requires the longest time. The remaining air can be expelled via the regular route through the valve. The $C_v$ of a QEV should be larger than the $C_{vs}$ of the combined upstream paraphernalia.

Let us solve a problem both without and then with QEVs to observe the impact on stroke times. Survey 8-1 (at the end of the chapter) is a dual-pressure solution without the use of QEVs. The schematic for this survey is shown in Fig. 8.10. Briefly, we are using a 2-in-bore × 6-in stroke, in a horizontal position, requiring a different mass to move in each direction (110 lb/30 lb), one in 0.2 s and the other in 0.15 s. We are employing a 60-in length of steel conductor having a volume of 8.71 in$^3$ with two long radius bends to bridge the misalignment

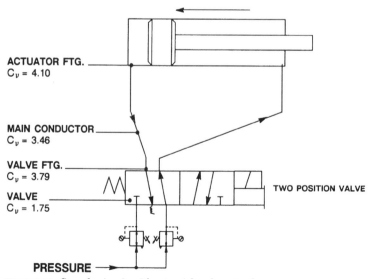

**Figure 8.10**  Sample circuit without quick-exhaust valves.

between the cylinder and valve ports. The cylinder has a volume of 18.85 in³ for the extend portion and 17.00 in³ for the retract portion. The $C_v$ value of each item is indicated on the schematic in Fig. 8.10. The total $C_{vs}$ of each leg is 1.36 in its current configuration.

By using a single-direction air valve, the trapped air cannot be released until the inherent check in the QEV is opened, which is possible only by shifting the power valve to the alternate position. This shifting releases the pressure on the trapped end, allowing the integral check to open, thus permitting the air to exhaust via the short quick route through the QEV rather than embark on the long time-consuming journey via the conductor, fittings, and valve. Figure 8.11 represents such a condition. The Fig. 8.11 components are identical to those used as in Fig. 8.10, with the addition of the QEVs. I would like to draw your attention to the fact that in many instances the QEV has a different $C_v$ depending on the direction the air is flowing. In

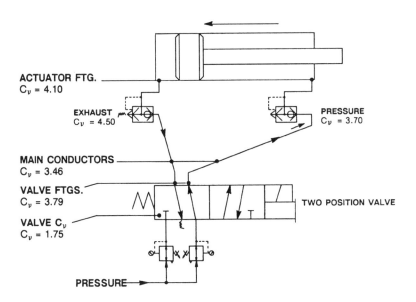

Pressure leg $C_{vs}$  =  **1.28** (Combination of 1.75, 3.79, 3.46, 3.70, 4.10)

Exhaust leg $C_{vs}$  =  **3.03** (Combination of 4.10, 4.50)

Combined legs  =  **1.18**

Combined legs without Q.E.V.'s Figure #10  =  **0.96** (1.36 x 0.707)

**Figure 8.11** Sample circuit with quick-exhaust valves. Retract-stroke $C_v$ schedule; extend-stroke $C_v$ schedule is identical, but legs are reversed.

this particular $\frac{3}{8}$-NPT unit, the path from the pressure port to the cylinder port (pressurizing the chamber) has a $C_v$ of 3.7. When the path is from the cylinder port to the exhaust port (evacuating the chamber), the $C_v$ is somewhat better: 4.5. This is rather typical of all QEVs. The principal duty is to evacuate the pressurized vessel or chamber as rapidly as possible, and thus the flow paths are designed to favor the exhaust function. The ensuing enhanced speed is a function of an improved $C_v$ for the exiting path and a reduced exhaust air mass.

Predicting the new speed is based on two ratios. The first ratio is the combined $C_{vs}$ of the extend and retract strokes as a numerator without the QEVs and a denominator based on eliminating components from the exhausting end and adding the pressurized $C_v$ component of the QEV to the filling end. It is well to remember that only for these QEV purposes do we consider the filling $C_v$ path along with the exhaust path. It is folded into the equation simply to obtain a relationship with the numerator which has the identical fill side without a QEV. In the second ratio the numerator is based on the reduced amount of air that has to be evacuated and the denominator is based on the full amount needed to be evacuated. Mathematically the predicted extend time computes as follows:

*The first ratio:* $C_v$ of the actuator fitting is 4.10, $C_v$ of conductor is 3.46, $C_v$ of valve fitting is 3.79, and valve $C_v$ is 1.75, for a grand total of 1.36. The numerator therefore becomes the combination of 1.36 and 1.36, which is *0.96.* The denominator becomes the combination of 1.36 for one leg combined with 3.7 (pressurized QEV $C_v$) and again combined with the other leg, which now consists of only the actuator fitting (4.10) and the exhaust $C_v$ of the QEV (4.5) for a total of *1.18.*

*The second ratio:* The numerator consists of the exhaust cylinder volume only or 17.00 in³, and the denominator is the combination of the cylinder and conductor volume, which amounts to 17.00 plus 8.71 or *25.71* in³.

The final predicted extend time is 0.11 s, and the equation using the ratios to yield the result is (0.96/1.18)(17.00/25.71)0.2 s for the extend-stroke time.

In the same fashion the final predicted retract-stroke time is 0.08 s, and the necessary equation is (0.96/1.18)(18.85/27.56)0.15 (the results are given in Survey 8-1*a.*). The retract time is beyond the terminal-velocity time and thus cannot reach 0.08 s. The minimum it can reach is 0.09 s, as indicated in the survey printout. Nevertheless, it indicates that we could reduce the pressures if we desired to remain with the initial performance times of 0.20/0.15 s, and save on horsepower to boot.

From our accumulated understanding, you can appreciate the fact that the load on the cylinder is now more than that at 0.20/0.15 s because the piston is evidently moving faster. This is because the acceleration increases, as it is inversely related to time. Therefore, the acceleration force ($F = Mz$) portion of the total load on the cylinder will escalate. The consequence is that the time cannot be 0.11/0.08 but the cylinder moves more slowly because of the increased total load. To establish the specific times, a series of iterations are required. The object is to match the loads to the performance times (to two decimal places) that can be attained. Survey 8-2[1] lists the results. The actual times that can be attained are 0.17/0.11. The extend load increased, because of the reduced time, by 30 percent and the retract load increased by almost 60 percent for the same reason. Nonetheless, this very clearly indicates the advantage of QEVs, for faster times are achievable with the identical pressures since we have an improved $C_{vs}$ (for increased airflow capability) in conjunction with a reduced air mass to evacuate.

To achieve maximum speed, whether with or without a dwell at the end of the stroke, it is essential that the air be evacuated prior to the inception of piston movement. In this way there is as little exhaust-pressure burden placed on the piston. This is in line with reducing as many barriers to speed as we can practically and effortlessly bring about. If the end result is to generate as many cycles per minute as possible, it would behoove one to eliminate the hesitation or dwell at both start and termination of the stroke, so as to create a direction reversal of the piston as quickly as possible. Thus, continuous cycling can be realized with essentially minuscule end cylinder impact. If a process dwell is required at the end of the stroke, we can then institute one of the methods described earlier to obtain the speed without any undo end impact. The use of two-directional air-control valves mated directly to each cylinder end port will generate these desired results. Figure 8.12 is the schematic for this plan.

It should be noted that we have observed, in extremely ultra-high-speed applications, even with the prior evacuation of the entrapped air (commencing with atmospheric pressure in the opposing chamber), an increased pressure in the presumably evacuated chamber.

---

[1] In order to simulate conditions we used 0 in of conductor, which skewed the air per cycle, operating air cost per year, and horsepower. They should all be 30 percent greater because that is the conductors' contribution. The cost per 1000 units is affected by only $0.01 because the operating-cost segment in the total cost was only $0.04, and therefore a 30 percent increase raised that to $0.05. This raised the cost from $12.70 per 1000 units to $12.71 per 1000 units.

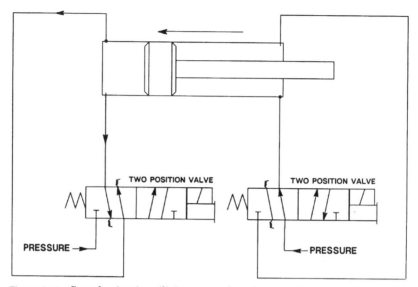

**Figure 8.12**  Sample circuit utilizing two valves for preexhausting cylinders to achieve optimum speeds. This system can take advantage of dual-flowing either or both valves to accelerate the stroke in either or both directions. (See Fig. 8.3 for an example.) In this arrangement, when springs are in command, the right valve has single pressure and the left valve has dual exhaust. When the solenoids are in command, the right valve has dual exhaust and the left valve has single pressure.

This piston's high-speed movement increased the pressure in the adjacent chamber because of its inability to evacuate this compacting of the air effect. Increasing the exhaust $C_{vs}$ would rectify this condition. However, in some instances an impact condition can arise as a result that must be addressed by one of the methods suggested earlier.

The first of the two indispensable basic ingredients essential to accomplishing the tasks described above is the ability for each directional air-control valve to operate independently. In turn, each air valve is used interchangeably as a directional power valve to operate the cylinder as well as a QEV. The second is to fire the air-control valve intended for use as a QEV before firing the one being used as a directional control valve to power the cylinder. This obviously is possible only because there are two valves functioning independently. For additional evacuation capability, if that is essential, one can dual-flow the valve being used as a QEV. If rapid movement is vital and a dwell is required at the end of a stroke, sensors can be arranged at the limits of the stroke to momentarily reverse the valve's role from a QEV (to dump the air as rapidly as possible) to a directional air-control valve (to gently settle the piston on the end block).

Let us solve the preceding problem (see Survey 8-3[2]) and determine the additional speed that can be gained by this two-valve approach. We would be able to reduce the extend time to 0.15 s by using the identical pressure of 66 psig and preexhausting the 67 psig prior to extending the piston. Using the same method, we can reduce the retract time to 0.10 s. *To summarize:* The performance times would be 0.20/0.15 s without QEVs; 0.17/0.11 s with QEVs; and 0.15/0.10 with two valves alternately used as power and QEVs. It would also be possible to reduce the pressures from 66/67 psig for the QEV approach and still further for the twin-valve technique if the intent would be to maintain the 0.20/0.15 s. An added dividend would be the commensurate reductions in horsepower needs. It is also interesting to examine the increasing total loads imposed on the cylinder as the speeds increased.

0.20/0.15-s performance times; 113/55 lb

0.17/0.11-s performance times; 146/88 lb

0.15/0.10-s performance times; 166/116 lb

Once again, there is no need to settle for the traditional solutions as there are a vast number of nontraditional ones waiting to become the norm. The rub is that one must avail oneself of every opportunity presented.

> *"It would be the height of folly—and self-defeating—to think that things never heretofore done can be accomplished without means never heretofore tried."*
> SIR FRANCIS BACON

---

[2]There are two parts to this survey. The first, entitled "extend," uses for purposes of calculating a very low retract pressure to simulate the residual pressure left after the major air mass has been preevacuated. Therefore, only the extend information is valid, and the hp indicated essentially applies to the extend portion only. The second part, entitled "return," is therefore applicable to the return portion, and the same holds for its hp requirement. The entire hp requirement would thus be the summation of the two as we are actually using the elevated pressures. We used the reduced pressures, as that's what they were at the commencement of the stroke, due to preexhaustion, permitting us to solve for the piston stroke times. The costs are also the addition of the two surveys for the very same reason.

```
NUMATICS NUMASIZING (R) SUMMARY SHEET                Date:   04/10/95
NU301EED  Ver 3.01 (c) 1989 Numatics, Inc.          SURVEY # 8-1
========================================================================
Prepared for:                    Prepared by:    Michael Liberty
Company:                         Company:        Numatics Inc.
Address:                         Address:        1450 N. Milford Rd.
City,State,Zip:                  City,State,Zip: Highland, Mi. 48357
Telephone #                      Telephone #     (810) 887-4111
Fax #                            Fax #           (810) 887-9190
------------------------------------------------------------------------
                                 Avg/Tot/Oth    Extend    Retract
INITIAL CUSTOMER PARAMETERS:
  Total weight of load (lbs)                     100.00    30.00
  Angle of load from horizontal        0
  Coefficient of Friction           0.30
  Number of actuators                 1
  Total load per actuator (lbs)                  112.70    55.44
  Minimum line pressure (PSIG)      100
  Design pressure used (PSIG)                     66.0     67.0
  Shifts/day (1 shift=120,000 m/yr)   2.0
  Cycles per year               6127660

ACTUATOR:
  Description:  Single Rod Conventional Actuator with 3/8 NPT ports
  Bore/stroke/rod        2.00" bore x 6.00" stroke x 0.625" rod
  Fitting                          1/2" - 3/8 NPT STR

CONDUCTOR & ASSOCIATED COMPONENTS:
  Branch conductor /leg                  N/A
  Branch manifold fitting /leg           N/A
  Branch cond equiv ftg lg /leg (in)     N/A
  Quick disconnect model /leg            N/A
  In line flow control model /leg               NONE      NONE
  Main conductor        1/2 metal tube  60" long with 0.0 elbow(s)
  Main manifold fitting                  N/A
  Main cond equiv ftg lg (in)             0

VALVE ASSEMBLY & ASSOCIATED COMPONENTS:
  Description    2 Pos L2 on 3/8 NPT base with ext reg
  Fitting                          1/2" - 3/8 NPT STR
  Silencer model                   N/A

SYSTEM PERFORMANCE TIMES:
  Att'n stroke time (sec)                         0.20      0.15
  Required stroke time (sec)                      0.20      0.15
  Stroke time @ term vel (sec)                    0.10      0.09
  Att'n cyclic rate (CPM)            25.53
  Required cyclic rate (CPM)        25.53
  Cyclic rate @ term vel (CPM)      27.40
  System delay time (sec)           0.023
  Dwell time after stroke (sec)                   1.00      1.00

SYSTEM INFORMATION:
  Required system Cv                              1.36      1.36
  Attained system Cv                              1.36      1.36
  Att'n system air flow (SCFM)                    26.3      33.0
  Att'n branch air vel (400 FPS max)      N/A            N/A
  Att'n main air vel (400 FPS max)                84       109
  Att'n % delta p (46% max)                        6        10
  % Act. capacity used (75% max)                  54        29
  Min pres necessary for ld w/S.F. (PSIG)        47.8      26.1
  Air per cycle (SCF)                0.17
  Att'n act leakage cost/yr @ $ 0.30 /KSCF   55    19        36
  Att'n operating air cost/yr @ $ 0.30 /KSCF 313   161       152
  Cost /1000 cyc @ att'n times @ $ 20.00 /hr 13.12
  Att'n power input total (HP)       1.04

COMMENTS:
  Dual pressure approach w/o the use of Quick Exhaust Valves
```

```
NUMATICS NUMASIZING (R) SUMMARY SHEET              Date:    04/10/95
NU301EED   Ver 3.01 (c) 1989 Numatics, Inc.        SURVEY # 8-1
================================================================================
Prepared for:                Prepared by:    Michael Liberty
Company:                     Company:        Numatics Inc.
Address:                     Address:        1450 N. Milford Rd.
City,State,Zip:              City,State,Zip: Highland, Mi. 48357
Telephone #                  Telephone #     (810) 887-4111
Fax #                        Fax #           (810) 887-9190
--------------------------------------------------------------------------------
                                                Extend     Retract
Cv DATA PER ACTUATOR

Actuator Fitting Cv                             4.10        4.10
Flow Control Free Flow Cv from Chart            N/A         N/A
Flow Control Adjustable Cv from Chart           N/A         N/A
Flow Control Adjustable Cv Used                 N/A         N/A
Quick Disconnect Cv                             N/A         N/A
Branch Conductor Cv                             N/A         N/A
Additional Cv Due to Elbows in Branch Conductor N/A         N/A
Branch Conductor Manifold Fitting Cv            N/A         N/A

Cv DATA - TOTAL SYSTEM

Actuator Fitting Cv                             4.10        4.10
Flow Control Free Flow Cv from Chart            N/A         N/A
Flow Control Adjustable Cv from Chart           N/A         N/A
Flow Control Adjustable Cv Used                 N/A         N/A
Quick Disconnect Cv                             N/A         N/A
Branch Conductor Cv                             N/A         N/A
Additional Cv Due to Elbows in Branch Conductor N/A         N/A
Branch Conductor Manifold Fitting Cv            N/A         N/A
Main Conductor Cv                               3.46        3.46
Additional Cv Due to Elbows in Main Conductor   N/A         N/A
Main Conductor Manifold Fitting Cv              N/A         N/A
Silencer Cv                                     N/A         N/A
Valve Fitting Cv                                3.79        3.79
Valve Cv                                        1.75        1.75
Sandwich Regulator Cv                           N/A         N/A
Sandwich Speed Control Cv from Chart            N/A         N/A
Sandwich Speed Control Cv Used                  N/A         N/A
Sandwich Check Valve Cv (3 pos valve only)      N/A         N/A


Attained system Cv                              1.36        1.36

Required system Cv                              1.36        1.36

Flow Control Adjustable Cv Suggested            N/A         N/A
Valve Cv Suggested                              1.75        1.75
Sandwich Speed Control Cv Suggested             N/A         N/A
```

```
NUMATICS NUMASIZING (R) SUMMARY SHEET                    Date:    04/10/95
NU301EED  Ver 3.01 (c) 1989 Numatics, Inc.              SURVEY # 8-1a
=========================================================================
Prepared for:                  Prepared by:    Michael Liberty
Company:                       Company:        Numatics Inc.
Address:                       Address:        1450 N. Milford Rd.
City,State,Zip:                City,State,Zip: Highland, Mi. 48357
Telephone #                    Telephone #     (810) 887-4111
Fax #                          Fax #           (810) 887-9190
-------------------------------------------------------------------------
                                          Avg/Tot/Oth   Extend    Retract
INITIAL CUSTOMER PARAMETERS:
Total weight of load (lbs)                             100.00      30.00
Angle of load from horizontal               0
Coefficient of Friction                     0.30
Number of actuators                         1
Total load per actuator (lbs)                          112.70      55.44
Minimum line pressure (PSIG)                100
Design pressure used (PSIG)                             66.0       67.0
Shifts/day (1 shift=120,000 m/yr)           2.0
Cycles per year                             6127660

ACTUATOR:
Description:  Single Rod Conventional Actuator with 1/2 NPT ports
Bore/stroke/rod            2.00" bore x 6.00" stroke x 0.625" rod
Fitting                    3/4" - 1/2 NPT STR

CONDUCTOR & ASSOCIATED COMPONENTS:
Branch conductor /leg                  N/A
Branch manifold fitting /leg           N/A
Branch cond equiv ftg lg /leg (in)     N/A
Quick disconnect model /leg            N/A
In line flow control model /leg                        NONE       NONE
Main conductor             3/4 metal tube  0.1" long with 0.0 elbow(s)
Main manifold fitting                  N/A
Main cond equiv ftg lg (in)            0

VALVE ASSEMBLY & ASSOCIATED COMPONENTS:
Description    2 Pos L2 on 1/2 NPT base with ext reg
Fitting                            3/4" - 1/2 NPT STR
Silencer model                     N/A

SYSTEM PERFORMANCE TIMES:
Att'n stroke time (sec)                                0.11 ?     0.08 ?
Required stroke time (sec)                             0.20       0.15
Stroke time @ term vel (sec)                          0.06       0.05
Att'n cyclic rate (CPM)                     27.35
Required cyclic rate (CPM)                  25.53
Cyclic rate @ term vel (CPM)                28.50
System delay time (sec)                     0.023
Dwell time after stroke (sec)                          1.00       1.00

SYSTEM INFORMATION:
Required system Cv                                     0.90       0.93
Attained system Cv                                     1.66 ?     1.66 ?
Att'n system air flow (SCFM)                33.0                  38.9
Att'n branch air vel (400 FPS max)     N/A            N/A
Att'n main air vel (400 FPS max)                      46         56
Att'n % delta p (46% max)                             7          10
% Act. capacity used (75% max)                        54         29
Min pres necessary for 1d w/S.F. (PSIG)               47.8       26.1
Air per cycle (SCF)                         0.11
Att'n act leakage cost/yr @ $ 0.30 /KSCF    55        19         37
Att'n operating air cost/yr @ $ 0.30 /KSCF  226       118        108
Cost /1000 cyc @ att'n times @ $ 20.00 /hr  12.23
Att'n power input total (HP)                0.79

COMMENTS:
Dual pressure approach w/the use of Q. E. V.'s, but prior to recalculating
time (equivalent Cvs and exhaust air to simulate Q.E.V.'s)
```

```
NUMATICS NUMASIZING (R) SUMMARY SHEET               Date:   04/10/95
NU301EED  Ver 3.01 (c) 1989 Numatics, Inc.          SURVEY # 8-1a
==================================================================
Prepared for:                 Prepared by:   Michael Liberty
Company:                      Company:       Numatics Inc.
Address:                      Address:       1450 N. Milford Rd.
City,State,Zip:               City,State,Zip: Highland, Mi. 48357
Telephone #                   Telephone #    (810) 887-4111
Fax #                         Fax #          (810) 887-9190
------------------------------------------------------------------
                                              Extend    Retract
Cv DATA PER ACTUATOR

Actuator Fitting Cv                           7.26      7.26
Flow Control Free Flow Cv from Chart          N/A       N/A
Flow Control Adjustable Cv from Chart         N/A       N/A
Flow Control Adjustable Cv Used               N/A       N/A
Quick Disconnect Cv                           N/A       N/A
Branch Conductor Cv                           N/A       N/A
Additional Cv Due to Elbows in Branch Conductor  N/A    N/A
Branch Conductor Manifold Fitting Cv          N/A       N/A

Cv DATA - TOTAL SYSTEM

Actuator Fitting Cv                           7.26      7.26
Flow Control Free Flow Cv from Chart          N/A       N/A
Flow Control Adjustable Cv from Chart         N/A       N/A
Flow Control Adjustable Cv Used               N/A       N/A
Quick Disconnect Cv                           N/A       N/A
Branch Conductor Cv                           N/A       N/A
Additional Cv Due to Elbows in Branch Conductor  N/A    N/A
Branch Conductor Manifold Fitting Cv          N/A       N/A
Main Conductor Cv                             251.09    251.09
Additional Cv Due to Elbows in Main Conductor N/A       N/A
Main Conductor Manifold Fitting Cv            N/A       N/A
Silencer Cv                                   N/A       N/A
Valve Fitting Cv                              7.26      7.26
Valve Cv                                      1.75      1.75
Sandwich Regulator Cv                         N/A       N/A
Sandwich Speed Control Cv from Chart          N/A       N/A
Sandwich Speed Control Cv Used                N/A       N/A
Sandwich Check Valve Cv (3 pos valve only)    N/A       N/A


Attained system Cv                            1.66      1.66

Required system Cv                            0.90      0.93

Flow Control Adjustable Cv Suggested          N/A       N/A
Valve Cv Suggested                            0.92      0.95
Sandwich Speed Control Cv Suggested           1.08      1.13
```

```
NUMATICS NUMASIZING (R) SUMMARY SHEET                    Date:  04/10/95
NU301EED  Ver 3.01 (c) 1989 Numatics, Inc.              SURVEY # 8-2
=========================================================================
Prepared for:                      Prepared by:      Michael Liberty
Company:                           Company:          Numatics Inc.
Address:                           Address:          1450 N. Milford Rd.
City,State,Zip:                    City,State,Zip:   Highland, Mi. 48357
Telephone #                        Telephone #       (810) 887-4111
Fax #                              Fax #             (810) 887-9190
-------------------------------------------------------------------------
                                   Avg/Tot/Oth      Extend      Retract
INITIAL CUSTOMER PARAMETERS:
  Total weight of load (lbs)                         100.00       30.00
  Angle of load from horizontal          0
  Coefficient of Friction             0.30
  Number of actuators                    1
  Total load per actuator (lbs)                      145.58       88.09
  Minimum line pressure (PSIG)         100
  Design pressure used (PSIG)                          66.0        67.0
  Shifts/day (1 shift=120,000 m/yr)    2.0
  Cycles per year                  6316259

ACTUATOR:
  Description:   Single Rod Conventional Actuator with 1/2 NPT ports
  Bore/stroke/rod          2.00" bore x 6.00" stroke x 0.625" rod
  Fitting                              3/4" - 1/2 NPT STR

CONDUCTOR & ASSOCIATED COMPONENTS:
  Branch conductor /leg                    N/A
  Branch manifold fitting /leg             N/A
  Branch cond equiv ftg lg /leg (in)       N/A
  Quick disconnect model /leg              N/A
  In line flow control model /leg                    NONE        NONE
  Main conductor           3/4 metal tube  0.1" long with 0.0 elbow(s)
  Main manifold fitting                    N/A
  Main cond equiv ftg lg (in)                0

VALVE ASSEMBLY & ASSOCIATED COMPONENTS:
  Description    2 Pos L2 on 1/2 NPT base with ext reg
  Fitting                              3/4" - 1/2 NPT STR
  Silencer model                       N/A

SYSTEM PERFORMANCE TIMES:
  Att'n stroke time (sec)                             0.17        0.11
  Required stroke time (sec)                          0.17        0.11
  Stroke time @ term vel (sec)                        0.06        0.05
  Att'n cyclic rate (CPM)            26.33
  Required cyclic rate (CPM)         26.32
  Cyclic rate @ term vel (CPM)       28.50
  System delay time (sec)            0.023
  Dwell time after stroke (sec)                       1.00        1.00

SYSTEM INFORMATION:
  Required system Cv                                  1.65        1.65
  Attained system Cv                                  1.66        1.66
  Att'n system air flow (SCFM)                        21.5        29.5
  Att'n branch air vel (400 FPS max)       N/A            N/A
  Att'n main air vel (400 FPS max)                     29          40
  Att'n % delta p (46% max)                             3           5
  % Act. capacity used (75% max)                       70          46
  Min pres necessary for ld w/S.F. (PSIG)            61.8        41.4
  Air per cycle (SCF)                 0.11
  Att'n act leakage cost/yr @ $ 0.30 /KSCF    55       19          36
  Att'n operating air cost/yr @ $ 0.30 /KSCF 218      114         104
  Cost /1000 cyc @ att'n times @ $ 20.00 /hr 12.70
  Att'n power input total (HP)        0.77

COMMENTS:
  Dual pressure approach w/the use of Q. E. V.'s, after recalculating time
  (equivalent Cvs and exhaust air to simulate Q.E.V.'s)
```

```
NUMATICS NUMASIZING (R) SUMMARY SHEET              Date:    04/10/95
NU301EED  Ver 3.01 (c) 1989 Numatics, Inc.        SURVEY # 8-2
================================================================================
Prepared for:                    Prepared by:    Michael Liberty
Company:                         Company:        Numatics Inc.
Address:                         Address:        1450 N. Milford Rd.
City,State,Zip:                  City,State,Zip: Highland, Mi. 48357
Telephone #                      Telephone #     (810) 887-4111
Fax #                            Fax #           (810) 887-9190
--------------------------------------------------------------------------------
                                                 Extend     Retract
Cv DATA PER ACTUATOR

Actuator Fitting Cv                                7.26       7.26
Flow Control Free Flow Cv from Chart               N/A        N/A
Flow Control Adjustable Cv from Chart              N/A        N/A
Flow Control Adjustable Cv Used                    N/A        N/A
Quick Disconnect Cv                                N/A        N/A
Branch Conductor Cv                                N/A        N/A
Additional Cv Due to Elbows in Branch Conductor    N/A        N/A
Branch Conductor Manifold Fitting Cv               N/A        N/A

Cv DATA - TOTAL SYSTEM

Actuator Fitting Cv                                7.26       7.26
Flow Control Free Flow Cv from Chart               N/A        N/A
Flow Control Adjustable Cv from Chart              N/A        N/A
Flow Control Adjustable Cv Used                    N/A        N/A
Quick Disconnect Cv                                N/A        N/A
Branch Conductor Cv                                N/A        N/A
Additional Cv Due to Elbows in Branch Conductor    N/A        N/A
Branch Conductor Manifold Fitting Cv               N/A        N/A
Main Conductor Cv                                251.09     251.09
Additional Cv Due to Elbows in Main Conductor      N/A        N/A
Main Conductor Manifold Fitting Cv                 N/A        N/A
Silencer Cv                                        N/A        N/A
Valve Fitting Cv                                   7.26       7.26
Valve Cv                                           1.75       1.75
Sandwich Regulator Cv                              N/A        N/A
Sandwich Speed Control Cv from Chart               N/A        N/A
Sandwich Speed Control Cv Used                     N/A        N/A
Sandwich Check Valve Cv (3 pos valve only)         N/A        N/A


Attained system Cv                                 1.66       1.66

Required system Cv                                 1.65       1.65

Flow Control Adjustable Cv Suggested               N/A        N/A
Valve Cv Suggested                                 1.75       1.74
Sandwich Speed Control Cv Suggested               27.46      19.72
```

```
NUMATICS NUMASIZING (R) SUMMARY SHEET                    Date:    04/10/95
NU301EED  Ver 3.01 (c) 1989 Numatics, Inc.              SURVEY # 8-3 Ext
=========================================================================
Prepared for:                    Prepared by:    Michael Liberty
Company:                         Company:        Numatics Inc.
Address:                         Address:        1450 N. Milford Rd.
City,State,Zip:                  City,State,Zip: Highland, Mi. 48357
Telephone #                      Telephone #     (810) 887-4111
Fax #                            Fax #           (810) 887-9190
-------------------------------------------------------------------------
                                          Avg/Tot/Oth    Extend    Retract
INITIAL CUSTOMER PARAMETERS:
Total weight of load (lbs)                               100.00      0.00
Angle of load from horizontal                0
Coefficient of Friction                      0.30
Number of actuators                          1
Total load per actuator (lbs)                            165.87      5.00
Minimum line pressure (PSIG)                 100
Design pressure used (PSIG)                               66.0       1.8
Shifts/day (1 shift=120,000 m/yr)            2.0
Cycles per year                              47104

ACTUATOR:
Description:    Single Rod Conventional Actuator with 1/2 NPT ports
Bore/stroke/rod                 2.00" bore x 6.00" stroke x 0.625" rod
Fitting                                      3/4" - 1/2 NPT STR

CONDUCTOR & ASSOCIATED COMPONENTS:
Branch conductor /leg                        N/A
Branch manifold fitting /leg                 N/A
Branch cond equiv ftg lg /leg (in)           N/A
Quick disconnect model /leg                  N/A
In line flow control model /leg                           NONE       NONE
Main conductor                  3/4 metal tube  0.1" long with 0.0 elbow(s)
Main manifold fitting                        N/A
Main cond equiv ftg lg (in)                  0

VALVE ASSEMBLY & ASSOCIATED COMPONENTS:
Description     2 Pos L2 on 1/2 NPT base with ext reg
Fitting                                      3/4" - 1/2 NPT STR
Silencer model                               N/A

SYSTEM PERFORMANCE TIMES:
Att'n stroke time (sec)                                   0.15      303.55
Required stroke time (sec)                                0.15      303.55
Stroke time @ term vel (sec)                             0.06        0.05
Att'n cyclic rate (CPM)                      0.20
Required cyclic rate (CPM)                   0.20
Cyclic rate @ term vel (CPM)                 28.50
System delay time (sec)                      0.023
Dwell time after stroke (sec)                            1.00        1.00

SYSTEM INFORMATION:
Required system Cv                                       1.66        1.66
Attained system Cv                                       1.66        1.66
Att'n system air flow (SCFM)                             23.3        0.0
Att'n branch air vel (400 FPS max)           N/A                N/A
Att'n main air vel (400 FPS max)                        32           0
Att'n % delta p (46% max)                               3            0
% Act. capacity used (75% max)                          80 ?       100 ?
Min pres necessary for 1d w/S.F. (PSIG)                 70.4         2.4
Air per cycle (SCF)                          0.07
Att'n act leakage cost/yr @ $ 0.30 /KSCF                2            2
Att'n operating air cost/yr @ $ 0.30 /KSCF              1            0
Cost /1000 cyc @ att'n times @ $ 20.00 /hr   1698.43
Att'n power input total (HP)                 0.01

COMMENTS:
Dual pressure approach using two valves one at each port of the cylinder
enabling the air mass to be preexhausted (only extend results are valid)
```

```
NUMATICS NUMASIZING (R) SUMMARY SHEET              Date:   04/10/95
NU301EED  Ver 3.01 (c) 1989 Numatics, Inc.         SURVEY # 8-3 Ext
===================================================================
Prepared for:                 Prepared by:   Michael Liberty
Company:                      Company:       Numatics Inc.
Address:                      Address:       1450 N. Milford Rd.
City,State,Zip:               City,State,Zip: Highland, Mi. 48357
Telephone #                   Telephone #    (810) 887-4111
Fax #                         Fax #          (810) 887-9190
-------------------------------------------------------------------
                                              Extend      Retract
Cv DATA PER ACTUATOR

Actuator Fitting Cv                            7.26        7.26
Flow Control Free Flow Cv from Chart           N/A         N/A
Flow Control Adjustable Cv from Chart          N/A         N/A
Flow Control Adjustable Cv Used                N/A         N/A
Quick Disconnect Cv                            N/A         N/A
Branch Conductor Cv                            N/A         N/A
Additional Cv Due to Elbows in Branch Conductor N/A        N/A
Branch Conductor Manifold Fitting Cv           N/A         N/A

Cv DATA - TOTAL SYSTEM

Actuator Fitting Cv                            7.26        7.26
Flow Control Free Flow Cv from Chart           N/A         N/A
Flow Control Adjustable Cv from Chart          N/A         N/A
Flow Control Adjustable Cv Used                N/A         N/A
Quick Disconnect Cv                            N/A         N/A
Branch Conductor Cv                            N/A         N/A
Additional Cv Due to Elbows in Branch Conductor N/A        N/A
Branch Conductor Manifold Fitting Cv           N/A         N/A
Main Conductor Cv                            251.09      251.09
Additional Cv Due to Elbows in Main Conductor  N/A         N/A
Main Conductor Manifold Fitting Cv             N/A         N/A
Silencer Cv                                    N/A         N/A
Valve Fitting Cv                               7.26        7.26
Valve Cv                                       1.75        1.75
Sandwich Regulator Cv                          N/A         N/A
Sandwich Speed Control Cv from Chart           N/A         N/A
Sandwich Speed Control Cv Used                 N/A         N/A
Sandwich Check Valve Cv (3 pos valve only)     N/A         N/A


Attained system Cv                             1.66        1.66

Required system Cv                             1.66        1.66

Flow Control Adjustable Cv Suggested           N/A         N/A
Valve Cv Suggested                             1.75        1.74
Sandwich Speed Control Cv Suggested            N/A         N/A
```

```
NUMATICS NUMASIZING (R) SUMMARY SHEET              Date:   04/10/95
NU301EED  Ver 3.01 (c) 1989 Numatics, Inc.         SURVEY # 8-3 Ret
==================================================================
Prepared for:              Prepared by:     Michael Liberty
Company:                   Company:         Numatics Inc.
Address:                   Address:         1450 N. Milford Rd.
City,State,Zip:            City,State,Zip:  Highland, Mi. 48357
Telephone #                Telephone #      (810) 887-4111
Fax #                      Fax #            (810) 887-9190
------------------------------------------------------------------
                               Avg/Tot/Oth    Extend     Retract
INITIAL CUSTOMER PARAMETERS:
 Total weight of load (lbs)                    0.00       30.00
 Angle of load from horizontal      0
 Coefficient of Friction          0.30
 Number of actuators                1
 Total load per actuator (lbs)                 5.00      116.37
 Minimum line pressure (PSIG)     100
 Design pressure used (PSIG)                   1.6        67.0
 Shifts/day (1 shift=120,000 m/yr)  2.0
 Cycles per year                 57018

ACTUATOR:
 Description:   Single Rod Conventional Actuator with 1/2 NPT ports
 Bore/stroke/rod           2.00" bore x 6.00" stroke x 0.625" rod
 Fitting                   3/4" - 1/2 NPT STR

CONDUCTOR & ASSOCIATED COMPONENTS:
 Branch conductor /leg              N/A
 Branch manifold fitting /leg       N/A
 Branch cond equiv ftg lg /leg (in) N/A
 Quick disconnect model /leg        N/A
 In line flow control model /leg                NONE       NONE
 Main conductor           3/4 metal tube  0.1" long with 0.0 elbow(s)
 Main manifold fitting              N/A
 Main cond equiv ftg lg (in)         0

VALVE ASSEMBLY & ASSOCIATED COMPONENTS:
 Description    2 Pos L2 on 1/2 NPT base with ext reg
 Fitting                   3/4" - 1/2 NPT STR
 Silencer model            N/A

SYSTEM PERFORMANCE TIMES:
 Att'n stroke time (sec)                      250.46       0.10
 Required stroke time (sec)                   250.46       0.10
 Stroke time @ term vel (sec)                   0.06       0.05
 Att'n cyclic rate (CPM)            0.24
 Required cyclic rate (CPM)         0.24
 Cyclic rate @ term vel (CPM)      28.50
 System delay time (sec)           0.023
 Dwell time after stroke (sec)                  1.00       1.00

SYSTEM INFORMATION:
 Required system Cv                             1.66       1.66
 Attained system Cv                             1.66       1.66
 Att'n system air flow (SCFM)                   0.0        34.5
 Att'n branch air vel (400 FPS max)    N/A            N/A
 Att'n main air vel (400 FPS max)               0          48
 Att'n % delta p (46% max)                      0           7
 % Act. capacity used (75% max)                99 ?        61
 Min pres necessary for ld w/S.F. (PSIG)        2.1        54.7
 Air per cycle (SCF)               0.07
 Att'n act leakage cost/yr @ $ 0.30 /KSCF       1           0
 Att'n operating air cost/yr @ $ 0.30 /KSCF     1           1
 Cost /1000 cyc @ att'n times @ $ 20.00 /hr  1403.11
 Att'n power input total (HP)      0.01

COMMENTS:
 Dual pressure approach using two valves one at each port of the cylinder
 enabling the air mass to be preexhausted (only retract results are valid)
```

```
NUMATICS NUMASIZING (R) SUMMARY SHEET                    Date:    04/10/95
NU301EED   Ver 3.01 (c) 1989 Numatics, Inc.            SURVEY # 8-3 Ret
===========================================================================
Prepared for:                 Prepared by:     Michael Liberty
Company:                      Company:          Numatics Inc.
Address:                      Address:          1450 N. Milford Rd.
City,State,Zip:               City,State,Zip:   Highland, Mi. 48357
Telephone #                   Telephone #       (810) 887-4111
Fax #                         Fax #             (810) 887-9190
---------------------------------------------------------------------------
                                                 Extend      Retract
Cv DATA PER ACTUATOR

Actuator Fitting Cv                              7.26         7.26
Flow Control Free Flow Cv from Chart             N/A          N/A
Flow Control Adjustable Cv from Chart            N/A          N/A
Flow Control Adjustable Cv Used                  N/A          N/A
Quick Disconnect Cv                              N/A          N/A
Branch Conductor Cv                              N/A          N/A
Additional Cv Due to Elbows in Branch Conductor  N/A          N/A
Branch Conductor Manifold Fitting Cv             N/A          N/A

Cv DATA - TOTAL SYSTEM

Actuator Fitting Cv                              7.26         7.26
Flow Control Free Flow Cv from Chart             N/A          N/A
Flow Control Adjustable Cv from Chart            N/A          N/A
Flow Control Adjustable Cv Used                  N/A          N/A
Quick Disconnect Cv                              N/A          N/A
Branch Conductor Cv                              N/A          N/A
Additional Cv Due to Elbows in Branch Conductor  N/A          N/A
Branch Conductor Manifold Fitting Cv             N/A          N/A
Main Conductor Cv                                251.09       251.09
Additional Cv Due to Elbows in Main Conductor    N/A          N/A
Main Conductor Manifold Fitting Cv               N/A          N/A
Silencer Cv                                      N/A          N/A
Valve Fitting Cv                                 7.26         7.26
Valve Cv                                         1.75         1.75
Sandwich Regulator Cv                            N/A          N/A
Sandwich Speed Control Cv from Chart             N/A          N/A
Sandwich Speed Control Cv Used                   N/A          N/A
Sandwich Check Valve Cv (3 pos valve only)       N/A          N/A


Attained system Cv                               1.66         1.66

Required system Cv                               1.66         1.66

Flow Control Adjustable Cv Suggested             N/A          N/A
Valve Cv Suggested                               1.75         1.74
Sandwich Speed Control Cv Suggested              N/A          N/A
```

# 9

# Other Pneumatic Components and Parameters

## Vacuum

Thus far we have confined our discussions to pressures at or above *sea-level atmospheric conditions,* which is defined as any value above 0 psig or in absolute terms, above 14.7 psia. We will now delve into the *vacuum area,* which by definition is any pressure below this demarcation line and is commonly referred to as so many inches or millimeters of mercury. There are many ways of describing vacuum; for instance, $X$ inches of mercury can mean above absolute zero or below atmospheric pressure, depending on the discipline and formulas involved. An array of expressions delineating pressure and vacuum is given in Fig. 9.1. In Fig. 9.2 we have the various means of defining temperatures.

The majority of formulas that we will be dealing with primarily use inches of mercury below atmosphere; thus the maximum value will be 29.92 inches of mercury (inHg), which is the ultimate vacuum. This is totally different from our previous definitions of pressure and use of pressure in calculations in earlier chapters. Here we have a positive member specifying a maximum vacuum that we have been normally expressing as 0 psia. There is nothing wrong in expressing vacuum in any way that is convenient, so long as we are aware of the terms and their meanings.

Many individuals in the pneumatics community erroneously classify the vacuum range of pressures as negative pressures because they are below 0 psig, and thus anything less than 0 must be negative. As we now know, 0 psig is simply a contrived or arbitrary number used for convenience, and the actual pressure is 14.7 psia; therefore, there

| | Gage Pressure PSIG | Absolute Pressure PSIA | Normal Atmos-pheres | Inches Hg Pressure | Inches Hg Vacuum | Millimeters Hg or Torrs | Inches Water Pressure | Feet Water Pressure | Kg/cm² Pressure | Bars Pressure | Kilopascals -KPA (Pascal = N/m²) Pressure |
|---|---|---|---|---|---|---|---|---|---|---|---|
| | 100 | 114.7 | 7.8 | NA | NA | NA | NA | NA | 8.06 | 7.91 | 791 |
| | 50 | 64.7 | 4.4 | NA | NA | NA | NA | NA | 4.55 | 4.46 | 446 |
| Standard Atmosphere Conditions | 0 | 14.7 | 1 | 29.92 | 0 | 760 | 406.8 | 33.9 | 1.003 | 1.013 | 101.3 |
| | -0.2 | 14.5 | 0.99 | 29.54 | 0.38 | 750.3 | 401.6 | 33.5 | 1.02 | 1.00 | 100 |
| | -0.5 | 14.2 | 0.97 | 28.91 | 1.01 | 734.3 | 393.1 | 32.8 | 1.000 (1 atu) | 0.98 | 98 |
| | -13.7 | 1.0 | 0.068 | 2.04 | 27.88 | 51.7 | 27.7 | 2.3 | .07 | 0.69 | 6.9 |
| Absolute Zero Total Vacuum | -14.7 | 0 | 0 | 0 | 29.92 | 0 | 0 | 0 | 0 | 0 | 0 |

Figure 9.1  Pressure scales (not to scale). All readings are at 0°C except water, which is at 4°C.

| Water Boiling Point | 100°C | 373°K | 212°F | 672°R |
|---|---|---|---|---|
| | 30°C | 303°K | 86°F | 546°R |
| | 20°C | 293°K | 68°F | 528°R |
| Water Freezing Point | 0°C | 273°K | 32°F | 492°R |
| | −18°C | 255°K | 0°F | 460°R |
| CO₂ Freezing Point | −175°C | 98°K | −283°F | 177°R |
| Absolute Zero | −273°C | 0°K | −460°F | 0°R |
| | °Celsius | °Kelvin | °Fahrenheit | °Rankine |

**Figure 9.2**  Temperature scales (not to scale).

cannot be any negative pressure. Anything less than 14.7 psia is simply a smaller number until one reaches the absolute minimum, which is 0. We will now consider the dynamic property of airflow ($Q$, in scfm) under vacuum conditions, namely below atmospheric pressure. The result is somewhat different from that under an equivalent pressure condition above atmospheric pressure. We will compare the results for the extent of their differences and determine whether there is any consistent relationship:[1]

$$Q = 1.69 C_{vs} \quad (\text{inHg})^{0.5}$$

where $Q$ = flow, expressed in scfm (as in preceding chapters)
$C_{vs}$ = system $C_v$ involved in evacuation of vessel
inHg = pressure in inches of mercury below atmospheric pressure

In the following problem we will determine the flow $Q$ through an 0.080-in orifice having 100 percent coefficient of flow under the influence of 20 inHg (below atmosphere). For a well-rounded entrance, multiply the results by 97 percent. For a sharp-edged orifice, the multiplier may be 61 percent. For a complete discussion of this topic dealing with the relationship of the $C_v$ to the entry configuration of an orifice, see Chap. 2.

---

[1]The formula was developed by Numatics' testing laboratory from accumulated empirical data collected over the years as well as published data and catalogs from other fluid-power companies involved in production of vacuum pumps and associated devices.

The $C_v$ of the orifice is $29d^2$ or 0.186:

$$Q = 1.69 \times 0.186(20)^{0.5} = 1.41 \text{ scfm}$$

The 20-inHg vacuum reading is equivalent to 9.82 psi ($0.4912 \times 20$) below atmosphere or 4.88 psia ($14.7 - 9.82$). If we now have the same situation except above the sea-level atmospheric datum line or 24.52 psia ($9.82 + 14.7$), we will have a flow of

$$Q = 0.978C_v(\Delta pp_{2a})^{0.5} = 0.978 \times 0.186(9.82 \times 14.7)^{0.5} = 2.19$$

This is approximately 1.5 times what one can expect under vacuum conditions. (A text that I found to be most useful, practical, and informative which thoroughly discussed the subject and the underlying causes for the differences is *Compressed Air and Gas Handbook*.[2] This is especially worthwhile for the thermodynamics student.) Even though the air was flowing to atmosphere, it was not at critical, as the minimum that $p_{2a}$ could be is 14.7 psia, and not 0.533 of 24.52. The critical flow would have placed $p_{2a}$ at 13.07 ($0.533 \times 24.52$), which is not standard atmospheric pressure. Thus $p_{2a}$ is 60 percent ($14.7/24.52$) and $\Delta p$ is only 40 percent. Interestingly, if it was possible to flow at critical, $Q$ would be equal to 2.23 scfm ($Q = 0.488C_v \, p_{1a} = 0.488 \times 0.186 \times 24.52$), a variance of less than 2 percent and still approximately 1.5 times the flow under vacuum conditions. Obviously at any $p_1$ pressure above 12.88 psig (27.58 psia) it is possible to flow at critical since $p_{2a}$ would be a minimum of 14.7 psia ($27.58 \times 0.533$).

Let us solve the same problem for a vacuum which can reach very close to 29.92 inHg, which is essentially 0 psia (14.7 psi below standard atmospheric pressure):

$$Q = 1.69 \times 0.186(29.92 \text{ in})^{0.5} = 1.72 \text{ scfm}$$

The flow $Q$, under pressure conditions of 14.7 psi (29.92 inHg) above standard atmospheric pressure or 29.4 psia, is 2.67 scfm ($0.488 \times 0.186 \times 19.4$) and the relationship is the same approximate 1.5 ratio ($2.67/1.72$). This ratio holds true for essentially all pressurized flows below critical, close to critical, at critical, and above critical up to a maximum of 14.7 psig [29.92 inHg above atmospheric pressure ($2.03 \times 14.7$)], which is compared to the minimum of 29.92 inHg of vacuum (below atmospheric pressure). When the pressure condition is such that it cannot reach maximum flow because it is below critical, as

---

[2]John P. Rollins, ed., *Compressed Air and Gas Handbook*, Compressed Air and Gas Institute, New York, 1973.

2.46 psig (5 inHg above atmospheric pressure), the flow would come to 1.09 scfm. [*Note:* The minimum that $p_{2a}$ can be is standard atmospheric pressure (14.7 psia), and thus $\Delta p$ is 2.46 psi, i.e., $Q = 0.978C_{vs}$ $(\Delta pp_{2a})^{0.5} = 1.09$ scfm.] The vacuum flow resulting from 5 inHg is 0.70 scfm $[1.69C_{vs} \, (\text{inHg})^{0.5}]$, and thus under these conditions the ratio is still approximately 1.5 in favor of the pressurized flow over the vacuum flow. This relationship holds true for flow for the entire range of pressures from 29.92 inHg vacuum [14.7 psi below atmospheric pressure (maximum vacuum)] to 14.7 psi above atmospheric pressure. This is a rather interesting phenomenon that we observed and deserves closer scrutiny (in my estimation, an excellent subject for a Ph.D. program).

## Leakage

The following method can be quite useful in establishing the amount of leakage from a gasket surface or from an installed component where it would be difficult or inconvenient to install a flow meter. The object is to use the conventional soap solution around the suspected area and determine the size of the soap bubble along with the number emanating from the source per minute [i.e., bubbles per minute (bpm)].

The pressure required to form a bubble is negligible, and we can therefore assume that the air pressure in the component under test $(p_a)$ is exhausting to atmosphere via the soap bubble (pressure inside the bubble is considered to be the same as outside the bubble). The formula for a bubble or essentially a sphere is $4\pi r^3/3$ or $\pi d^3/6$. (*Note: r* and $d$ are expressed in inches as we are maintaining the imperial system of terms, as that's what we have been using all along.)

Let us combine the number of bubbles per minute and the dimension of the sphere into one formula to arrive at the leak rate. Leakage is usually expressed in standard cubic centimeters per minute (sccm), for scfm is much too large a term (*note:* although we use the *imperial system,* somehow leak rates are expressed in metric terminology, namely, sccm; there are 2.54 centimeters per inch):

$$\frac{(\pi d^3)(\text{bpm})(2.54)^3}{6} \quad \text{which becomes} \quad 8.58d^3 \text{ bpm}$$

Let us use the following example to become conversant with this formula. The number of bubbles per minute emanating from the device is 22 bpm; the diameter of the bubble is 0.50 in:

$$\text{Leakage} = 8.58(0.50)^3 \times 22 = 23.6 \text{ sccm}$$

## Hydraulic $C_v$ versus Pneumatic $C_v$

There is some confusion regarding the flow of liquids as opposed to gases through the same valve because both use the same term $C_v$ to express their capability, yet the same number is not applicable to the two media. There should be different nomenclature describing the two, for one is approximately 91 percent of the other. Let me explain. The formula for determining $C_v$ for hydraulics is as follows:

$$C_v = \frac{G}{(\Delta p/\text{sp.gr.})^{0.5}}$$

where $G$ is flow of a liquid in gallons per minute (gpm) and sp.gr. denotes specific gravity of the liquid in question.

A valve having a $C_v$ of 1.0 is capable of flowing 1.0 gpm of a liquid with sp.gr. 1.0 under a pressure differential of 1.0 psi. This same valve when subjected to compressed air will have a $C_v$ of 1.1. As discussed previously, the formula for $C_v$ for compressed air (its gaseous specific gravity being equal to 1.0 for air at standard conditions) at 68°F flowing to atmosphere (critical) from 80 psig (94.7 psia) is $Q/0.489p_{1a}$. If we use the valve which had a $C_v$ equal to 1.0 hydraulically, it would flow 50.9 scfm. Applying the formula for a $p_{1a}$ of 94.7 psia would render a $C_v$ of 1.1. If we used a pneumatic valve having a $C_v$ of 1, it would render a $Q$ under the identical circumstances of 46.3 scfm. The relation between 46.3 and 50.9 is 91 percent. Since the $C_v$ varies directly as the flow ($Q$), then obviously 1.0/1.1 is essentially 91 percent as well. The lesson to be learned here is that a $C_v$ of 1.0 does not have the same meaning for hydraulics as it does for pneumatics.

### Compressor-Capability Problem

The following problem (Example 9.1), depicted in Fig. 9.3, will help tie in some of the foregoing principles as they relate to compressors.

**Example 9.1**   Referring to Fig. 9.3, determine (1) the capacity required for the compressor, in cfm at 100°F and 14.7 psia, assuming that it is operating continuously while all three processes, A, B, and C, are functioning constantly; and (2) the length of time the tank can supply the processes if there is an electrical failure.

We will ultimately determine the cfm necessary for process A by converting the mass of air to cfm at the required temperature (100°F) and pressure (14.7 psia). The process is operating at 90°F and 75 psia. The weight of air at 14.7 psia and 60°F (standard conditions) is 0.076 lbm/ft³ [see Chap. 3; (14.7 × 144/(60 + 460)53.3)]. At 90°F and 75 psia the weight would be 0.3684 lbm/ft³ [75 × 144/(90 + 460)53.3]. Since we require 8 lbm/min, the flow rate would be 21.71 cfm (8/0.3684). The compressor operates and delivers compressed air at 100°F, and thus the 21.71 cfm becomes 22.11 cfm [21.71(100 + 460)/(90 + 460)].

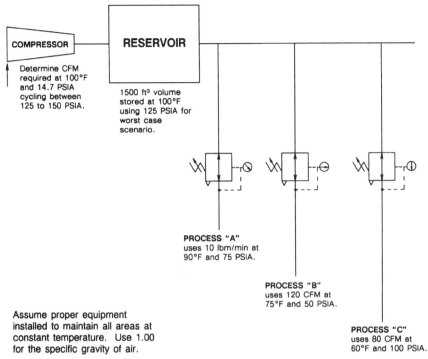

**Figure 9.3**  Layout of components of problem.

The air is compressed to 75 psia, and since we must know what amount is required at 14.7 psia, therefore 22.11 × 75/14.7 or 112.80 cfm. (*Notes:* (1) we converted the cfm to 100°F and 14.7 psia because that is what the capability of the compressor is expressed in as well as how we are storing the compressed air in the reservoir tank; and (2) for those who are more accustomed to compressed-air calculations, we could go directly to determining the amount of cfm necessary as opposed to taking several intermediary steps. We are performing it in this fashion for the benefit of those less conversant with the procedure.)

The density or mass of air per cubic foot (air/ft³) at 100°F and 14.7 psia (the required conditions) is 0.0709 [14.7 × 144/(100 + 460)53.3]. The flow rate necessary, in cfm at these conditions, would be 112.80 (8 lbm/min; 0.0709 lbm/ft³.

We now will take process B and correct for temperature and pressure: 120 cfm at 75°F and 50 psia becomes 427.24 cfm [120(100 + 460)50/(75 + 460)14.7] at 100°F and 14.7 psia. Next, we do the same for process C; specifically, 80 cfm at 60°F and 100 psia is 586.08 cfm [80(100 + 460)100/(60 + 460)14.7] at 100°F and 14.7 psia.

We can now total the three amounts for the necessary flow rate required of an air compressor running continuously:

$$112.80 + 427.24 + 586.08 = 1126.12 \text{ cfm}$$

A compressor delivering 1126.12 cfm at 100°F and corrected to 14.7 psia is required to operate on a continuous basis. The approximate range of cfm/hp for today's compressors, under these conditions, operating between 125 and 150 psia is 4.5 to 5.0. There is an empirical formula which zeros in on a figure which can be compared to the rule of thumb:

cfm/hp = (1470/kick-in pressure in psia)$^{0.625}$ = (1470/125)$^{0.625}$ = 4.67

This figure, as well as the range mentioned previously, is obviously subject to the manufacturer's specifications and should be ascertained. Nevertheless, if we use the 4.5 figure, the hp required will be 250 (1126.12/4.5). (*Hint:* Imposing a 2:1 or 3:1 ratio in order for the compressor to have some breathing time will bring the hp up to 500 or 750.)

The minimum pressure to which the 1500-cf (ft$^3$) tank can drop in order to adequately supply all the processes is 100 psia (process C). Assume the worst-case scenario, which would be for a power failure to occur just as the tank reaches the minimum pressure of 125 psia but prior to the compressor kicking in. We have at this moment only a 25-psi hedge, and thus only 2551 cf (1500 × 25/14.7) is available. Since we utilize 1126 cfm, we have only 2.26 min (2552/1126) for all the processes to function satisfactorily. We must determine whether 2.26 min is ample time to clear or shut down process C; if not, then obviously we require a larger tank. At this moment, once we have shut down process C, the next process on the agenda to study is process A, where the minimum operating pressure is 75 psia. We will further assume that the power failure occurred when we had only one person available to shut down these processes, and it took 1.5 min to deactivate process C. We will now determine the remaining pressure and volume in the reservoir tank in order to establish the amount of time remaining to suitably supply processes A and B in order to effect a proper shutdown. In 1.5 min we consumed 1689 cf (1126 × 1.5), leaving 11,066 cf available for future usage. The total cf available in the tank is 12,755 (1500 × 125/14.7). Since we reduced the content by 1689, we have left the 11,066, as stated above. We can solve for the remaining tank pressure in the following manner:

$$\frac{1500 p_{ax}}{14.7} = 11{,}066; \qquad p_{ax} = 108.44 \text{ psia}$$

Our pressure hedge now is 33.44 psi (108.44 − 75). The usage has been reduced to 540 cfm from 1126 because process C has been shut down. We have available 3412 cf (1500 × 33.44/14.7) in the tank. Therefore, the time available for shutdown is 6.32 min (3412/540). Assume that it took 2 min to shut down process A. We have consumed 1080 cf (540 × 2), leaving 9986 cf (11,066 − 1080) available for shutting down process B. Proceeding with the same calculations as above, we arrive at the remaining tank pressure: 97.9 psia (9986 × 14.7/1500). The pressure differential we enjoy to this point is 47.9 psi (97.9 − 50). We have available 4888 cf in the tank for this shutdown. Process B draws 113 cfm, and thus we have 43 min to complete the task. We require only 10 min, and thus have a reserve in the tank once the entire shutdown is accomplished. We have consumed 1130 cf (113 × 10), leaving 8856 cf (9986 − 1130) at a pressure of 86.8 psia remaining in the vessel (process B).

## Parallel-Surge-Tank Application

In all our discussions thus far we have been employing a surge tank as an intermediary between an upstream supply source and a down-

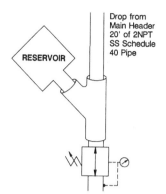

**Figure 9.4** Parallel-reservoir layout.

stream supply line, which forms a series configuration. We have often been asked to evaluate a circuit consisting of a surge tank and a supply line both feeding the downstream needs. In other words, the tank and the supply line would be oriented in parallel to provide the combined downstream needs as portrayed in Fig. 9.4. We will investigate such a parallel array and also compare the results to the standard series installation and assess the differences and relative merits of each. The typical conditions that one is confronted with is a machine operating with an existing supply line and an available pressure. The intent is to increase the productivity, requiring a new shorter time cycle and thus higher flow rate, which is unattainable under the present circumstances. Invariably there is very little room to locate a surge tank; the pressure cannot be increased, and the supply line is untouchable.

We have the following given conditions:

$Q_s$      The new, most demanding instantaneous flow rate for the entire system is 1500 scfm (cfm at atmospheric conditions of 60°F and 14.7 psia) required for the extend stroke is to be jointly delivered by the tank and upstream supply line. The extend stroke has as well the least amount of dwell time ($T_{we}$) to recharge the tank for the return stroke. The delivery pressure must be held continuously at 94.7 psia. (*Note:* The most flow we can depend on is 1300 scfm.)

$T_{we}$      The new required dwell time in seconds at the conclusion of the extend time is 1.3 s.

$T_e$      The new most stringent demand is the extend time, which is 0.35 s.

$V_T$      Tank size (i.e., volume; in ft$^3$) cannot be larger than 20 cf [150 gal ($V_{Tg}$)] because of space limitations.

$P_{1a}$      Assured available operating pressure remained the same: 114.7 psia.

Conductor    2-NPT SS Schedule 40 pipe (remained the same) having
$d$—internal diameter of 2.067 in; $f$—friction factor of 0.0166;
$l$—length of 240 in; $C_{vp}$—102 based on formula $C_v$ =
$33.2d^2(d/fl)^{0.5}$.

We need to determine the values for the following:

| | |
|---|---|
| $\Delta p_T$ | Pressure drop experienced in tank, expressed in psi |
| $\Delta p_p$ | Pressure drop experienced in stainless-steel pipe, expressed in psi |
| $V_u$ | Makeup air volume to be replenished into tank, expressed in scf |
| $Q_p$ | Flow contributed by 2-NPT supply line, expressed in scfm |
| $Q_T$ | Flow contributed by a surge tank $V_T$, expressed in scfm |

We will be using the following formulas derived and utilized earlier in
the text ($V$ in ft³, $Q$ in scfm throughout):

$$V_T = \frac{14.7V_u}{\Delta p_T} \quad \text{cf} \tag{9.1}$$

$$V_u = \frac{Q_T T_e}{60} \tag{9.2}$$

$$Q_s = Q_p + Q_T \tag{9.3}$$

$$Q_T = Q_s - Q_p \tag{9.3a}$$

$$\Delta p_p = \frac{p_{1a} - [p_{1a}^2 - 4.18(Q_p/C_{vp})^2]^{0.5}}{2} \tag{9.4}$$

By combining Eqs. (9.1) and (9.2), we arrive at the following:

$$V_T = \frac{14.7Q_T T_e}{60\Delta p_T}$$

and then substituting for $Q_T$ the expression (9.3a), we obtain

$$V_T = \frac{14.7(Q_s - Q_p)T_e}{60\Delta p_T}$$

Rearranging the terms, we obtain

$$\Delta p_T = \frac{14.7(Q_s - Q_p)T_e}{60V_T} \tag{9.5}$$

If the tank size were given in gallons, Eq. (9.5) would read as follows:

$$\Delta p_T = \frac{1.833T_e(Q_s - Q_p)}{V_{Tg}}$$

The key which permits us to solve for all the remaining unknowns is the fact that $\Delta p_p$ must equal $\Delta p_T$ as they are at the confluence of the supply sources, and thus the pressure conditions are identical. Each will experience the same pressure drop, thus concluding with the same pressure. This permits us to equate Eqs. (9.4) and (9.5) to obtain Eq. (9.6):

$$\frac{p_{1a} - [p_{1a}{}^2 - 4.18(Q_p/C_{vp})^2]^{0.5}}{2} = \frac{14.7(Q_s - Q_p)T_e}{60V_T} \qquad (9.6)$$

I will spare the reader the many involved steps and proceed directly to the assembled quadratic equation. We have taken care to eliminate the roots which are not applicable as a result of the multiple signs possible from the multiple quadratic equations involved:

$$\left(\frac{0.24T_e^2 C_{vp}^2}{V_T} + 4.18V_T\right)Q_p^2 + \left(0.98p_{1a}T_e C_{vp}^2 - \frac{0.48T_e^2 C_{vp}^2 Q_s}{V_T}\right)Q_p$$

$$+ \left(\frac{0.24T_e^2 C_{vp}^2 Q_s^2}{V_T} - 0.98p_{1a}T_e C_{vp}^2 Q_s\right) = 0$$

The three coefficients $a$, $b$, and $c$ are located respectively in front of $Q_p^2$, $Q_p$, and the last term. We can now generate the last quadratic equation by using the standard form for a second-degree equation:

$$Q_p = \frac{-b \pm (b^2 - 4ac)^{0.5}}{2a}$$

In our case the equation will read as follows, and here again we've taken care to use only the applicable root:

$$Q_p = (T_e C_{vp}^2 \frac{0.48T_e Q_s}{V_T} - 0.98p_{1a}) +$$

$$\frac{T_e C_{vp}^2(0.96p_{1a}^2 T_e C_{vp}^2 + 16.4V_T p_{1a}Q_s - 4T_e Q_s^2)^{0.5}}{0.48T_e^2 C_{vp}^2/V_T + 8.36V_T}$$

We will now utilize this equation by substituting all our known values and solve for $Q_p$. It is lengthy and involved but not difficult. We took the liberty of determining the $Q_p$ for 25-, 50-, 75-, 100-, and 125-gal tanks and the largest we can accommodate, a 150-gal tank (all standard):

| Tank size, gal | Flow rate, scfm |
|---|---|
| 25 | 1429 |
| 50 | 1370 |
| 75 | 1323 |
| 100 | 1275 |
| 125 | 1236 |
| 150 | 1202 |

The $Q_T$ would then respectively be for the 25- to 150-gal tanks: 71, 130, 177, 225, 264, and 298 scfm.

It would be wise at this stage to review how the $\Delta p_p / \Delta p_T$ varies with the different tank sizes:

| Tank size, gal | Pressure, psi |
|----------------|---------------|
| 25  | 1.82 |
| 50  | 1.67 |
| 75  | 1.52 |
| 100 | 1.44 |
| 125 | 1.35 |
| 150 | 1.28 |

It is interesting to note that as the tank size progressively increases, the drop in pressure decreases. This is quite logical, for although there is a greater demand put on the tank, there is considerably more air available.

Obviously if the guaranteed flow rate is only 1300 scfm, we would require the assistance of a tank that can furnish the remaining 200 scfm. A standard 100-gal tank is the smallest tank that can adequately fulfill the bill with 225 scfm.

Using Eq. (9.4) we calculate a $\Delta p_p$ of 1.44 psi, and Eq. (9.5) obviously renders the same for $\Delta p_T$ (we used these equations to obtain the $\Delta p$ for the various tank sizes stated above). This is certainly within the suggested 2-psi pressure drop. An important point to keep in mind is that even though we can flow 1300 scfm through the conductor, we will be flowing only 1275 scfm because of the extra capability of the tank. A tank of 11.4 cf (85.6 gal) would fit the bill exactly, but unfortunately it is not a standard. I've used a formula which I will introduce shortly to determine the specific size of the tank needed.

Immediately downstream of the "Y" fitting is a regulator to reduce the 100 psig or better to the required 80 psig, which must be able to pass 1500 scfm under these conditions. It is interesting to note that a 2-NPT pipe is capable of flowing 1500 scfm at a delivery pressure of 100 psig for a 20-ft length experiencing only a 2-psi pressure drop [using Eq. (9.4)]. This would be fine in terms of the conductor. A suggestion at this point may be for the facilities engineer to carefully investigate the compressed-air requirements and recommend additional compressor capacity, as the existing piping system is capable of handling the greater demand if it were available. However, this is a future solution, and an immediate one is demanded now.

The next item we wish to determine is whether there is sufficient time to recharge the tank that was depleted of 1.31 scf ($225 \times 0.35/60$)

during the extend stroke. Once the operating drain is complete, we have 1300 scfm resupplying the tank or 21.67 scf per second (scfs), and since we have 1.3 s of dwell time, we can replenish up to 28.2 scf (21.67 × 1.3), which is more than adequate. It will take only 0.061 s (1.31/21.67) to recharge the tank. Two notes are appropriate here:

1. I have not considered the $C_v$ of the tank fitting simply because it is so large in relation to all other components that it will have no perceptible impact on the results obtained. Also, the tank is mated directly to the 2-NPT "Y" fitting. It has an equivalent length of approximately 187 in, rendering a $C_v$ of 373 [$33.22d^2(d/fl)^{0.5}$]. For purposes of determining the fill time in the event the $C_v$ is appreciable, it would be folded into the pipe $C_v$ of 102, thereby reducing it to 98 (combining $C_v$ values). The flow, as a result, is reduced from 1300 to 1224 scfm (used in the equation $Q = 0.978C_{vp}(\Delta pp_{2a})^{0.5}$ given in earlier chapters]. The new fill time is 0.064 s: not much of a variance from 0.061 s because in our case there was little restriction but worth going through the exercise to understand the methodology. It is important to keep in mind that the drain from the tank was based on a flow of 225 scfm (1275 scfm from the conductor) during the operating stroke, and the pressure drop experienced at the end of the operating stroke was 1.44 psi. This should not be confused with the refill flow which is occurring at the end of the operating stroke and can supply air at 1300 scfm, except for the added restriction reducing it to 1224 scfm. The point here is that the 1300-scfm flow is not impaired, as this aspect does not contend with the added constraint, which comes into play only when the operation ceases and the refilling mode is in effect. Then and only then does the restricted 1224 scfm take come into play since it must contend with the added burden of additional components.

2. Since the "Y" fitting represents the convergence of two flows, it cannot be considered a parallel arrangement as far as the refill calculations are concerned. It is a series circuit feeding air from the conductor around the bend into the tank. At times a shunt is provided to minimize this circuitous route if it is excessive. In our case it was not.

Let us consider several variations of the preceding problem and solve for $C_{vp}$, assuming that the other variables are known, and do the same for $T_e$ and $V_T$ ($V$ in ft³, $Q$ in scfm unless otherwise indicated). We will require the following three equations [derived from Eq. (9.6)] to calculate for these properties:

$$C_{vp} = \frac{Q_p}{[0.23T_e p_{1a}(Q_s - Q_p)/V_T] - \{0.057[(Q_s - Q_p)T_e/V_T]^2\}^{0.5}} \qquad (9.6a)$$

$$T_e = \frac{2.04V_T\{p_{1a} - [p_{1a}^2 - 4.18(Q_p/C_{vp})^2]^{0.5}\}}{Q_s - Q_p} \qquad (9.6b)$$

$$V_T = \frac{T_e(Q_s - Q_p)}{2.04\{p_{1a} - [p_{1a}^2 - 4.18(Q_p/C_{vp})^2]^{0.5}\}} \qquad (9.6c)$$

For Eq. (9.6a) we will assume the following new given conditions: $Q_p$ cannot be continually sustained at greater than the reduced rate of 1200 scfm (now requiring a $V_{Tg}$ of 150-gal tank or $V_T$ of 20 cf); however, we wish to know whether the existing conductor diameter is adequate for the purpose when $T_e$ is equal to only 0.25 s (previously it was 0.35 s); the remaining conditions of $p_{1a} = 114.7$ psia and $Q_s = 1500$ scfm hold.

Solving for $C_{vp}$ renders an answer of 102 (when $T_e = 0.35$), which is precisely what we should obtain as we solved this essentially backward for the 150-gal-tank problem encountered earlier. Just to refresh our memories, a 2-NPT stainless-steel Schedule 40 pipe having an ID of 2.067 in yields a $C_{vp}$ of 102. Assuming now that we use the newly anticipated time of 0.25 s, the $C_{vp}$ would come to 120, requiring the next size or 2½-NPT pipe having a diameter of 2.469 in, which would render a $C_{vp}$ of 162. We would then recalculate the $\Delta p$ values and any of the other necessary information as refill time, etc. for the increased value of the $C_{vp}$.

We can, in turn, use Eqs. (9.6b) and (9.6c) to resolve any other aspect of the circuit if we know or can determine the other variables for their respective equations. The purpose of having all the equations available is to have the one unknown isolated in order to solve for it. Earlier we spoke of determining a specific tank size if all other variables have been established. That is the purpose of Eq. (9.6c), which, when utilized, renders a tank size of 11.4 cf with an associated $\Delta p$ of 1.5 psi. Quickly solving this using the series formula [Eq. (9.6c)] we obtain the identical result of 11.4 cf for a $\Delta p$ of 1.5 psi, a $Q_T$ of 200 scfm ($Q_s - Q_p = 1500$ scfm $- 1300$ scfm), and a $T_e$ of 0.35 s ($14.7Q_TT_e/60\Delta p_T = 14.7 \times 200 \times 0.35/60 \times 1.5$).

As far as the size of the tank is concerned, there is no difference whether it is located in the circuit in series or in what we have come to call the *parallel-flow arrangement*. However, the major advantage in the parallel flow is that there is a smaller $\Delta p$ loss, which occurs, as we've seen, at the juncture. In the *series-flow arrangement* we have the addition of the pipe losses and the tank losses. In our case we experienced a 1.44-psi total loss in the parallel composite circuit, whereas if it were in series, it would be the tank pressure drop in addition to the 1.44 psi. This was amply demonstrated in the Chap. 7 sections on receiver tanks. We can conclude then if too great a pressure drop is detrimental to the circuit, then it's wise to use the parallel method if it can be located in close proximity to a "Y" or "tee" connection emanating from the drop line.

[*Note:* I would like to briefly mention the impact if the parallel-tank arrangement is located remote from the intersection with the drop line. We had a situation where the pressure drop was 1.44 psi. Obviously we would not be able to maintain it because of the increased resistance. We would have to determine what the $C_{vs}$ of this auxiliary circuit would be and, by following the methods used in the Chap. 7 sections on tank sizing, arrive at a tank with its series conductor size under the maximum pressure drop of 2 psi. Having that information, we can use Eqs. (9.6*a*) to (9.6*c*) to arrive at the necessary results for selecting the settings and sizing the remainder of the circuit. The advantage of a parallel arrangement may be negated or even worsened when compared to a series circuit. This would depend on the remoteness of the tank. We can readily conclude that the real advantage, as we've mentioned several times, is if the tank can be close-coupled to the drop line. If it cannot, it may be wise to use the series approach unless space limitations or configuration factors prohibit the use of a series tank.]

The next element, if one has an ample pressure drop window to work within, would be to consider which layout offers the most convenient installation. The last factor of concern is space constraints for a specific tank size, and thus one would select the scheme which would present the optimum configuration.

It may be superfluous to state that the reserve cycles are identical for the same size tank. The refill time, however, will vary between a series and parallel network depending on the remoteness of the tank in the parallel arrangement from the point of intersection with the drop. As pointed out earlier that extra piping and/or fitting must be added to the drop length for correct results.

## Manometer Problem

Find the difference in pressure [expressed in kilopascals (kPa)] between the air and water compartments as depicted in Fig. 9.5.

**Example 9.2**   In Fig. 9.5 we have the following conditions:

1 bar = 100 kPa = 14.5 psi; therefore 6.9 kPa = 1 psi

Density of water is 62.316 lb/ft$^3$ at 68°F

Specific gravity of mercury is 13.546 at 68°F

Density of air is 0.076 lb/ft$^3$ at 68°F

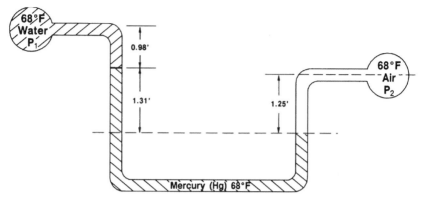

**Figure 9.5**  Configuration of sample manometer problem.

Also

$$p_1 + \frac{62.316 \times 0.98}{144} + \frac{62.316 \times 13.546 \times 1.31}{144} = p_2 + \frac{0.076 \times 1.25}{144}$$

$$p_1 - p_2 = 0.424 + 7.679 - 0.00066 = 8.102 \text{ psi}$$

$$8.102 \text{ psi} \times 6.9 = 55.9 \text{ kPa}$$

## Fill and Exhaust Vessel Times

Previously we were intent on designing tanks or vessels to suit applications with specific time constraints. What we are primarily interested in now is to turn the request around and be able to predict the elapsed time to either fill or exhaust an existing vessel. A specific example would be to determine the time required to rapidly fill tires on a production line to a required pressure with an initial higher starting pressure. A sensor would detect when the vessel (tires in this instance) reaches the desired fill pressure and shuts off the fill valve. The leak portion of the cycle follows immediately, and the same sensor can detect whether there is a greater or lesser pressure decay, within a given permitted time period, than specified. If the case is greater, the vessel is rejected; if not, it passes. (There are several interesting circuits suggested in a bulletin entitled *Leak Sensing* which describe several arrangements to sense minute variations in pressure.[3]

---

[3]*Leak Sensing* (manual), Numatics, Inc., 1972.

Filling to a desired pressure with the same pressure would take too long, thereby preventing adequate time to perform the leak test. Thus, we need some means of predicting the expired time with this initial elevated pressure method just described with various $C_{vs}$ combinations. Another application would be to fill, with a higher initial pressure, a gasoline tank on a conveyor to some low fill pressure also for leak testing. Again, a sensor would be used to detect the moment when the pressure has reached the desired fill level to close a valve to prevent any further charging. The same concept and reason applies for the need to predict elapsed fill times here as with the automobile tires. In addition, the prediction of exhaust times is pertinent. Another task is to predict the elapsed time involved in filling a welding gun cylinder from the soft-touch low pressure to the required higher welding pressure with various combinations of valves, etc. Another valuable area for this concept would be its application to predicting the filling time of a reservoir during the dwell period of the cylinder cycle as we've discussed in Chap. 7 and earlier in this chapter. To the casual observer, the averaging method of flows for this purpose may be adequate and logical, but for the student or serious pneumatics designer it is inadequate. By the same token, it is just as advisable to have the ability to predict elapsed times to exhaust all these vessels under different pressures and component combinations. There are many fields, as you can see, which can benefit from a method that can accurately suggest both fill and exhaust times. This is precisely why we had undertaken the task of investigating this subject and developed an equation to closely approximate the fill and exhaust times of a vessel when it is used strictly as a reservoir. The raison d'être for this section is to share this information, for the results can be considerably different from the usual means we have been using to date. In fact, the tank sizing method to charge a tank to the filling pressure that we—as well as most practitioners of pneumatics—have employed over the years is based on an erroneous proposition. Namely, the premise that the flow is linear and therefore the average at the initial differential and the final differential between tank and fill pressure. The flow at the final condition is zero since the pressure differential at that moment is essentially zero. In other words, we divided the initial flow in half for purposes of calculating the flow to be used. We will shortly compare results to see the extent of the deviations due to this mistaken reasoning.

Here, as in the past, we conducted an extensive testing program to accumulate the data for this segment. This time we conducted our tests with somewhat more sophisticated equipment than we did 25 years ago. The final equations are based on over 250,000 data points that we amassed for this purpose, and fortunately it wasn't as time-consuming to collect as those required for our Numasizing database. The need to throw out stray results for fear of generating errors due to manually recording the data was almost entirely eliminated.

The following is the final form of the formula, expressing the interrelationships between pressures, tank size, $C_v$, and filling time, which rendered a correlation of 99.0 percent:

$p_1$    Available pressure to fill vessel, psig

$p_2$    Desired pressure to fill vessel, psig

$T$    Filling time to reach $p_2$ from 0 psig using $p_1$, s

$T_{21}$    Elapsed time to reach $p_1$ from $p_2$, s

$V_T$    Tank volume, ft$^3$

$\pi$    Expressed in radians; therefore 180°

$C_{vs}$    System $C_v$

$$\Phi = \frac{5.644Vp_1^{0.215}}{C_{vs}}$$

$$p_2 = p_1\sin\frac{\pi T}{\Phi} \tag{9.7}$$

$$= \frac{p_1\sin 31.892TC_{vs}}{Vp_1^{0.215}} \tag{9.8}$$

In Eq. (9.7) the sine is expressed in radians, whereas in Eqs. (9.8) to (9.12) it is in degrees, which is the more familiar term one uses. By rearranging the terms we can extract each variable and solve for it independently if the other three are known:

$$T = \frac{0.0314Vp_1^{0.215}\sin^{-1}(p_2/p_1)}{C_{vs}} \tag{9.9}$$

$$V = \frac{31.892TC_{vs}}{p_1^{0.215}\sin^{-1}(p_2/p_1)} \tag{9.10}$$

$$C_{vs} = \frac{0.0314Vp_1^{0.215}\sin^{-1}(p_2/p_1)}{T} \tag{9.11}$$

$$T_{12} = \frac{0.0314Vp_1^{0.215}[(90 - \sin^{-1}(p_2/p_1)]}{C_{vs}} \tag{9.12}$$

There are several very significant elements we have failed to include in all of the equations. They are temperature and heat gains and losses. They were far beyond our ability to monitor and record. The information is most difficult to capture even with very sensitive instrumentation, as the equipment must also be extremely rapid to detect and relate the specific temperature to the event as it is occurring. Even though we recognized the relevance and importance, we had to seek another property which we were able to observe which is directly tied to temperature and heat. We also recognize the shortcomings and inaccuracies of this approach. Nevertheless we submit the results with all the inherent weaknesses as we found nothing else available. Our profound wish is for someone to pick up the baton and revise or improve upon these meager beginnings, for we consider it a launching point only. Nevertheless, the results we obtain using the proposed equations more closely approximate the actual results than does any other technique which is currently in vogue.

From a logical point of view, whether one fills to 12.65 psig (27.35 psia) with an initial pressure of 40 psig (54.7 psia) or to 32.65 psig (47.35 psia) with an initial pressure of 80 psig (94.7 psia), the elapsed time should be identical under ideal conditions, for the containers were both filled to 50 percent of the starting fill pressure. Pressure should not enter into the equation. As you can see from the formulas we have arrived at, we are utilizing pressure only because we were unable to monitor the variables that are affected. However, since we live in the real world, pressure does vary and reflects the combined effects of the other properties. Thus, pressure is directly related to temperature and heat gains and losses and was a convenient property which was within our ability to observe and scrutinize. Thus the equations we arrived at utilized pressure because it is influenced and can be monitored easily.

The example that I will be using is the first fill-time problem of Chap. 7. Let me briefly restate the pertinent information. The lowest line pressure encountered can be as low as 70 psig. Usually it hovers around 80 psig, and at times it can reach 90 psig, the purported available line pressure. We used 70 psig as we were designing for the worst-case condition. During the fill cycle we started at 149 scfm and 65.5 psig and ended at 0 scfm when we ostensibly reached 70 psig. Theoretically, we never reach the full line pressure in the vessel. It's like taking a step one half the distance to the wall each stride. From a hypothetical point of view, the individual will never reach the wall. From a practical point of view, one does reach the wall since the final strides become so small that they can be considered insignificant. Suppose that we have a 10-ft³ surge tank. The $C_{vs}$ of the supply line to the tank amounted to 7.64. Our average supply was 1.24 scfs [(149 + 0)/(2 × 60)], and since we required to replace 2.98 scf into the vessel, it rendered a time of 2.4 s (2.98/1.24). Many of us appreciated the fact and understand that it is not a linear function and would more closely approximate $\frac{1}{3}$ (149/3 = 49.7) based on the stride analogy rather than the straight average of $\frac{1}{2}$ (149/2 = 74.5) we use. By using the $\frac{1}{3}$ figure, a rendered flow of 49.7 scfm (0.83 scfs) ensues, and thus a fill time of 3.6 s results. We suspected it would behave more like its electrical counterpart, a capacitor. Interestingly, the results of the investigation proved to be more complex, which eventually furnished us with the preceding basic equation [Eq. (9.8)] with its variations. In using the formula with the same available pressure condition of 70 psig, we find it would take 2.12 s to fill a corresponding 10-ft$^3$ vessel from an identical initial pressure of 65.5 psig instead of 2.4 or 3.6 s, as was the case in Chap. 7. Before we analyze the results, let us quickly go through the mathematics. We will use the Eq. (9.8) formula twice: (1) to determine the elapsed time to reach 70 psig starting from 0 psig with an initial pressure of 70 psig available; and (2) to determine the elapsed time to reach 65.5 psig also originating with 0 psig from the same initial pressure of 70 psig. We can then subtract the two, which renders the time necessary to go from 65.5 to 70 psig, the eventual figure we are searching for:

$$T = \frac{[0.0314 V p_1^{0.215} \sin^{-1}(p_2/p_2)]}{C_{vs}}$$

$$= \frac{0.0314 \times 10 \times 2.493 \times 90}{7.64} = 9.21 \text{ s}$$

$$= \frac{0.0314 \times 10 \times 2.493 \times 69.34}{7.64} = 7.09 \text{ s}$$

The elapsed time to proceed from 65.5 to 70 psig is 9.21 − 7.09 = 2.12 s. Or, we can apply Eq. (9.11) directly and obtain the 2.12 s. A sufficient difference exists between the new approach and the conventional methods to cause one to reflect on which is the more appropriate strategy to follow.

This leaves us on the horns of a dilemma, for it implies, at least in this instance, that either of the methods currently employed to determine the fill time generates a result which is slower than the result(s) we obtain empirically. Let us quickly review the fill time for the tank resulting from the dual-pressure solution in Chap. 7 and observe whether it follows the same trend. Briefly, we required a 25-gal tank, which is 3.4 cf. The available pressure remained 70 psig, but we were able to dip to 60 psig (recalling that the maximum regulated operating pressure was 40 psig). The result, using the traditional average method, yields an elapsed time of 2.95 s, and by the one-third ($\frac{1}{3}$) method, the time amounts to 4.4 s. The empirical approach renders an elapsed time of only 1.08 s. So here, too, the results using the conventional methods are slower. We speculate that the major reason for this shortened fill time is due to the increase in temperature during the filling cycle, which is simultaneously raising the pressure as it is normally increasing because of the surge of filling a lower-pressure vessel with an elevated pressure.

As we've stated before, it is just as important to be able to predict exhaust times of chambers as it is to be able to predict their fill times. Tires, gasoline tanks, surge vessels, etc. must be filled within a specific timeframe and must also be evacuated within a certain period. Along with our recent fill testing data, we also accrued a healthy array of exhaust data. From this data we were able to develop an exhaust-time equation which achieved a 99.1 percent correlation.

The equation relating pressures (initial and final), $C_{vs}$, tank size, and evacuating time turned out to be considerably more elaborate than the fill equation. The following is the equation which ties in these properties; the connotations of the terms are identical to those used above for the fill equations:

$$p_2 = p_1 e^a - [(0.14C_{vs}^{1.04})V^{-1.09}]T \tag{9.13}$$

$$a = -bV^c T p_1^d$$

$$b = -0.02 + 1.02C_{vs}$$

$$c = -0.83 + 0.04 \ln C_{vs}$$

$$d = -0.31 - 0.03 \ln V$$

There is always a great deal of interest in comparing fill time to exhaust time to establish which would be concluded sooner. For example, to fill the preceding 17,280-in$^3$ tank initially at atmospheric pressure to 70 psig with a starting pressure of 70 psig and a $C_{vs}$ of 7.64 would take 9.21 s. Using Eq. (9.13) to determine the elapsed time to empty this tank back to atmospheric pressure, keeping all things equal, would take longer: 13.8 s. To fill to 65.5 psig, again under the same conditions, would take 7.09 s. To evacuate the tank down to 4.5 psig (so as to keep the differentials the same; filling 65.5 of a possible 70 and by the same token, dumping 65.5 of a possible 70 psig) would consume 8.9 s. Again the exhausting function is slower. An interesting conclusion one draws from these results is that to fill the last 4.5 psi requires 2.12 s (our earlier problem: 9.21 − 7.09), whereas to exhaust the last 4.5 psi necessitates 4.9 s (13.8 − 8.9). This follows the prevailing, "logical," conclusion that it takes longer to empty a vessel than it does to fill it. This has been essentially a given since, for fill-

| Fill Time in Seconds | Final Pressure PSIG | Final Pressure PSIG | Exhaust Time in Seconds |
|:---:|:---:|:---:|:---:|
| 0.00 | 0.0 | 70.0 | 0.00 |
| 0.38 | 4.5 | 65.5 | 0.23 |
| 0.84 | 10.0 | 60.0 | 0.53 |
| 1.27 | 15.0 | 55.0 | 0.83 |
| 1.70 | 20.0 | 50.0 | 1.16 |
| 2.60 | 30.0 | 40.0 | 1.92 |
| 3.57 | 40.0 | 30.0 | 2.90 |
| 4.66 | 50.0 | 20.0 | 4.27 |
| 5.44 | 56.0 | 14.0 | 5.44 |
| 6.04 | 60.0 | 10.0 | 6.54 |
| 7.09 | 65.5 | 4.5 | 8.90 |
| 9.21 | 70.0 | 0.0 | 13.75 |

Pressure available is 70 PSIG for filling results.

Starting pressure is 70 PSIG for exhausting results.

$C_{vs}$ is 7.64

Tank Volume is 17,280 cubic inches.

**Figure 9.6**   Fill time versus exhaust time.

ing, there is a continuous supply of energy available; whereas for exhausting, there is a continual depleting source of energy contributing to the evacuation of the vessel.

Let us review some resulting times where we fill only a small percentage of the potential pressure available so as to hasten the fill portion of the cycle time. We will compare those to the exhausting time necessary to purge this low pressure from the chamber and observe whether the pattern continues where filling time is faster than exhausting time. Still maintaining the same components and initial pressure, we find that it takes 0.38 s to fill to 4.5 psig, whereas it takes only 0.23 s to exhaust 4.5 psi to 65.5 psig from a starting pressure of 70 psig. In both cases we kept the same differentials as we did earlier. The chart in Fig. 9.6 shows the inversion where the fill time overtakes the exhaust time. The exhaust time from 70 psig to 14 psig is 5.44 s, and the filling time to 56 psig is 5.44 s.

These inversions occur at different percentages of the initial pressure depending on the $C_{vs}$, tank size, and the initial pressure itself. This appears to be going contrary to the considered, speculated, popular belief on the topic up to a point. Beyond, the process follows the accepted line of reasoning that fill time is faster than exhaust time. The interesting aspect is that it doesn't comply with the prevailing rationale at every stage. Thus we encounter another area of fluid dynamics which warrants intensive investigations, perhaps by some additional enthusiastic pneumatics student(s).

*"We are continually faced with great opportunities brilliantly disguised as insolvable problems."*
ANONYMOUS

# 10

# Pneumatic Venting

A wise preacher of a congregation had a very effective formula for the success of his sermons. It was a three-pronged attack; he first told the assembly what he was going to tell them, then he told them and finally restated what he just told them. Permit me the same latitude, and let us review the salient features covered thus far as I've already emulated the preacher's first two points and perhaps went overboard:

1. Keep conductor lengths to a minimum.
2. Keep the conductor path as straight as possible. Sharp cosmetic bends improve appearance but waste energy. Whenever you must negotiate conductor turns, be generous and use a bend radius of at least 10 times the ID (inner diameter) of the conductor. Use sharp-right-angle turns sparingly.
3. Increasing the conductor diameter will result in improved conductor $C_v$ and thus the flow rate (cpm) but will also cause the volume to increase; the conductor must be filled and evacuated each cycle, which takes time, thus impairing the cpm. Therefore, each application should be carefully weighed to arrive at the optimum conductor.
4. If the customer's objective is to render the maximum cpm, then a cylinder bore should be selected such that the force generated will be approximately twice the load. [*Note:* For every pressure and load condition there is only one cylinder bore size (assuming that the stroke is kept constant), which will produce the maximum cpm. If the objective is to conserve compressed air, then the bore should be as small as possible and the pressure as high as possible (within range of practical delivery pressures) so that the force is kept at, but never below, a  minimum of 1.33 times the load. If pressure in a plant is a problem, the minimum achievable with the appropriate cylinder bore should be used, but again the rendered force should never drop below 1.33 times the load.]

5. Actuator stroke length should be no more than required. Obviously, the longer the stroke length, the more energy is necessary to fill the vessel.

6. Air valves can be oversized, for future expansion, as they do not waste energy, similar to an electrical switch.

7. Overpressurizing a circuit beyond a certain point does not increase cylinder speed but does waste air. Every actuator reaches terminal velocity under a particular set of pressure conditions and load requirements.

8. If the application calls for two different loads or times for the extend and retract strokes, it is a good candidate for dual pressures. Intelligent use of multipressure usage conserves air in the majority of dual-pressure air cylinder applications: (*Note:* A sizable benefit can also be gained by applying this dual-pressure concept: reduced cylinder rod and piston air leakage. Leakage is essentially proportional to pressure and is an unavoidable industrial headache. Thus, by lowering the pressure wherever possible, this problem becomes manageable and less expensive.)

9. A $C_v$ evaluation of all the components of a circuit should be conducted before placing the usual onus for poor cylinder performance time on the valve.

10. Receivers will not always improve productivity.

11. The arbitrary use of flow controls is not suggested.

12. Using a single flow control for the control of only one leg of a circuit is not only permissible but warranted in some cases.

13. The least restrictive connecting paths of a flow control is not necessarily the opposing ports.

14. A potential pneumatics customer may have various objectives in viewing a circuit, such as increased productivity, optimal utilization of compressed-air usage, minimum-size circuit members, and energy or space conservation. Each carries specific-size components; e.g., the valve appropriate to satisfy the purchasing agent desiring the minimum size may be totally inappropriate for the facilities engineer requiring optimum utilization of compressed air. It is highly unlikely that the same component as a valve is capable of satisfying all objectives. There is no such thing as the best valve for a particular circuit; it must be accompanied with an objective.

15. Often dual-pressurizing a cylinder in conjunction with either one flow control (as exemplified in Surveys 10-1 and 10-2 (at end of chapter) or two flow controls may be in order. If that is the case, the procedure should be to reduce the pressure(s) to the minimum level (within suggested parameters) before adjusting the flow control(s) to fine-tune the cylinder speed to achieve the required time(s). It is not advisable to drop the pressure(s) to the point where the speed of the

cylinder is achieved without the use of flow control(s) because the pressure(s) may be below those that render a sufficient safety factor. The other aspect is to reduce pressure(s) first to the minimum permissible level in order to conserve energy before proceeding to throttle the flow controls. If the flow controls are throttled first to achieve the desired time(s), then no efficiencies can be gained by dual-pressurizing, as we are leaving no margin for pressure adjustment. In reviewing Survey 10-1, one sees that 59.5/12 psig is all that is necessary to achieve the 1.00/0.25-s stroke time(s). However, the 59.5 psig moves the load using 90 percent of the cylinder capacity. To bring it down to the preferred 75 percent, a pressure of 71.6 psig is required. If the pressure is increased to that level, the piston would be going too rapidly, and thus a flow control would effectively reduce the air flow, thus throttling it to the specified time. The retract portion is fine, and thus the need for a flow control does not exist. The results are clearly shown in Survey 10-2.

16. For dedicated compressors, the preferred on time should be one third that of the off time and at worst, one half.

17. The speed of the cylinder is a function of: (1) the $C_{vs}$ of the entire circuit, (2) the total circuit volume because it is continually filled and exhausted, and (3) the accelerating force essential to propel the load. It is well to remember when using a cylinder chart to establish the cylinder bore for raising a weight that only the weight of the load is considered, which is fine for slow-moving objects. To make my point, let us determine the bore diameter to raise a 490-lb weight 12 in in 3 s with 100 psig. On the basis of paragraph 4 above, we will use a 33 percent safety factor (SF), rendering a load of 653.3 lb. The method would be to find the intersection on a graph or chart for 653 lb and 100 psig and read the bore diameter. The figures on the graph and chart are based on $F = PA$ and would thus yield a 2.88-in bore. We can select the next-larger standard metric size of 80 mm (3.15 in) or English size of 3.25 in. There would be no fault to find with this approach at the required time of 3 s since the accelerating load is only 3.4 lb. The small accelerating force would increase the load to 493.4 lbf and, when multiplied by the SF of 1.33, would render a 656 lbf required of the cylinder, which essentially raised the load insignificantly from the 653 lb originally arrived at. However, if the time to raise this 490-lb load were reduced to 0.3 s, the accelerating load on the cylinder would be 338 lb, thus increasing the total force required of the cylinder to 828 lb and with a SF to 1100 lb. This is the figure one must now use to enter the graph or chart, even though it deals with the same weight of 490 lb, yielding a cylinder diameter of 3.74 in. In this instance we would select either a metric size of 100 mm (3.94 in) or an English size of 4 in. It is quite evident that without

taking into consideration all the aspects of a moving mass, one cannot expect to arrive at a suitable answer. In the first solution we used dual pressures and flow controls with a valve having a $C_v$ of 0.4. For the second we used dual pressures and a valve having a $C_v$ of 5.7. It is most illuminating to see the vast differences in the component needs for each problem (see Surveys 10-3 and 10-4) even though they have many similarities.

18. Provisions should be made initially to compensate for the shrinkage of the inside diameter of a conductor over an extended period of time. Actually conductors and fittings suffer a double penalty because not only is the internal diameter shrinking by virtue of deposits, but the internal friction factor is continually getting worse.

19. The resulting combination of two or more $C_v$ values will always be smaller than the smallest $C_v$ in the group because the answer is obtained by adding their reciprocals.

I would like to dwell somewhat on paragraphs 3, 9, and 17. Specifically, they deal with $C_v$, volume, and acceleration. One must consider not only all these properties but all components for the entire circuit as well in order to properly evaluate the impact on the performance times. It is unwise and inaccurate to isolate a single component to determine the effect it can have on the cyclic rate of the actuator even if all the physical properties are included. They must all be weighed jointly. In Chap. 5 we used five conductors having the characteristics indicated in Fig. 10.1.

I would strongly discourage anyone from simply diagnosing a conductor's property and from this drawing the conclusion that it would improve or worsen the actuator's performance. Using a quotient of merely the $C_v$ of the conductors, the results, as stated so often and of which we are all well aware by now, would lead us down the primrose path. The first quotient consists of just the $C_v$ where the numerator is the known $C_v$ and the denominator is the proposed $C_v$. If the result is less than 1, it indicates an improvement. If greater than 1, a deteriorating consequence would ensue. Even if the quotient included the volume (proposed over the known value), it would still lead one astray, as indicated in this case. The quotient must be composed of the $C_{vs}$ and the entire system volume. As you can see, there is an optimum condition of either a ½- or ¾-NPT conductor which was not evident by any other means. By multiplying the quotient by the known $T_e$, we arrive at the predicted $T_e$ for the proposed case. Since we have not included the acceleration component, the results are somewhat skewed from the computed-program results.

One of the outcomes we hope to realize is to help dissolve some of the mysticism surrounding this topic. Another accomplishment would

| Size NPT | Volume in.$^3$ | $C_v$ | Quotient w/o Volume | Quotient w/ Volume |
|----------|---------------|-------|---------------------|--------------------|
| 3/8      | 22.91         | 2.96  | 1.00                | 1.00               |
| 1/2      | 36.46         | 5.48  | 0.54                | 0.86               |
| 3/4      | 63.99         | 11.47 | 0.26                | 0.72               |
| 1        | 103.71        | 21.69 | 0.14                | 0.62               |
| 1 1/4    | 179.49        | 44.51 | 0.07                | 0.52               |

(a)

| Conductor NPT | $C_{vs}$ | Volume* | System Quotient | Calculated $T_e$ | Actual $T_e$ |
|---------------|----------|---------|-----------------|------------------|--------------|
| 3/8           | 1.89     | 113.0   | 1.00            | 0.41             | 0.41         |
| 1/2           | 2.62     | 126.6   | 0.81            | 0.33             | 0.36         |
| 3/4           | 3.20     | 154.1   | 0.81            | 0.33             | 0.36         |
| 1             | 3.34     | 193.8   | 0.97            | 0.40             | 0.41         |
| 1 1/4         | 3.38     | 269.6   | 1.33            | 0.55             | 0.51         |

(b)

**Figure 10.1** (*a*) Schedule 40 pipe properties 10 ft long; (*b*) system properties with 3.25 × 12-in-bore actuator.

be to eradicate a bit of the vast sea of irrationality that pervades the subject. Our aspirations may be too ambitious, but if we can create an ounce of skepticism in the minds of those applying the current modus operandi, we will consider it an excellent beginning.

Some of you readers may have been exposed to the concept of dual-pressurizing an actuator and the potential benefits derived therefrom prior to reading this text. It was a case of trial and error in the selection of the components and pressures to establish the desired performance times. However, we have eliminated the chance solution for the minimum pressures. We have developed a unique method which allows you to correctly predict these two distinct pressures necessary to propel even two different loads at the designated performance times. This requires a departure from the accepted techniques, and anything new is difficult to assimilate. To understand the underlying proposition is one thing; to be willing to incorporate it into your analysis is another. To use the proposition is the ultimate acceptance, and to realize the inherent savings is conclusive evidence of its viability. Let us assume that we have accomplished the first three elements, for they are relatively easy to achieve compared to the last. Deriving the benefits in the form of savings is always the most difficult, especially in this situation, not because of any technical encumbrances, but rather because of existing and entrenched practices.

The purpose of the written word in an academic text, specifically texts devoted to the physical sciences or engineering, is vastly different from that in a fiction novel or biographical volume. This may be an oversimplification of categorizing books into only three broad classifications. Forgive me if this offends the authors of novels or biographies, for it certainly is not the intent. My point is simply to emphasize that a scientific monograph differs from the others. Webster defines a *textbook* as a book giving instructions in the principles of a subject of study, specifically one used as the basis of a course of study. A *novel* is defined as a relatively long fictional prose narrative with a more or less complex plot or pattern of events, about human beings, their feelings, thoughts, actions, etc. A novel is intended primarily for entertainment, and if there is a message to be shared, all well and good. The focus of an engineering textbook is to impart information and knowledge. If it can be conveyed in an interesting and absorbing manner, so much the better. A good scientific text should be enlightening by bringing freshness to an old topic or revealing a newly conceived subject. Readers (and students) use an engineering text for the purpose of learning with the eventual objective, once having successfully mastered the material, of applying the information for solving the practical engineering problems that they will encounter. The readers obviously must understand and believe in the tenets espoused in the text and should confirm their validity before proceeding with their implementation. Then, once convinced that they understand these tenets, the readers should have the wherewithal to execute them at the place of employment to gain the benefits. Therein lies the rub, for if it is not possible to implement the theory, it is simply a hollow victory. All the means may be available and in place at some firms, except the responsibility for exercising the specifying and purchasing option or to have an input in its outcome because of the internal organizational structure of that firm. This is one of the most crucial elements in the sequence of operations of a business. Many large manufacturing companies are missing the boat and will continue to miss the boat unless they alter their practices of split purchasing and specifying functions. It is not that individuals do not possess responsibilities; rather, it is that if one locates a potential savings in an area which is outside one's province, there is very little likelihood that it can be realized. Over the past few decades a system has evolved in the pneumatics field whereby the purchasing and specifying roles of the components are divided and delegated among three different disciplines. More often than not, one branch will unearth a savings which is applicable to another area but is unable or unwilling to effect the change because the gains will be outside that branch's province and the costs will be within that province. It is essential in order to gain the full profits from these dual-pressure concepts that there be a single person or committee with complete authority for purchasing and specifying. In this manner the fruits can be harvested even if the components are specified by one group for the interest of another. To be short-sighted or insular and think narrowly can only penalize the corporation's competitiveness. The predicament arises because the distribution of the component responsibilities is divided. However, the one component interacts with the others, and in most cases the components are totally dependent on one another. It therefore seems quite ludicrous to separate the functions, but that is basically what is occurring in some industries today. And yet, this comparison represents only a portion of the obstacle as we shall soon see.

Currently in the hierarchy of many large plants the managing, purchasing, and/or specifying activities are arranged essentially into three groups alluded to earlier: the facilities, mechanical, and controls sections. The facilities group would be responsible for specifying and purchasing compressors, reservoirs, refrigerant dryers, etc. The mechanical group would specify and order actuators. The controls group would specify and order valves, regulators, etc. All these components are seemingly discrete, independent parts of a whole where each is unaffected by the action of the other; obviously they are not, just as the parts of a body are not. For example, a facilities engineer who might find it advantageous to employ dual-pressure components for a proposed incoming assembly line, in order to utilize the existing limited compressor capacity more wisely, would have no or very little input into the required regulator specifying process. The mechanical people neither have any jurisdiction or input in the specifications and/or purchasing of regulators, as that function falls under the aegis of the controls group. The controls people, who specify valves, regulators, filters, etc., do not benefit directly from this added expense and thus have no interest in acquiring them. In fact, it would perhaps place them over budget, which certainly would thwart any possibility of including the additional regulators in a purchase order.

The purchasing departments being involved in the current trend of disinflationary practices are demanding that their suppliers drop their prices by a few percentage points. This makes for very difficult relations, much to the chagrin of the supplier. However, here we have a concept made available by the supplier that would save the corporation energy dollars, yet frequently the specific individual(s) exposed to it would turn a deaf ear because of lack of direct departmental justification. Assuming that the controls people recognize the advantages in a particular application of dual-pressuring an actuator and desire to alter the bore size, they may be unable to effect a change because it is outside their bailiwick. The mechanical people hesitate to request the larger item as it necessitates laying out more funds, and once again the only one that stands to gain is another department, and thus any proposed change may be difficult to defend under the existing corporate makeup. Although, if assessed on a corporate basis, the extra equipment can pay for itself within 3 months and thereafter, all the energy or productivity savings are essentially bottom-line profit. I am certain that somewhere in these organizations there is someone who, if made aware of these practices, will demand that they be modified. This appeal is specifically intended for that person's ears.

Several years ago I was struck by a cover story in a major engineering periodical documenting and extolling the virtues of concurrent engineering. The accomplishments were literally awesome. These same individuals who hesitate to execute these principles as they apply to their respective departments compliment themselves as part of the corporation for the success of the concurrent engineering project that was accomplished in the other fields of design and manufacturing engineering. They are either unwilling or, more likely, unable to apply these notions to their areas, which can prove to be just as beneficial. It's obvious that any of the three disciplines can discover a cost-saving process, product, or concept, but if it is outside their realm of responsibility, there is very little chance of getting it approved. Perhaps highlighting it may stimulate the proper individuals to apply concurrent thinking to many other areas and make the obvious recognition. that it is not restricted simply to simultaneous engineering between product and manufacturing engineering.

Division of responsibility inhibits optimum selection of components, preventing maximum productivity, energy conservation, optimum utilization of energy, minimum-size elements, or whatever. If one does not view the entire picture or circuit, one cannot possibly make a proper choice except by happenstance. There is the obvious synergistic effect when coordinating activities, which today is called *simultaneous* or *concurrent* or whatever *engineering, specifying,* or *purchasing.*

The relationship between vendor and user should not be confrontational but rather one of mutual respect with each sensitive to the needs of the other. If it is essential to reduce costs to enjoy a competitive edge, does it really make any difference how or where in the overall business process it was accomplished? The decisive element is that the resultant bottom line indicates that the profit has been realized. The supplier can be most useful if the problem is attacked from this vantage point. This is precisely the gains that can be gleaned without experiencing any pain, to either buyer or seller, from this cooperative effort of applying the dual-pressure process.

I will not burden you with all the details involved in my attempts to communicate with governmental agencies, spanning a time period from Presidents Nixon to Bush, concerning the dual-pressure concept. Attempting to convince them and what it can realize for the United

States if implemented even partially is almost a hopeless cause. I use the word *almost* because one must never throw in the towel, and one must be forever resolute. Calvin Coolidge once said, "Nothing in the world can take the place of persistence. Talent will not; nothing is more common than unsuccessful men with talent. Genius will not; unrewarded genius is almost a proverb. Education will not; the world is full of educated derelicts. Persistence and determination alone are omnipotent." The slogan "press on" has solved many problems, whether it be hunger, the environment, or our limited energy resources. So with dogged perseverance we continue. Perhaps, if Calvin Coolidge were president now, we could make some inroads.

We are "wasteful"; we are continually improving but still considerably worse than our formidable competitors. Unfortunately, this epithet applies to all sectors of our industrial, commercial, and residential community. I am singling out only the compressed-air portion of the industrial community. We were so infuriated at the Iraqi army torching the oil fields of Kuwait prior to their departure for a multiplicity of reasons, not the least of which was wastefulness. We have methods to reduce some of our wastefulness in the pneumatics field, and if we do not exercise them, we are just as guilty as the retreating army of Iraq. Yet when presented with these facts, people tend to disregard them because we neither see the smoke, smell the fumes, nor inhale the noxious gases. Aldous Huxley put it very succinctly when he said, "Facts do not cease to exist because they are ignored."

This seems to be a propitious location to discuss the latest statistics for 1993 from the Energy Information Administration (EIA). In reading them, I noticed that we lapsed back into our old habits, for our imports of total energy consumed jumped from 23.9 to 25.2 percent with petroleum leading the way, advancing from 7.89 to 8.53 million barrels per day (mbpd). Fossil fuels represented 88.4 percent of the energy consumed for 1993, as opposed to 88.3 percent for 1992 (not significant, except for the fact that we are proceeding in the wrong direction). The present administration still has no cohesive energy plan to combat or at least manage this enormous oil dependence, which is thrusting us further into debt as evidenced by the following statistics. In the year 1992 the 7.89-mbpd consumer glut was responsible for a good measure of the 37.73 billion-dollar value of fossil-fuel net imports. In 1993 that figure soared to 38.13 billion dollars to a great degree because of the increase to 8.53 mbpd of imports. For a detailed discussion and representative graphs on this topic, up to 1992, which was the most recent year for which complete statistics are available, see Chap. 1.

We did not ask the appropriate or even inappropriate bureaus for endorsements nor approval, just an acknowledgment of the existence of energy-saving methods. These plans can be suggested to industry and perhaps apply efficiency grades to their air circuits as boiler, furnace, and air-conditioner manufacturers do. Or a rating system can be employed, as is done for insulation ($R$ and $U$ factors) and automobiles [miles per gallon (mpg)]. In like fashion, industry can seek the most efficient employment of compressed air by conducting an economic-feasibility study. This, along with some other pertinent information, can then be the basis for an intelligent judgment call for pneumatic circuits. Without this knowledge, any low-energy-efficient, oversized, or low-productivity pneumatic circuit would be admissible because there is no yardstick for comparison. Industry is ignorant of its existence. This calls for agencies to assist in making this information available, which is a deviation from traditional avenues of approach and difficult to do, much less to accept in principle.

Allow me to venture into another hallowed area; utilities. An interesting convergence of two circumstances has occurred in the past few decades: (1) the drying up of investment capital with respect to utilities, due primarily to the anti-nuclear-power syndrome; and (2) the cost to conserve per kilowatt, including incentives, which is considerably less expensive than the cost to build per kilowatt.[1] Utilities must continually assess their future needs so as to be able to keep pace with the commercial-industrial-residential growth requirements. As a result of the prospects mentioned above, it is quite apparent as to which was and still is the best strategy to proceed with for their immediate future demands. We have approached several utilities that have shown a keen interest in this dual-pressure concept because they have recognized the potential benefit they can glean from it. It is difficult to understand why more have not evinced an interest, but that is not the subject of this discussion at the moment. They acknowledge the fact that eventually they will have to build, and this represents a significant area to capitalize on since it gives them the essential breather. The conventional approaches of preaching conservation and efficiency in the lighting, motors, heating, and air-conditioning fields have, by and large, been exploited, leaving only incremental improvements possible in these areas. They have made a considerable amount of energy available. Yet, there is room for further gains with the infusion of this new dual-pressure concept. As we've mentioned earlier,[2] 7.5 percent of the energy costs incurred in a

---

[1]A. H. Rosenfeld and D. Hafemeister, "Energy-Efficient Buildings," *Scientific American*, April 1988; broadcast of Morning Edition (7:30 AM) in early May 1994 on station WFUM (NPR) by R. Charles on nuclear reactors: "$125 to conserve with incentives per kilowatthour; $1500 to construct a traditional coal-fired facility to produce 1 kWh; $5000 to construct a nuclear-powered utility to produce 1 kWh."

[2]See Chap. 1, Fig. 1.3.

plant stem directly from producing compressed air. Saving 20 percent of this amount will reduce the industrial energy bill by 1.5 percent. Now, that ain't hay. So, why aren't they showing an overwhelming interest in this technique? To a great measure they mimic the words of the governmental agencies, "We cannot show partiality even if it is beneficial as it would be considered discriminatory." I suspect that with all the difficulties and differences the utilities are experiencing with the Nuclear Regulatory Agency, Environmental Protection Agency, and Occupational Safety and Health Administration, one cannot blame them for being somewhat gun-shy. However, those are not the only options open to them, as is the case for the government. They, as we've suggested with the government, have alternatives that they already apply and impose on the automotive industry, the food industry, or the pharmaceutical industry, to name just a few. It also is done in such a manner so as to avoid the discriminating label. Or, they can do the same as the air-conditioning, furnace, hot-water-heater, motor, and refrigeration industries, to name only a few which operate under an accepted industry-standard efficiency guideline. The point is that there are alternatives, and hiding under the discriminating label is a copout.

The argument could be made that explicit condemnations of this nature do not constitute a proper form for a scientific text. Obviously, I do not agree. In fact, as far as my personal opinion is concerned, I consider it to be a noble cause and thus not taking undue license. Therefore, if these critiques are excluded from the text, I would judge it to be deficient and the author to be negligent. It is essential, if we desire to be a successful nation, to be competitive and assertive. To that end we cannot afford to sit around and hope that things will improve. We must not hand over to our grandchildren and great grandchildren the same archaic attitudes and practices which prevent our success. We must all participate and take an active role in all aspects of the process. We must view the entire picture. We must be responsible for taking a concept from inception through teaching and implementation to the final conclusion (in this case) of saving energy, improving productivity, etc., or we've dropped the ball. If it takes exposing some of the wrongs of our corporate culture or governmental institutions, so be it. Perhaps this will serve as a bellweather. If in some small measure the censure in this text aids in awakening some dormant thoughts in some individuals and they respond by altering the practices so that their objectives are fully realized, then I would deem it to be a victory. Fulfilling only the teaching aspect without being able to achieve the desired end objective is incomplete and unacceptable. In today's world economic climate there is no plausible explanation in defense of such practices, and there is no explanation necessary to support amending them. Authors would be remiss if they did not attempt to cover all the considerations of the process. It would then be up to the readers and their colleagues to consummate the entire plan.

Allow me the courtesy to stray for a moment to relate, in my estimation, a relevant short tale I came across several years ago. This is a little story about four people named Everybody, Somebody, Anybody, and Nobody. There was an important job to be done, and Everybody was sure that Somebody would do it, and it ended up that Nobody did it. Somebody got angry about that, because it was Everybody's job. Everybody thought Anybody could do it, but Nobody realized that Everybody wouldn't do it. It ended up that Everybody blamed Somebody when Nobody did what Anybody could have done.

There are many more areas which require—no, demand—attention, such as the ability to estimate the effect of quick-exhaust valves on cylinder speeds, and having the wherewithal to predict cylinder response times of air over oil circuits. It would be magnificent to be able to predict filling times for blow molding equipment, both plastic and glass. It would make the design of the single- and multicavity molds and their worm-trail-like galleries more efficient for improved productivity. The labyrinthine air passages for operating complex functions of multicavity injection-molding dies is an area worth pursuing. The filling time of airbags for clamping as well as performing punch-press, heat-sealing, etc. functions is another region seeking answers. This is clearly a hybrid device, for it is neither a vessel nor a cylinder in the strictest sense but is widely accepted and used today with very little operating information.

We have formulated methods by which conductors, fittings, air cylinders, etc. can all be expressed by a common denominator. Although tests performed at the Numatics laboratories have verified that these methods are satisfactory for general selection purposes, we feel they can be further refined, improved, and enhanced. This should be viewed as just another step in understanding the complexities and interrelationships between an actuator, conductor, and fittings. It is presented as the beginning of a topic which helps shed light on operating a pneumatic system more wisely, more productively, and more efficiently. As is the case with all subjects, the better informed one is, the more intelligent are the decisions.

Doctoral students exploring the field for stimulating thesis projects tend to select the exotic areas of lasers, plasma physics, scanning tunneling electron microscopes, superconductors, and photovoltaic technology which must all appear more exciting than the seemingly mundane subjects of pneumatics and hydraulics. Personally, my colleagues and I find the thirst for knowledge in the prosaic field of pneumatics equally compelling. Some individuals are inclined to overlook entire disciplines because they are assumed to be complete and closed to fresh notions. They should know better and are taught to resist this type of reasoning. There is an entire world to be discovered in the field of fluid dynamics and, more importantly, correcting some concepts based on hearsay and emotion rather than logic and reason leading to poor and, even worse, wrong decisions. This attitude toward the routine is not reflective of all but is far too typical of many, and helps explain why youth is more fascinated with the unusual. Therefore, I invite the young and old alike to investigate the archaic fields, for the world will always need to be enlightened and require coherent explanations of the old as well as the new in order to have a better comprehension of a subject.

Just a few territories for Somebody to explore, not Anybody, for Everybody is not sufficiently skilled and, as expected, Nobody may wind up investigating it. We aspire to spark sufficient interest in all readers to continue to strive to eliminate waste and improve productivity (indicating another form of waste) which will directly benefit the readers and their educational institute, firm, and country and the world at large, for we really are only one community.

There have been very few changes, from a technical viewpoint, in how pneumatic systems have been engineered and built in the past several decades. The electrical actuating networks have changed, but most of the basic pneumatic techniques and practices of using compressed air have remained essentially the same. Recognizing the growing need for a more sophisticated method of sizing pneumatic components, because the existing selections were both costly and consumers of energy, we decided to reevaluate the conventional means to determine how they could be revised and improved on to build a more efficient pneumatic circuit. The use of the dual-pressure procedure with its ensuing ability to predict them, to achieve specific cylinder stroke times, fills this vacuum, for it offers an excellent opportunity to not only save energy but to increase productivity.

*"In an information society, education is no mere amenity; it is the prime tool for growing people and profits."*
JOHN NAISBITT, AUTHOR OF *MEGATRENDS*

*"This time, like all times, is a very good one if we but know what to do with it."*
RALPH WALDO EMERSON

```
NUMATICS NUMASIZING (R) SUMMARY SHEET                    Date:   04/10/95
NU301EED  Ver 3.01 (c) 1989 Numatics, Inc.              SURVEY # 10-1
========================================================================
Prepared for:                     Prepared by:    Michael Liberty
Company:                          Company:        Numatics Inc.
Address:                          Address:        1450 N. Milford Rd.
City,State,Zip:                   City,State,Zip: Highland, Mi. 48357
Telephone #                       Telephone #     (810) 887-4111
Fax #                             Fax #           (810) 887-9190
------------------------------------------------------------------------
                                  Avg/Tot/Oth    Extend    Retract
INITIAL CUSTOMER PARAMETERS:
  Total weight of load (lbs)                      250.00    -50.00
  Angle of load from horizontal         90
  Coefficient of Friction             0.00
  Number of actuators                    1
  Total load per actuator (lbs)                   263.52    -19.39
  Minimum line pressure (PSIG)         100
  Design pressure used (PSIG)                      59.5      12.0
  Shifts/day (1 shift=120,000 m/yr)    2.0
  Cycles per year                   3600000

ACTUATOR:
  Description:   Single Rod High Flow Numatics Actuator with 3/8 NPT ports
  Bore/stroke/rod          2.50" bore x 6.00" stroke x 0.625" rod
  Fitting                  1/2" - 3/8 NPT STR

CONDUCTOR & ASSOCIATED COMPONENTS:
  Branch conductor /leg                N/A
  Branch manifold fitting /leg         N/A
  Branch cond equiv ftg lg /leg (in)   N/A
  Quick disconnect model /leg          N/A
  In line flow control model /leg                 NONE      NONE
  Main conductor           1/2" rubber hose 48" long with 0.0 elbow(s)
  Main manifold fitting                N/A
  Main cond equiv ftg lg (in)            0

VALVE ASSEMBLY & ASSOCIATED COMPONENTS:
  Description    2 Pos Mk15 on 3/8 NPT base with ext reg
  Fitting                  1/2" - 3/8 NPT STR
  Silencer model           N/A

SYSTEM PERFORMANCE TIMES:
  Att'n stroke time (sec)                          1.00      0.25
  Required stroke time (sec)                       1.00      0.25
  Stroke time @ term vel (sec)                     0.14      0.13
  Att'n cyclic rate (CPM)             15.01
  Required cyclic rate (CPM)          15.00
  Cyclic rate @ term vel (CPM)        19.82
  System delay time (sec)             0.025
  Dwell time after stroke (sec)                    1.00      1.75

SYSTEM INFORMATION:
  Required system Cv                               1.33      1.31
  Attained system Cv                               1.33      1.33
  Att'n system air flow (SCFM)                     6.8       9.5
  Att'n branch air vel (400 FPS max)       N/A           N/A
  Att'n main air vel (400 FPS max)                 17        69
  Att'n % delta p (46% max)                        1         8
  % Act. capacity used (75% max)                   90 ?     -35
  Min pres necessary for ld w/S.F. (PSIG)          71.6     -5.6
  Air per cycle (SCF)                 0.15
  Att'n act leakage cost/yr @ $ 0.30 /KSCF   25    18        6
  Att'n operating air cost/yr @ $ 0.30 /KSCF 165   123       42
  Cost /1000 cyc @ att'n times @ $ 20.00 /hr 22.25
  Att'n power input total (HP)        0.54

COMMENTS:
  Extend stroke pressure is the only pressure below the permissible level. Must
  raise it to 71.6 PSIG which is the min req'd for a S.F. of 75%.
```

```
NUMATICS NUMASIZING (R) SUMMARY SHEET              Date:   04/10/95
NU301EED  Ver 3.01 (c) 1989 Numatics, Inc.         SURVEY # 10-1
=====================================================================
Prepared for:              Prepared by:    Michael Liberty
Company:                   Company:        Numatics Inc.
Address:                   Address:        1450 N. Milford Rd.
City,State,Zip:            City,State,Zip: Highland, Mi. 48357
Telephone #                Telephone #     (810) 887-4111
Fax #                      Fax #           (810) 887-9190
---------------------------------------------------------------------
                                             Extend    Retract

Cv DATA PER ACTUATOR

Actuator Fitting Cv                           4.29      4.29
Flow Control Free Flow Cv from Chart          N/A       N/A
Flow Control Adjustable Cv from Chart         N/A       N/A
Flow Control Adjustable Cv Used               N/A       N/A
Quick Disconnect Cv                           N/A       N/A
Branch Conductor Cv                           N/A       N/A
Additional Cv Due to Elbows in Branch Conductor  N/A    N/A
Branch Conductor Manifold Fitting Cv          N/A       N/A

Cv DATA - TOTAL SYSTEM

Actuator Fitting Cv                           4.29      4.29
Flow Control Free Flow Cv from Chart          N/A       N/A
Flow Control Adjustable Cv from Chart         N/A       N/A
Flow Control Adjustable Cv Used               N/A       N/A
Quick Disconnect Cv                           N/A       N/A
Branch Conductor Cv                           N/A       N/A
Additional Cv Due to Elbows in Branch Conductor  N/A    N/A
Branch Conductor Manifold Fitting Cv          N/A       N/A
Main Conductor Cv                             5.61      5.61
Additional Cv Due to Elbows in Main Conductor N/A       N/A
Main Conductor Manifold Fitting Cv            N/A       N/A
Silencer Cv                                   N/A       N/A
Valve Fitting Cv                              3.79      3.79
Valve Cv                                      1.56      1.56
Sandwich Regulator Cv                         N/A       N/A
Sandwich Speed Control Cv from Chart          N/A       N/A
Sandwich Speed Control Cv Used                N/A       N/A
Sandwich Check Valve Cv (3 pos valve only)    N/A       N/A


Attained system Cv                            1.33      1.33

Required system Cv                            1.33      1.31

Flow Control Adjustable Cv Suggested          N/A       N/A
Valve Cv Suggested                            1.56      1.56
Sandwich Speed Control Cv Suggested           N/A       7.45
```

```
NUMATICS NUMASIZING (R) SUMMARY SHEET                    Date:   04/10/95
NU301EED  Ver 3.01 (c) 1989 Numatics, Inc.              SURVEY # 10-2
========================================================================
Prepared for:                       Prepared by:   Michael Liberty
Company:                            Company:       Numatics Inc.
Address:                            Address:       1450 N. Milford Rd.
City,State,Zip:                     City,State,Zip: Highland, Mi. 48357
Telephone #                         Telephone #    (810) 887-4111
Fax #                               Fax #          (810) 887-9190
------------------------------------------------------------------------
                                    Avg/Tot/Oth    Extend     Retract
INITIAL CUSTOMER PARAMETERS:
  Total weight of load (lbs)                       250.00     -50.00
  Angle of load from horizontal          90
  Coefficient of Friction              0.00
  Number of actuators                     1
  Total load per actuator (lbs)                    263.52     -19.39
  Minimum line pressure (PSIG)          100
  Design pressure used (PSIG)                        71.6       19.0
  Shifts/day (1 shift=120,000 m/yr)     2.0
  Cycles per year                   3600000

ACTUATOR:
  Description:   Single Rod High Flow Numatics Actuator with 3/8 NPT ports
  Bore/stroke/rod            2.50" bore x 6.00" stroke x 0.625" rod
  Fitting                    1/2" - 3/8 NPT STR

CONDUCTOR & ASSOCIATED COMPONENTS:
  Branch conductor /leg                     N/A
  Branch manifold fitting /leg              N/A
  Branch cond equiv ftg lg /leg (in)        N/A
  Quick disconnect model /leg               N/A
  In line flow control model /leg                     3FC2B      NONE
  Main conductor             1/2" rubber hose 48" long with 0.0 elbow(s)
  Main manifold fitting                     N/A
  Main cond equiv ftg lg (in)                 0

VALVE ASSEMBLY & ASSOCIATED COMPONENTS:
  Description     2 Pos Mk15 on 3/8 NPT base with ext reg
  Fitting                    1/2" - 3/8 NPT STR
  Silencer model             N/A

SYSTEM PERFORMANCE TIMES:
  Att'n stroke time (sec)                           1.00       0.25
  Required stroke time (sec)                        1.00       0.25
  Stroke time @ term vel (sec)                      0.38       0.15
  Att'n cyclic rate (CPM)               14.99
  Required cyclic rate (CPM)            15.00
  Cyclic rate @ term vel (CPM)          18.30
  System delay time (sec)               0.025
  Dwell time after stroke (sec)                     1.00       1.75

SYSTEM INFORMATION:
  Required system Cv                                0.50       1.22
  Attained system Cv                                0.50       1.20
  Att'n system air flow (SCFM)                       7.9       11.7
  Att'n branch air vel (400 FPS max)      N/A              N/A
  Att'n main air vel (400 FPS max)                   17         69
  Att'n % delta p (46% max)                           4         10
  % Act. capacity used (75% max)                     75        -22
  Min pres necessary for ld w/S.F. (PSIG)          71.6       -5.6
  Air per cycle (SCF)                    0.18
  Att'n act leakage cost/yr @ $ 0.30 /KSCF   32       22         10
  Att'n operating air cost/yr @ $ 0.30 /KSCF 196     143         53
  Cost /1000 cyc @ att'n times @ $ 20.00 /hr 22.30
  Att'n power input total (HP)           0.64
```

COMMENTS:
Raised extend pressure to min acceptable level & used a FC to fine tune
stroke time to desired performance time.

```
NUMATICS NUMASIZING (R) SUMMARY SHEET                Date:   04/10/95
NU301EED  Ver 3.01 (c) 1989 Numatics, Inc.          SURVEY # 10-2
======================================================================
Prepared for:              Prepared by:    Michael Liberty
Company:                   Company:        Numatics Inc.
Address:                   Address:        1450 N. Milford Rd.
City,State,Zip:            City,State,Zip: Highland, Mi. 48357
Telephone #                Telephone #     (810) 887-4111
Fax #                      Fax #           (810) 887-9190
----------------------------------------------------------------------
                                                 Extend     Retract
Cv DATA PER ACTUATOR

Actuator Fitting Cv                               4.29        4.29
Flow Control Free Flow Cv from Chart              2.86        N/A
Flow Control Adjustable Cv from Chart             2.54        N/A
Flow Control Adjustable Cv Used                   0.53        N/A
Quick Disconnect Cv                               N/A         N/A
Branch Conductor Cv                               N/A         N/A
Additional Cv Due to Elbows in Branch Conductor   N/A         N/A
Branch Conductor Manifold Fitting Cv              N/A         N/A

Cv DATA - TOTAL SYSTEM

Actuator Fitting Cv                               4.29        4.29
Flow Control Free Flow Cv from Chart              2.86        N/A
Flow Control Adjustable Cv from Chart             2.54        N/A
Flow Control Adjustable Cv Used                   0.53        N/A
Quick Disconnect Cv                               N/A         N/A
Branch Conductor Cv                               N/A         N/A
Additional Cv Due to Elbows in Branch Conductor   N/A         N/A
Branch Conductor Manifold Fitting Cv              N/A         N/A
Main Conductor Cv                                 5.61        5.61
Additional Cv Due to Elbows in Main Conductor     N/A         N/A
Main Conductor Manifold Fitting Cv                N/A         N/A
Silencer Cv                                       N/A         N/A
Valve Fitting Cv                                  3.79        3.79
Valve Cv                                          1.56        1.56
Sandwich Regulator Cv                             N/A         N/A
Sandwich Speed Control Cv from Chart              N/A         N/A
Sandwich Speed Control Cv Used                    N/A         N/A
Sandwich Check Valve Cv (3 pos valve only)        N/A         N/A


Attained system Cv                                0.50        1.20

Required system Cv                                0.50        1.22

Flow Control Adjustable Cv Suggested              0.53        N/A
Valve Cv Suggested                                1.56        1.58
Sandwich Speed Control Cv Suggested               N/A         N/A
```

```
NUMATICS NUMASIZING (R) SUMMARY SHEET                     Date:   04/10/95
NU301EED  Ver 3.01 (c) 1989 Numatics, Inc.                SURVEY # 10-3
==============================================================================
Prepared for:                  Prepared by:    Michael Liberty
Company:                       Company:        Numatics Inc.
Address:                       Address:        1450 N. Milford Rd.
City,State,Zip:                City,State,Zip: Highland, Mi. 48357
Telephone #                    Telephone #     (810) 887-4111
Fax #                          Fax #           (810) 887-9190
------------------------------------------------------------------------------
                                 Avg/Tot/Oth     Extend      Retract
INITIAL CUSTOMER PARAMETERS:
  Total weight of load (lbs)                      490.00     -100.00
  Angle of load from horizontal          90
  Coefficient of Friction              0.00
  Number of actuators                     1
  Total load per actuator (lbs)                   500.86      -91.83
  Minimum line pressure (PSIG)          125
  Design pressure used (PSIG)                      80.5        10.0
  Shifts/day (1 shift=120,000 m/yr)      2.0
  Cycles per year                   1440000

ACTUATOR:
  Description:  Single Rod High Flow Numatics Actuator with 1/2 NPT ports
  Bore/stroke/rod            3.25" bore x 12.00" stroke x 1.000" rod
  Fitting                              3/8" - 1/2 NPT STR

CONDUCTOR & ASSOCIATED COMPONENTS:
  Branch conductor /leg                  N/A
  Branch manifold fitting /leg           N/A
  Branch cond equiv ftg lg /leg (in)     N/A
  Quick disconnect model /leg            N/A
  In line flow control model /leg                 4FC3B       4FC3B
  Main conductor        3/8" rubber hose 36" long with 0.0 elbow(s)
  Main manifold fitting                  N/A
  Main cond equiv ftg lg (in)             0

VALVE ASSEMBLY & ASSOCIATED COMPONENTS:
  Description    2 Pos Mk 7 on 1/4 NPT base with ext reg
  Fitting                              3/8" - 1/4 NPT STR
  Silencer model                         N/A

SYSTEM PERFORMANCE TIMES:
  Att'n stroke time (sec)                         3.00        3.00
  Required stroke time (sec)                      3.00        3.00
  Stroke time @ term vel (sec)                    1.38        2.10
  Att'n cyclic rate (CPM)                6.00
  Required cyclic rate (CPM)             6.00
  Cyclic rate @ term vel (CPM)           8.02
  System delay time (sec)               0.022
  Dwell time after stroke (sec)                   1.00        3.00

SYSTEM INFORMATION:
  Required system Cv                              0.37        0.22
  Attained system Cv                              0.36        0.22
  Att'n system air flow (SCFM)                    7.7         1.8
  Att'n branch air vel (400 FPS max)    N/A            N/A
  Att'n main air vel (400 FPS max)                28          28
  Att'n % delta p (46% max)                       6           14
  % Act. capacity used (75% max)                  75         -122
  Min pres necessary for ld w/S.F. (PSIG)         80.5       -16.3
  Air per cycle (SCF)                   0.48
  Att'n act leakage cost/yr @ $ 0.32 /KSCF   37           28          10
  Att'n operating air cost/yr @ $ 0.32 /KSCF 221         179          42
  Cost /1000 cyc @ att'n times @ $ 20.00 /hr 55.75
  Att'n power input total (HP)         0.77

COMMENTS:
```

```
NUMATICS NUMASIZING (R) SUMMARY SHEET              Date:  04/10/95
NU301EED  Ver 3.01 (c) 1989 Numatics, Inc.         SURVEY # 10-3
=================================================================
Prepared for:                 Prepared by:   Michael Liberty
Company:                      Company:       Numatics Inc.
Address:                      Address:       1450 N. Milford Rd.
City,State,Zip:               City,State,Zip: Highland, Mi. 48357
Telephone #                   Telephone #    (810) 887-4111
Fax #                         Fax #          (810) 887-9190
-----------------------------------------------------------------
                                              Extend    Retract

Cv DATA PER ACTUATOR

Actuator Fitting Cv                            2.55       2.55
Flow Control Free Flow Cv from Chart           6.36       6.36
Flow Control Adjustable Cv from Chart          5.83       5.83
Flow Control Adjustable Cv Used                0.94       0.26
Quick Disconnect Cv                            N/A        N/A
Branch Conductor Cv                            N/A        N/A
Additional Cv Due to Elbows in Branch Conductor N/A       N/A
Branch Conductor Manifold Fitting Cv           N/A        N/A

Cv DATA - TOTAL SYSTEM

Actuator Fitting Cv                            2.55       2.55
Flow Control Free Flow Cv from Chart           6.36       6.36
Flow Control Adjustable Cv from Chart          5.83       5.83
Flow Control Adjustable Cv Used                0.94       0.94
Quick Disconnect Cv                            N/A        N/A
Branch Conductor Cv                            N/A        N/A
Additional Cv Due to Elbows in Branch Conductor N/A       N/A
Branch Conductor Manifold Fitting Cv           N/A        N/A
Main Conductor Cv                              3.08       3.08
Additional Cv Due to Elbows in Main Conductor  N/A        N/A
Main Conductor Manifold Fitting Cv             N/A        N/A
Silencer Cv                                    N/A        N/A
Valve Fitting Cv                               2.25       2.25
Valve Cv                                       0.41       0.41
Sandwich Regulator Cv                          N/A        N/A
Sandwich Speed Control Cv from Chart           N/A        N/A
Sandwich Speed Control Cv Used                 N/A        N/A
Sandwich Check Valve Cv (3 pos valve only)     N/A        N/A


Attained system Cv                             0.36       0.22

Required system Cv                             0.37       0.22

Flow Control Adjustable Cv Suggested           0.99       0.26
Valve Cv Suggested                             0.41       0.42
Sandwich Speed Control Cv Suggested            N/A        N/A
```

```
NUMATICS NUMASIZING (R) SUMMARY SHEET                    Date:   04/10/95
NU301EED  Ver 3.01 (c) 1989 Numatics, Inc.              SURVEY # 10-4
================================================================================
Prepared for:                    Prepared by:     Michael Liberty
Company:                         Company:         Numatics Inc.
Address:                         Address:         1450 N. Milford Rd.
City,State,Zip:                  City,State,Zip:  Highland, Mi. 48357
Telephone #                      Telephone #      (810) 887-4111
Fax #                            Fax #            (810) 887-9190
--------------------------------------------------------------------------------
                                     Avg/Tot/Oth    Extend      Retract
INITIAL CUSTOMER PARAMETERS:
  Total weight of load (lbs)                        490.00      -100.00
  Angle of load from horizontal          90
  Coefficient of Friction              0.00
  Number of actuators                     1
  Total load per actuator (lbs)                     837.63      -21.73
  Minimum line pressure (PSIG)          125
  Design pressure used (PSIG)                        95.3        22.4
  Shifts/day (1 shift=120,000 m/yr)     2.0
  Cycles per year                   3130435

ACTUATOR:
  Description:   Single Rod High Flow Numatics Actuator with 1 NPT ports
  Bore/stroke/rod          4.00" bore x 12.00" stroke x 1.000" rod
  Fitting                          1" - 1 NPT STR

CONDUCTOR & ASSOCIATED COMPONENTS:
  Branch conductor /leg            N/A
  Branch manifold fitting /leg     N/A
  Branch cond equiv ftg Ig /leg (in)  N/A
  Quick disconnect model /leg      N/A
  In line flow control model /leg                   NONE        NONE
  Main conductor       1" rubber hose 36" long with 0.0 elbow(s)
  Main manifold fitting            N/A
  Main cond equiv ftg Ig (in)        0

VALVE ASSEMBLY & ASSOCIATED COMPONENTS:
  Description    2 Pos Mk 55 on 1 NPT base with ext req
  Fitting                          1" - 1 NPT STR
  Silencer model                   N/A

SYSTEM PERFORMANCE TIMES:
  Att'n stroke time (sec)                            0.30        0.30
  Required stroke time (sec)                         0.30        0.30
  Stroke time @ term vel (sec)                       0.17        0.16
  Att'n cyclic rate (CPM)             13.05
  Required cyclic rate (CPM)          13.05
  Cyclic rate @ term vel (CPM)        13.88
  System delay time (sec)            0.023
  Dwell time after stroke (sec)                      1.00        3.00

SYSTEM INFORMATION:
  Required system Cv                                 5.52        5.45
  Attained system Cv                                 5.21        5.21
  Att'n system air flow (SCFM)                      155.1       50.2
  Att'n branch air vel (400 FPS max)      N/A                N/A
  Att'n main air vel (400 FPS max)                   69          66
  Att'n % delta p (46% max)                           8           8
  % Act. capacity used (75% max)                     70          -8
  Min pres necessary for ld w/S.F. (PSIG)            88.9        -2.5
  Air per cycle (SCF)                  1.02
  Att'n act leakage cost/yr @ $ 0.32 /KSCF   58      28          29
  Att'n operating air cost/yr @ $ 0.32 /KSCF 1026    778         248
  Cost /1000 cyc @ att'n times @ $ 20.00 /hr 25.88
  Att'n power input total (HP)          3.24

COMMENTS:
```

```
NUMATICS NUMASIZING (R) SUMMARY SHEET              Date:   04/10/95
NU301EED  Ver 3.01 (c) 1989 Numatics, Inc.         SURVEY # 10-4
==================================================================
Prepared for:             Prepared by:    Michael Liberty
Company:                  Company:        Numatics Inc.
Address:                  Address:        1450 N. Milford Rd.
City,State,Zip:           City,State,Zip: Highland, Mi. 48357
Telephone #               Telephone #     (810) 887-4111
Fax #                     Fax #           (810) 887-9190
------------------------------------------------------------------
                                           Extend      Retract
Cv DATA PER ACTUATOR

Actuator Fitting Cv                         19.91       19.91
Flow Control Free Flow Cv from Chart         N/A         N/A
Flow Control Adjustable Cv from Chart        N/A         N/A
Flow Control Adjustable Cv Used              N/A         N/A
Quick Disconnect Cv                          N/A         N/A
Branch Conductor Cv                          N/A         N/A
Additional Cv Due to Elbows in Branch Conductor   N/A    N/A
Branch Conductor Manifold Fitting Cv         N/A         N/A

Cv DATA - TOTAL SYSTEM

Actuator Fitting Cv                         19.91       19.91
Flow Control Free Flow Cv from Chart         N/A         N/A
Flow Control Adjustable Cv from Chart        N/A         N/A
Flow Control Adjustable Cv Used              N/A         N/A
Quick Disconnect Cv                          N/A         N/A
Branch Conductor Cv                          N/A         N/A
Additional Cv Due to Elbows in Branch Conductor   N/A    N/A
Branch Conductor Manifold Fitting Cv         N/A         N/A
Main Conductor Cv                           38.84       38.84
Additional Cv Due to Elbows in Main Conductor     N/A    N/A
Main Conductor Manifold Fitting Cv           N/A         N/A
Silencer Cv                                  N/A         N/A
Valve Fitting Cv                            17.61       17.61
Valve Cv                                     5.73        5.73
Sandwich Regulator Cv                        N/A         N/A
Sandwich Speed Control Cv from Chart         N/A         N/A
Sandwich Speed Control Cv Used               N/A         N/A
Sandwich Check Valve Cv (3 pos valve only)   N/A         N/A


Attained system Cv                           5.21        5.21

Required system Cv                           5.52        5.45

Flow Control Adjustable Cv Suggested         N/A         N/A
Valve Cv Suggested                           6.15        6.06
Sandwich Speed Control Cv Suggested          N/A         N/A
```

# Nomenclature

## Symbols

| | |
|---|---|
| $a$ | Area, in square inches |
| $A$ | Area, in square feet |
| $c_p$ | Specific heat of a fluid at constant pressure |
| $c_v$ | Specific heat of a fluid at constant volume |
| $C_d$ | Coefficient of discharge |
| $C_n$ | Electrical conductance, in siemens or mhos |
| $C_v$ | Pneumatic conductance |
| $d$ | Diameter, in inches |
| $D$ | Diameter, in feet |
| $E$ | Impressed voltage, in volts |
| $f$ | Friction factor of internal surface of a conductor or an actuator |
| $F$ | Pound force |
| $g$ | Acceleration due to gravity, in feet per square second (32.2 ft/s$^2$) |
| $G$ | Ratio of molecular weight (MW) of gas under test to that of air (MW of air is 28.98; MW of gas used is 28.98; sometimes referred to as *specific gravity* |
| $I$ | Current, in amperes |
| $J$ | Mechanical equivalent of heat (778 ft•lb/Btu) |
| $k$ | Specific-heat ratio $c_p/c_v$ (isentropic coefficient) |
| k | Kilo or 1000 |
| $K$ | Multiplying factor for a conductor; loss coefficient for a fitting |
| $l$ | Length, in inches |
| $L$ | Length, in feet; load to which the actuator is exposed, expressed in pound force |
| $m$ | Mass, in slugs (lb•s$^2$/ft) or $W/g$ |
| $M$ | Molecular weight |

| | |
|---|---|
| $n$ | Number of units |
| $p$ | Pressure, in pounds per square inch |
| $P$ | Pressure, in pounds per square foot |
| $Q$ | Flow, in standard cubic feet per minute or cubic feet per minute |
| $r$ | Radius, in inches |
| $R$ | Resistance, in ohms; universal gas constant |
| $R_a$ | Gas constant for air |
| Re | Reynolds number |
| $s$ | Stroke, in inches |
| $S$ | Stroke, in feet |
| $T$ | Time, in seconds |
| $u$ | Coefficient of friction between two surfaces |
| $v$ | Velocity, in feet per second or feet per minute |
| $V$ | Volume, in cubic inches or cubic feet |
| $V_g$ | Tank capacity, in gallons |
| $w$ | Specific weight, in pounds mass per cubic foot $= W/V$ |
| $W$ | Weight, in pounds mass (lbm) or pounds force (lbf) depending on whether it's a load (force) or a weight (mass) |
| $X$ | Exhaust |
| $Z$ | Acceleration, expressed in inches or feet per square second |
| | |
| $\Gamma$ | Temperature appropriately specified |
| $\gamma$ | Critical ratio |
| $\Delta$ | Differential or pressure drop; e.g., $\Delta p$ is pressure differential expressed in lb/in$^2$ |
| $\varepsilon$ | Absolute roughness |
| $\eta$ | Polytropic coefficient |
| $\theta$ | Angle, in degrees |
| $\mu$ | Dynamic viscosity |
| $\Phi$ | Combined quantities |
| $\mu_c$ | Dynamic viscosity, in centipoise |
| $\nu$ | Kinematic viscosity |
| $\rho$ | Density, in lbm$\bullet$s$^2$/ft$^4$ or slugs/ft$^3$ $= w/g$ |
| $\Omega$ | electrical resistance, ohms |
| $\nu'$ | Specific volume, in ft$^3$/lbm $= V/W = 1/w$ |

## Subscripts

| | |
|---|---|
| 1 | Initial condition |
| 2 | Final condition |
| a | Absolute; air |
| c | Sound |
| C | Cylinder |
| d | Dynamic or moving |
| D | Drop |
| e | Extend |
| f | Friction |
| F | Fitting |
| FC | Flow control |
| g | Gallons |
| m | Static or motionless |
| M u | Makeup |
| $n$ | Terminal velocity |
| o | Orifice |
| p | Conductor |
| r | Retract |
| s | System |
| t | Total |
| T | Tank volume, in ft$^3$ |
| w | Dwell |
| $x$ | Unknown |
| v | Valve |

## Abbreviations and Acronyms

| | |
|---|---|
| bhp | Brake horsepower |
| bpd | Barrels (of oil) per day (also boopd) |
| bpdoe | Barrels (of oil) per day of oil equivalent |
| bpm | Soap bubbles/min |
| Btu | British thermal unit (3413 Btu/kW) |
| cf | Cubic feet (ft$^3$) |
| cfm | Cubic feet per minute (ft$^3$/min) |
| ci | Cubic inches (in$^3$) |
| cm | Centimeters |
| cpm | Cycles per minute |

| | |
|---|---|
| cps | Cycles per second |
| CRT | Cathode-ray tube (oscilloscope) |
| fps | Feet per second (ft/s) |
| ft | Foot or feet |
| gpm | Gallons per minute (gal/min) |
| Hg | Symbol for the chemical element mercury |
| hp | Horsepower (1 hp = 550 ft•lb/s) |
| ID | Inside (inner) diameter |
| kscf | 1000 standard cubic feet |
| kW | Kilowatts (0.746 kW = 1 hp) |
| kWh | Kilowatthour |
| lbf | Pounds force |
| lbm | Pounds mass |
| min | Minute |
| mbpd | Million barrels per day |
| mph | Miles per hour |
| MW | Molecular weight |
| NPT | National pipe thread |
| OEM | Original equipment manufacturer |
| OWS | One-way shutoff |
| pcf | Pounds per cubic foot (lb/ft$^3$) |
| psfa | lb/ft$^2$ absolute |
| psfg | lb/ft$^2$ gauge |
| psia | lb/inch$^2$ absolute |
| psig | lb/in$^2$ gauge |
| OD | Outside (outer) diameter |
| QEV | Quick-exhaust valve |
| quad | 1 quadrillion Btu ($1 \times 10^{15}$ Btu) |
| rpm | Revolutions per minute |
| s | Second |
| sccm | Standard cubic centimeters per minute (cm$^3$/min) |
| scf | Standard cubic feet (ft$^3$) |
| scfm | Standard cubic feet per minute (ft$^3$/min) |
| scfs | Standard cubic feet per second (ft$^3$/s) |
| sci | Standard cubic inches (in$^3$) |
| scis | Standard cubic inches per second (in$^3$/s) |
| SF | Safety factor |
| TWS | Two-way shutoff |

# Index

## ABOUT THE AUTHOR

Henry Fleischer, P.E., CMFgE, is Vice President of Research and Development for Numatics, Inc., a manufacturer of pneumatic components for industry. He was awarded the 1985 Outstanding Engineer in Industry for Michigan by the Michigan Society of Professional Engineers. He received his Master of Science degree in Mechanical Engineering from Columbia University. Mr. Fleischer lectures widely on pneumatics throughout the world and is the coauthor of *Practical Air Valve Sizing*, as well as numerous articles on various aspects of compressed air technology.